Collins *Advanced Modular Sciences*

Physics

A2

Series Editor: John Avison

Dave Kelly

This book has been designed to support AQA Physics specification A. It contains some material which has been added in order to clarify the specification. The examination will be limited to material set out in the specification document.

Published by HarperCollins*Publishers* Limited
77-85 Fulham Palace Road
Hammersmith
London
W6 8JB

www.CollinsEducation.com
Online support for schools and colleges

© Dave Kelly 2001
First published 2001
ISBN 0 00 327756 9

Dave Kelly asserts the moral right to be identified as the author of this work.

British Library Cataloguing in Publication Data
A catalogue record for this publication is available from the British Library

Cover design by Chi Leung
Design by Ken Vail Graphic Design
Edited by Mike Nugent
Illustrations by Illustrated Arts and Peter Harper
Picture research by Caroline Thompson
Index by Julie Rimington
Production by Kathryn Botterill
Commissioned by Martin Davies
Project management by Pat Winter

Printed and bound by Scotprint

The publisher wishes to thank the Assessment and Qualifications Alliance for permission to reproduce examination questions.

You might also like to visit
www.**fire**and**water**.com
The book lover's website

WAVES, FIELDS AND NUCLEAR ENERGY

NUCLEAR INSTABILITY

Acknowledgements

Every effort has been made to contact the holders of copyright material, but if any have been inadvertently overlooked the publishers will be pleased to make the necessary arrangements at the first opportunity.

The publishers would like to thank the following for permission to reproduce photographs (T = Top, B = Bottom, C = Centre, L= Left, R = Right):

Ace Photoagency/K Phillips, 107, Jigsaw 2, 142BR, D Kerwin, 150CR;
Allsport/B Martin, 69B;
Alton Towers, 62L&R;
Associated Press Ltd, 16B, 112T;
Photos from www.JohnBirdsall.co.uk, 2B, 15;
J Allan Cash Ltd, 141;
Dukane Corporation – Ultrasonics Division, 2T;
Photo courtesy of Crizal® by Essilor, premium anti-reflective lenses, 42T;
Mary Evans Picture Library, 132;
Vivien Fifield, 105;
French Tourist Board, 28TL;
Leslie Garland Picture Library, 12B, 20B, 63B, 104BL;
GettyOne Stone, 65, 69T;
Peter Gould, 59;
Ronald Grant Archive, 78;
Sally & Richard Greenhill, 3C, 16TL;
Hewlett Packard Ltd, 50, 53L;
JET Joint Undertaking, Abingdon, Oxfordshire, 127;
Mark Jordan, 142CR;
Kos Picture Source, 104BC, De Tierida Bros, 20T;
Andrew Lambert, 2C, 6T, 16TC, 31, 37, 38, 42C, 44, 51, 89T, 153;
Military Picture Library/G Lee, 66L, T Fisher, 28CR, R Adshead, 28BCR, S McConnell, 29L;
John Millar Photography, 86TL;
NASA, 79, 81, 83T;
Image courtesy of Jabez McClelland, Electron Physics Group,

National Institute of Standards and Technology, Gaithersburg, MD, USA, 34;
National Maritime Museum, London, 6B;
NOAA/National Geophysical Data Center, 20CR;
Northern Picture Library, 70;
Novosti Picture Library, 138TC;
'PA' Photos, 7, 63C,
Poloroid AG, 27CR;
RAF School of Aviation Medicine, 62B, 66R;
Redferns, 17TL, 33;
Rex Features Ltd, 130B, 142T;
Bernard Richardson, Department of Physics and Astronomy, Cardiff University, 32;
SCALA, 5;
Science Photo Library, 12T, 17TR, 27L, 36, 43, 45, 47, 53T, 64, 72, 74, 76, 77, 78, 83B, 86TR&B, 87, 89CR, 90, 91, 94, 97CR, 98TR, 99, 100, 104BR, 108, 120, 121, 123, 124, 125B, 126, 130T&CR, 133, 139, 142BL, 144, 147, 150T, 151, 152, 155, 156, 157;
Science and Society Picture Library, 3L;
www.shoutpictures.com, 28TC;
FSP/Novosti/Gamma, 117L, Gamma Press, 138TL;
The Stock Market, 104T, 110;
UKAEA Photographic Library, 28B, 98TL, 112B, 113, 117TR, 122, 125T.

Front cover:
All images supplied by: Science Photo Library

Waves & Oscillations

To the student

This book covers the content needed for the AQA Specification A in Physics at A2-level. It aims to give you the information you need to get a good grade and to make your study of advanced science successful and interesting. Science is constantly evolving and, wherever possible, modern issues and problems have been used to make your study stimulating and to encourage you to continue studying science after you complete your current course.

Using the book

Don't try to achieve too much in one reading session. Science is complex and some demanding ideas need to be supported with a lot of facts. Trying to take in too much at one time can make you lose sight of the most important ideas – all you see is a mass of information.

Each chapter starts by showing how the science you will learn is applied somewhere in the world. At other points in the chapter you may find more examples of the way the science you are covering is used. These detailed contexts are not needed for your examination but should help to strengthen your understanding of the subject.

The numbered questions in the main text allow you to check that you have understood what is being explained. These are all short and straightforward in style – there are no trick questions. Don't be tempted to pass over these questions, they will give you new insights into the work. Answers are given in the back of the book.

The Key Facts for each section summarise the information you will need in your examination. However, the examination will test your ability to apply these facts rather than simply to remember them. The main text in the book explains these facts. The application boxes encourage you to apply them in new situations. Occasional extension boxes provide extra detail not required for your examination. These are interesting to read and will support your studies beyond A2-level.

Past paper questions are included at the end of each chapter. These will help you to test yourself against the sorts of questions that will come up in your examination. There is also a section that covers synoptic assessment questions to help you prepare for the synoptic element of your final examination.

Good luck!

1 Oscillations

For hundreds of years, people have used nails, screws and glue to join things together. As the use of plastic goods has grown, solvent-based adhesives have become one of the main ways of joining components together. But every year thousands of tonnes of these toxic solvents end up in the atmosphere. However, there are better, cleaner ways to join plastics. Ultrasonic welding uses high-frequency vibrations to melt adjacent faces into each other. These oscillations are well beyond the range of human hearing with frequencies from 20 to 40 kHz.

High-power ultrasonic technology is not limited to welding. Oscillations are used for producing fine sprays, inserting fasteners, mixing emulsion paints and increasingly for cleaning. Delicate

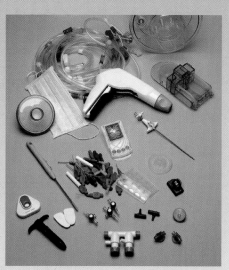

Videocassettes, car dashboards, blister packs for tablets, plastic cups and children's toys are all made using ultrasonic welding. Critical items in medical life support systems, like facemasks and blood filters, are made this way; ultrasonic welding is clean and reliable.

machinery or glassware is placed into a tank of water and detergent. A vibrating plate (transducer) on the bottom of the tank then makes the liquid vibrate at a high frequency (typically 33 000 Hz). When the vibrations reach the surface of the

The tip of a ballpoint pen is only about 9 mm long and 0.9 mm in diameter, and has a 'dead' hole which is difficult to clean. After manufacture the tips are covered with turning oil and have tiny shavings stuck inside. These would prevent the pen from writing smoothly. Organic solvents (such as trichloroethene) were needed to clean the pens, but this has been replaced by ultrasonic cleaning, which uses only mild aqueous detergents.

parts to be cleaned, they create microbubbles that implode, reaching a pressure 1000 times greater than atmospheric. This phenomenon, known as cavitation, provides the energy that helps the detergent to remove dirt from surfaces.

Ultrasonic waves have many other uses; the sonar systems for boats, fetal scanners in maternity units and motion sensors in burglar alarms. These all rely on the properties of high-frequency vibrations.

1.1 Oscillating systems

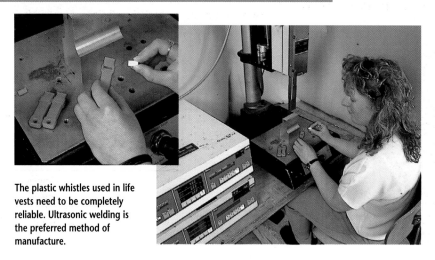

The plastic whistles used in life vests need to be completely reliable. Ultrasonic welding is the preferred method of manufacture.

An ultrasonic welder transfers energy from an electrical vibrator, known as a **transducer**, to the plastic. Although the transducer may be large, the energy is needed in a small region of the plastic. The transducer is fitted with a specially shaped 'horn' to concentrate the vibrations in a small space. This boosts the **amplitude** and energy of vibration, making it large enough for welding or cutting. Both the transducer and horn oscillate naturally at their own **frequency**. There is a link between the amplitude and frequency of the oscillations and the energy that is stored.

Fig. 1 Ultrasonic welding apparatus

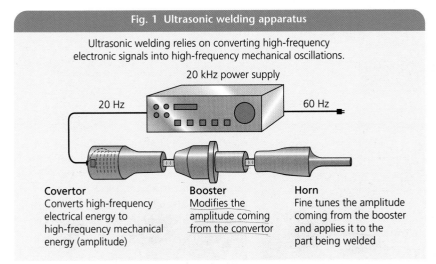

Ultrasonic welding relies on converting high-frequency electronic signals into high-frequency mechanical oscillations.

20 kHz power supply

20 Hz   60 Hz

Covertor
Converts high-frequency electrical energy to high-frequency mechanical energy (amplitude)

Booster
Modifies the amplitude coming from the convertor

Horn
Fine tunes the amplitude coming from the booster and applies it to the part being welded

Fig. 2 Energy transfer in a horizontal mass–spring system

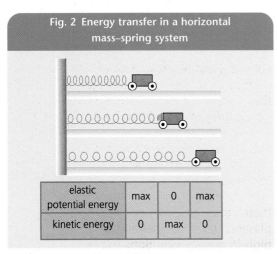

elastic potential energy	max	0	max
kinetic energy	0	max	0

Fig. 3 Energy transfer for a pendulum

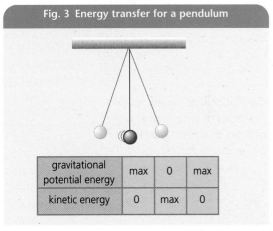

gravitational potential energy	max	0	max
kinetic energy	0	max	0

Energy and oscillations

Swinging pendulums, masses hanging on springs and an atom vibrating in a solid are all examples of oscillatory motion. The repetitive to-and-fro movement relies on an object storing energy when it is disturbed from rest. This stored energy enables the object to move back again.

For example, a horizontal mass–spring system (Fig. 2) stores **potential energy** in the elastic strain of the spring. When the mass is released it accelerates and the potential energy is transferred as **kinetic energy** of the mass. The mass overshoots its original position and compresses the spring, transferring kinetic energy back to potential energy in the spring. This transfer of potential energy to kinetic energy, back to potential energy and so on, happens in all mechanical oscillations.

When a pendulum is released, gravitational potential energy is transferred to kinetic energy as the mass accelerates (Fig. 3). After the pendulum has passed the middle of its oscillation, it slows down as kinetic energy is transferred back to potential energy.

The pendulum and the mass are examples of symmetrical oscillations: the same amount of potential energy is stored on both sides of the oscillation. If no energy is lost by the system the total energy, E, will remain constant throughout the oscillation and will always be the sum of the potential energy (E_p) and the kinetic energy (E_k).

Fig. 4 Energy transfer during an oscillation

For an undamped mechanical oscillation, one in which no energy is transferred from the system, the total energy is constant and is always the sum of the potential energy and the kinetic energy: $E = E_p + E_k$.

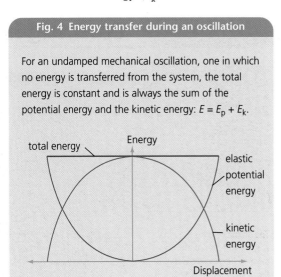

total energy

Energy

elastic potential energy

kinetic energy

Displacement

Pendulums and masses on springs are examples of oscillatory motion.

Fig. 5 Energy transfer in a vertical mass–spring system

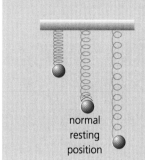

gravitational potential energy	elastic potential energy	overall potential energy	kinetic energy
high	low	max	0
		min	max
low	high	max	0

normal resting position

At the centre of the oscillation all of this potential energy has been transferred to kinetic energy:

Kinetic energy $= E_k = 0.02$ J.

Since $E_k = \frac{1}{2}mv^2$,

$$v = \sqrt{\frac{2E_k}{m}} = 0.45 \text{ m s}^{-1}$$

1 A mass on a spring that oscillates vertically stores energy both as gravitational potential energy and as elastic potential energy in the stretched spring. Complete the table next to the spring in Fig. 5 by identifying where the maximum, minimum and zero values occur.

To get more energy we need bigger oscillations. For a horizontal mass–spring system, like the one in Fig. 2, the elastic strain energy in the spring depends on the amount it is stretched, and the spring constant, k. In fact the energy, E, stored in a stretched spring is given by:

$E = \frac{1}{2}ke^2$,

where e is the extension (see *AS Physics*, Chapter 13).

If the total energy, E, remains constant then all this potential energy will be transferred to kinetic energy as the mass passes through the centre of the oscillation. Suppose a 200 g mass is attached to a spring with a spring constant of 100 N m⁻¹. If the spring is stretched by 2 cm, we can calculate how fast the mass will be travelling when it passes through the centre of the oscillation.

Potential energy stored

$$= \frac{1}{2}ke^2$$
$$= 0.5 \times 100 \text{ N m}^{-1} \times (0.02)^2$$
$$= 0.02 \text{ J}$$

3 Suppose that the spring in the example above was stretched by 4 cm instead of 2 cm. Calculate the maximum velocity that the mass would reach.

4 A pendulum is made from a mass of 500 g hanging on a string. The pendulum is pulled back so that the mass is lifted through a vertical height of 5 cm. Calculate:
a The gravitational potential energy stored before the pendulum is released.
b The total energy of the oscillations.
c The highest velocity reached by the pendulum bob.

5 An ultrasound horn is a solid metal bar that oscillates like a mass–spring system. The mass depends on the mass of the bar and the spring constant is related to the stiffness (Young modulus) of the metal. Using the mass–spring model, predict how the size of oscillations would be affected by:
a doubling the energy of oscillation
b using a thicker bar
c using a less stiff material (lower Young modulus) with the same density.

$F = k \partial x$

f

E_k KE

APPLICATION	**Why do materials expand when they get hotter?**

Not all oscillations are symmetrical. On the symmetrical track (see below), the ball spends an equal time to the left and right of O. On the other track, it will spend a much longer time on the gentler slope. Its average position is therefore to the right of its resting position.

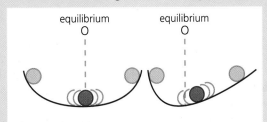

An atom bonded to another atom acts like a ball bearing on a track rolling back and forth. The asymmetric potential energy curve (pictured below) rises sharply if you try to squash two atoms together because they are not easily compressed. When you separate atoms, the force holding them together gradually gets smaller, so the potential energy rises and levels off at zero (the energy of completely separated atoms).

Given a certain amount of thermal energy, the atoms can oscillate. At energy E_1, the average position during the oscillation is about the same as the normal resting position. At a higher temperature, corresponding to energy E_2, the oscillation is not symmetrical: the atoms will spend more time being further

apart. Therefore the material has expanded at the higher temperature.

A large amount of energy can be enough to pull adjacent atoms or molecules apart. This is the basis of ultrasonic cleaning and mixing: the extreme vibrations open up 'cavities' inside liquids by overcoming forces of attraction between molecules.

2 The graph in Fig. 6 shows how potential energy varies with the separation for two atoms.

a Show the position of an atom when the temperature is at absolute zero.

b What would happen to the atom if it gained an amount of energy equal to E (as marked on Fig. 6)?

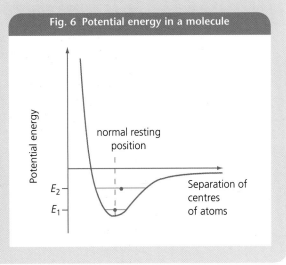

Fig. 6 Potential energy in a molecule

Period, frequency and amplitude

It was in Pisa Cathedral that the young Galileo is reputed to have made an important observation.

Galileo is said to have discovered one of the most important properties of oscillating objects, while watching lamps swinging in the cathedral at Pisa. He noticed that the swinging of the lamp gradually died down, but that the time for each swing stayed about the same (Fig. 7). He checked this by experiment using the most accurate timekeeping device available to him: the pulse in his wrist. This chance observation led to the invention of an accurate timing device, the simple pendulum, which revolutionised the study of motion.

A pendulum oscillates when it is disturbed from its resting place, or **equilibrium**

Fig. 7 The oscillations of a pendulum

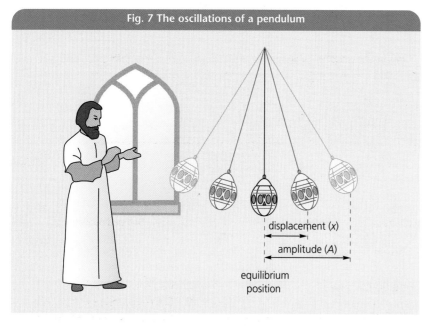

Fig. 8 One complete cycle

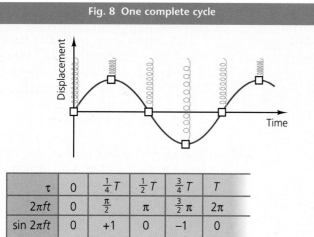

τ	0	$\frac{1}{4}T$	$\frac{1}{2}T$	$\frac{3}{4}T$	T
$2\pi ft$	0	$\frac{\pi}{2}$	π	$\frac{3}{2}\pi$	2π
$\sin 2\pi ft$	0	+1	0	−1	0

position. At any moment, the object has a certain displacement, x, from equilibrium. The maximum displacement of an object from its equilibrium position is called its amplitude, A. The displacement has a direction and is therefore a vector quantity, but amplitude is a scalar quantity.

After one complete **cycle** of an oscillation (Fig. 8), the object returns to the same position, travelling in the same direction.
The time for one complete cycle is called the period, T, of the oscillation. Regular oscillations are sometimes called 'periodic motion'.

The frequency, f, of an oscillation is the number of cycles in a given time. Frequency and period are related by the equations:

$$f = \frac{1}{T} \quad \text{or} \quad T = \frac{1}{f}$$

The metronome can beat out a regular rhythm even as its oscillations die away.

The SI unit of frequency is the hertz (Hz), where 1 Hz = 1 oscillation per second. These terms can be used to describe any oscillation.

Galileo's observation that period does not depend on amplitude seems to go against common sense. You might expect larger amplitude oscillations to take longer, because the pendulum bob has further to travel. However, a larger amplitude swing means more potential energy, which in turn means more kinetic energy. The bob travels faster, so it covers a larger distance in the same time.

Suppose that we could make an ideal pendulum that could swing without any

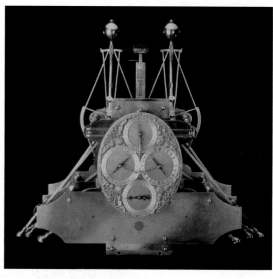

John Harrison used the oscillation of springs to regulate his timepiece H1 which was an important step towards improving navigation at sea.

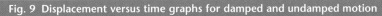

Fig. 9 Displacement versus time graphs for damped and undamped motion

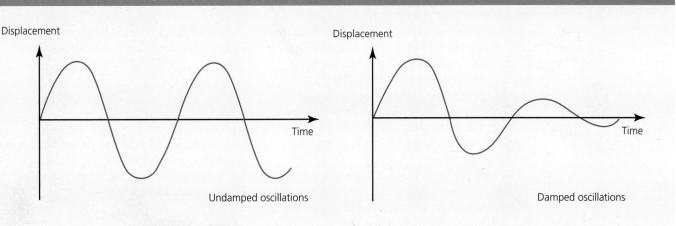

Displacement

Time

Undamped oscillations

Displacement

Time

Damped oscillations

friction or air resistance. This ideal pendulum would not transfer any energy to its surroundings and it would oscillate forever, with the same period of oscillation and the same amplitude. Real pendulums always transfer energy to their surroundings. The amplitude of the oscillations gets less as time goes on. We say that the oscillations are **damped** (Fig. 9). Galileo realised that this damping does not affect the period; as the oscillations die away they still beat out the same time.

Galileo's observations about the pendulum only hold true for fairly small-amplitude oscillations. To prove this, we need to use mathematical ideas about oscillating motion.

6 A mass suspended from a spring is pulled down and released. Sketch graphs on the same axes to show how displacement of the mass changes with time if:
a it is bouncing in air
b it is bouncing in water
c it is bouncing in oil.
Explain the differences in your graphs.

7 The water in a harbour rises and falls due to the tides with a period of approximately 12 hours. Find the frequency of the oscillation.

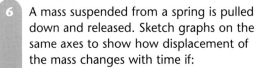

Sometimes damping is a desirable thing. The new bridge over the Thames had to be closed because its oscillations were insufficiently damped. It became difficult to walk across the bridge.

1.3 Simple harmonic motion

Ultrasonic processes, like welding or cleaning, rely on high-power oscillations at very high frequencies. High frequencies are useful because the accelerations and velocities involved are large – large enough to pull molecules apart. To understand this, we need to form a link between the way things oscillate and the acceleration and velocity of the oscillations.

A system will oscillate if there is a force acting on it that always tends to pull it back to its equilibrium position – a **restoring force**. For a swinging pendulum it is the combination of the forces of gravity and the tension in the string that always acts to bring the pendulum back to the centre of its swing. For many oscillating systems the restoring force increases as the object moves further from its resting place. If the restoring force, f, is directly proportional to the displacement from equilibrium, x, the oscillation is known as **simple harmonic motion (SHM)**.

For an object oscillating with simple harmonic motion,

$$f \propto -x$$

(The negative sign indicates that the force acts in the opposite direction to the displacement.)

Since force = mass × acceleration, if the object has a constant mass, we can write:

$$a \propto -x$$

Or, putting in a constant,

$$a = -\omega^2 x$$

where ω^2 is a constant. ω is sometimes referred to as the **angular frequency**, and it depends on the frequency, f, of the oscillations. In fact, $\omega = 2\pi f$ so the SHM equation can be written:

$$a = -(2\pi f)^2 x = -4\pi^2 f^2 x$$

An object that oscillates with SHM has its maximum acceleration when the displacement is greatest, i.e. when $x = A$. The acceleration is zero as the object passes through its equilibrium position, i.e. when $x = 0$.

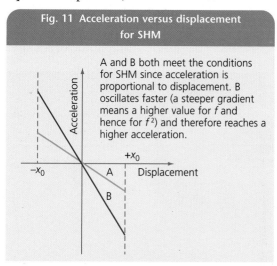

Fig. 11 Acceleration versus displacement for SHM

A and B both meet the conditions for SHM since acceleration is proportional to displacement. B oscillates faster (a steeper gradient means a higher value for f and hence for f^2) and therefore reaches a higher acceleration.

We can use this equation to calculate the accelerations involved in ultrasonic waves. An ultrasonic paint mixer uses a horn that vibrates with an amplitude of 55 µm at a frequency of 20 kHz. What is the maximum acceleration of the horn during its oscillation?

Using $a = -(2\pi f)^2 x$, the maximum acceleration is:

$$a = (2\pi f)^2 \times 55 \times 10^{-6} \, \text{m}$$

Since $2\pi f = 2\pi \times 20\,000 = 1.26 \times 10^5 \, \text{s}^{-1}$
$$a = (1.26 \times 10^5)^2 \times 55 \times 10^{-6} \, \text{m s}^{-2}$$
$$= 8.7 \times 10^5 \, \text{m s}^{-2}$$

Such a huge acceleration is enough to pull molecules apart, leaving empty spaces (cavities) in the liquid. When these cavities implode, high pressures are created which make the fluids mix.

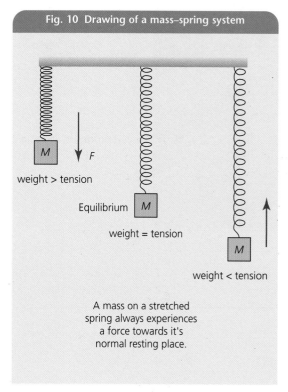

Fig. 10 Drawing of a mass–spring system

M F
weight > tension

Equilibrium   M
weight = tension

M
weight < tension

A mass on a stretched spring always experiences a force towards it's normal resting place.

8 Use the equation $a = -\omega^2 x$ to check the correct units for ω.

9 Sketch an oscillating pendulum and mark in the positions where the acceleration is greatest and where it is least.

10 An ultrasonic welder uses a tip that vibrates at a frequency of 25 kHz. If the tip's amplitude is 6.25×10^{-2} mm, calculate the maximum acceleration of the tip.

11 A spin drier that is loaded unevenly can vibrate quite violently. When this happens, any items that have been left on top of the spin drier may vibrate so strongly that they do not stay in contact with the surface. Explain why this happens.

How large is the acceleration of the vibrating surface when this starts to happen? If the spin drier is rotating at 1000 revolutions per minute, estimate the smallest amplitude of vibration that will just cause the items to leave the surface.

EXTENSION **The solution to the SHM equation**

If you are studying A-level mathematics and you are familiar with the process of differentiating, you might like to examine the solution to the simple harmonic equation. The SHM equation is a differential equation. It can be written

$$\frac{d^2 x}{dt^2} \propto -x$$

(remember $\frac{dx}{dt}$ is velocity and $\frac{d^2 x}{dt^2}$ is acceleration)

This equation can be solved to show how displacement varies with time. The exact solution depends on where the object is when you start timing. If we consider the case when the displacement is zero when time is zero, the solution is:

$$x = A \sin(2\pi ft)$$

We can show that this solution works by differentiating this expression with respect to time. Velocity is the rate of change of displacement with time. Mathematically this can be written dx/dt. If the displacement x is given by $x = A \sin(2\pi ft)$, then the velocity v is:

$$v = \frac{dx}{dt} = \frac{d}{dt}(A \sin(2\pi ft)) = -A\, 2\pi f \cos(2\pi ft)$$

Acceleration is the rate of change of velocity with time. Mathematically this can be written dv/dt. If we differentiate the expression for the velocity, we get:

$$a = \frac{dv}{dt} = \frac{d}{dt}(A\, 2\pi f \sin(2\pi ft)) = -A\,(2\pi f)^2 \sin(2\pi ft)$$

Since $A \sin(2\pi ft) = x$, this shows that

$$a = -(2\pi f)^2 x$$

or $\quad a = \frac{d^2 x}{dt^2} \propto -x$

■ For motion to be simple harmonic, the acceleration, a, must be proportional to the displacement, x, and in the opposite direction.

■ The acceleration of an object moving with SHM is given by $a = -4\pi^2 f^2 x$, where f is the frequency of the oscillation.

1.4 Visualising simple harmonic motion

Displacement and time

All objects that vibrate with simple harmonic motion have the same pattern of motion. Whether we consider a swinging pendulum, a vibrating molecule or the tip of an ultrasonic welder, the motion will follow the same rules. The change in displacement with time can be plotted using a position transducer and a datalogger to record the motion.

The displacement–time graph of a pendulum pulled to its maximum displacement and then released is shown in Fig. 13. The displacement, x, is related to the time, t, by the equation:

$$x = A \cos (2\pi f t)$$

We can use this equation to predict the position of an oscillating system at any time. The tides rise and fall with a motion that is approximately simple harmonic. If high tide is at 12.00 noon, the period of oscillation is roughly 12 hours and the amplitude of the oscillation is 2 m, we could calculate the height of the tide at any other time, say at 2.00 p.m.

$$f = \frac{1}{T} = \frac{1}{43\,200} = 2.31 \times 10^{-5}\ \text{Hz}$$

$$2\pi f = 1.45 \times 10^{-4}\ \text{rad s}^{-1}$$

Using $x = A \cos 2\pi f t$, for $t = 2$ hours = $2 \times 60 \times 60$ seconds = 7200 s

$$x = 2\ \text{m} \times \cos (1.45 \times 10^{-4} \times 7200) = 1.00\ \text{m}$$

Note that the angle $2\pi f t$ is in radians, so your calculator must be in radian mode when you do these calculations. See Chapter 5 for a full discussion of radians.

12 Find out how high the tide will be in another 2 hours, at 4.00 p.m.

13 A pendulum that is oscillating at 30 times per minute has an amplitude of 20 cm.
a Find its displacement 0.5 s after being released from its maximum displacement.
b Find its displacement 0.75 s after being released from its maximum displacement.

Velocity and time

Because velocity is defined as the change in displacement in a given time, $\Delta x/\Delta t$, the velocity at any given time is the gradient of the displacement–time graph.

Acceleration and time

Acceleration is the rate of change of velocity, $\Delta v/\Delta t$. The acceleration during SHM can be found by calculating the gradient of the velocity–time graph.

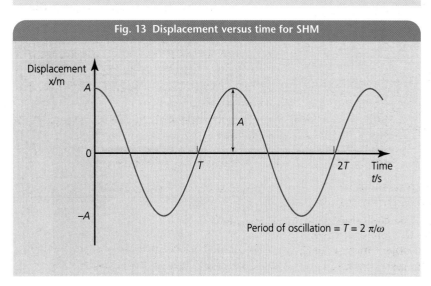

Fig. 12 Block diagram of a transducer and a datalogger

The position transducer produces a voltage that is proportional to the displacement of the oscillating mass. The datalogger records the changing voltage at a suitable rate and the voltage-time graph is plotted by the computer.

Mass-spring
Position transducer
Clamp
Clamp
Computer
Datalogger

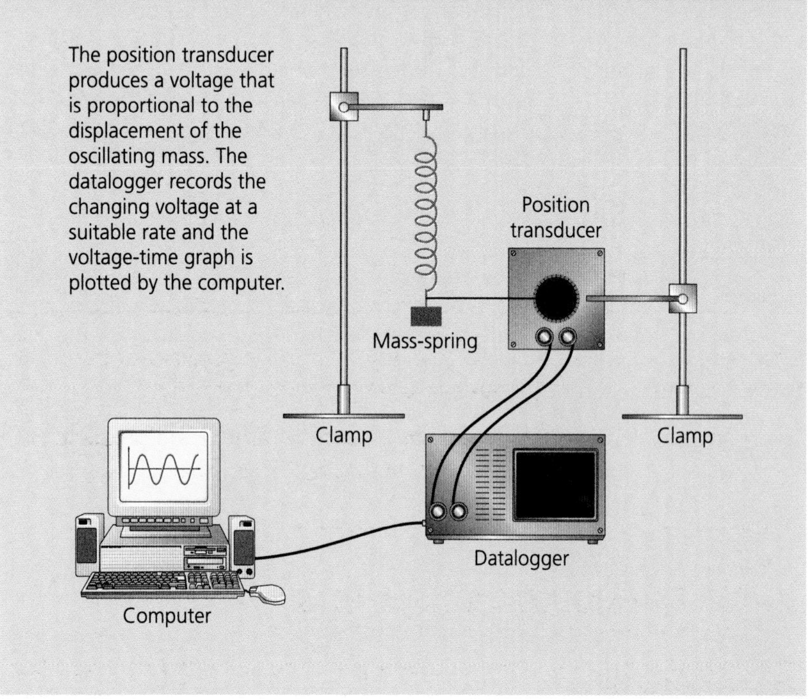

Fig. 13 Displacement versus time for SHM

Displacement x/m

Period of oscillation = $T = 2\pi/\omega$

Fig. 14 The variation of displacement and velocity versus time

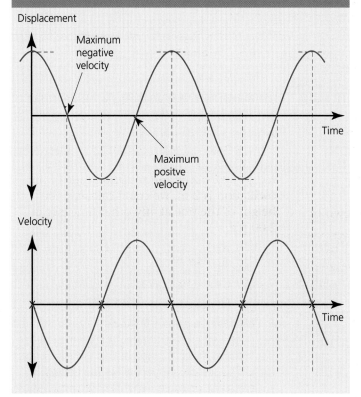

Fig. 15 The variation of velocity and acceleration versus time

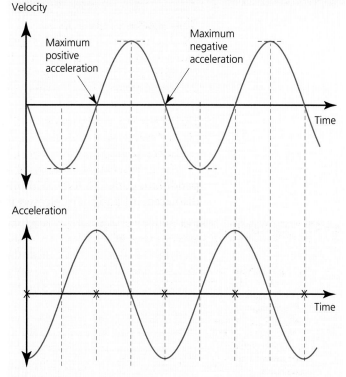

■ The displacement of an object that is vibrating with simple harmonic motion is given by $x = A \cos (2\pi f t)$.

■ The velocity at any time is the gradient of the displacement–time graph at that time.

■ The acceleration at a given time is the gradient of the velocity–time graph at that time.

1.5 The energy in simple harmonic oscillations

Some of the applications of ultrasonics rely on delivering a large amount of energy. In lithotripsy an ultrasonic shock wave is used to blast kidney stones apart. The patient is submerged in water to allow the energy of the ultrasonic vibrations to pass into the patient.

The use of ultrasonics often relies on transferring known quantities of energy. We can calculate the energy transferred during each oscillation by considering the forces involved.

The acceleration of an object moving with SHM is $a = -4\pi^2 f^2 x$, so the restoring force of the oscillating system is $F = ma = -4m\pi^2 f^2 x$, or, $F = -m\omega^2 x$ (where $\omega = 2\pi f$). To push the object slowly from equilibrium to a displacement x, you would need to exert a force that gradually increased in magnitude from zero to F, in the opposite direction to the restoring force. The average force exerted would be $-F/2$.

The potential energy stored is equal to the work done:

E_p = average force × distance

$$= \tfrac{1}{2}(0 + m\omega^2 x) \times x = \tfrac{1}{2}m\omega^2 x^2$$

$$E_p = \tfrac{1}{2}m\omega^2 x^2$$

When the object is at the extremes of its oscillation ($x = \pm A$), it has no kinetic energy.

The total energy, E, of the SHM is therefore equal to the maximum potential energy (the potential energy when $x = \pm A$), so $E = \frac{1}{2}m\omega^2A^2$.

At any instant,

$$E = E_p + E_k \text{ and } E_k = \frac{1}{2}mv^2,$$

so $\quad \frac{1}{2}m\omega^2A^2 = \frac{1}{2}m\omega^2x^2 + \frac{1}{2}mv^2$

Divide by $\frac{1}{2}m$:

$$\omega^2A^2 = \omega^2x^2 + v^2$$

so, $\qquad v^2 = \omega^2(A^2 - x^2)$

or $\qquad v = \pm 2\pi f \sqrt{A^2 - x^2}$

This last equation can be used to calculate the velocity and kinetic energy of an object at any position in its SHM.

An ultrasonic stapler can join pieces of recycled plastic together. The energy from the transducer is transferred to the plastic as heat, melting the staple into place. This works better than trying to use adhesives: recycled plastics contain impurities which make it difficult to glue them together.

Suppose the tip of the ultrasonic horn has an effective mass of 12 grams. To have enough energy to melt plastic, the staple needs to oscillate with an amplitude of 80 µm at 35 kHz. What ultrasound power would be needed to drive in 100 staples per minute?

First, we need to work out the energy of the stapler due to its simple harmonic motion:

From: $\quad E = \frac{1}{2}m\omega^2A^2$ and $\omega = 2\pi f$

$E = \frac{1}{2} \times 0.012 \text{ kg} \times (2\pi \times 35\ 000 \text{ s}^{-1})^2$
$\qquad \times (80 \times 10^{-6} \text{ m})^2$

$\qquad = 1.86 \text{ J}$

It takes 1.86 joules to melt each staple. Using power = energy/time, and time = $60/100 = 0.6$ seconds:

power = 1.86 J/0.6 s = 3.1 W

This power is easily achieved by ultrasonic transducers.

14 A mass of 1 kg is suspended from a spring with a spring constant, k, of 1000 N m^{-1}. The mass is pulled down and released so that it bounces with SHM of amplitude 2 cm.

a Use the equation $T = 2\pi\sqrt{m/k}$ to calculate the period of oscillation.

b Use the equation $v = \pm 2\pi f\sqrt{A^2 - x^2}$ to find the velocity and hence the kinetic energy of the mass. Complete this table and use it to sketch a graph of kinetic energy against displacement for the mass.

Displacement, x (metres)	Velocity (m s^{-1})	Kinetic energy (joules)
0.020		
0.015		
0.010		
0.005		
0.000		

1.6 Pendulums and springs

Two familiar oscillating systems are the simple pendulum and the mass–spring system. By considering the forces that act on these systems we can show that they move with simple harmonic motion and calculate the period of their oscillation.

Period of a pendulum

Suppose a bob of mass m is fixed to a string of length l (measured to the centre of the bob). The bob is displaced to one side to such a small extent that the vertical movement of the bob is negligible (Fig. 16).

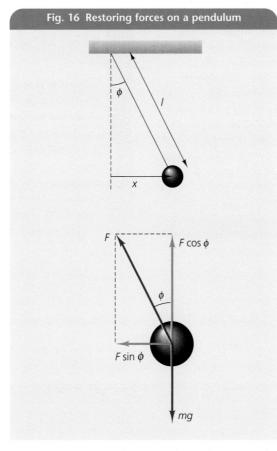

Fig. 16 Restoring forces on a pendulum

The tension in the string has a horizontal component which always acts towards the centre. Because oscillations are small, vertical accelerations are near zero, so the vertical component of tension roughly balances the weight of the bob:

$$F \cos \phi + mg \approx 0$$

For small angles, $\cos \phi \approx 1$. Therefore, for small angles:

$$F \approx -mg$$

The horizontal component of tension causes horizontal acceleration:

$$F \sin \phi = ma$$

Eliminating F from these equations gives:

$$-mg \sin \phi = ma$$

$$\sin \phi = -\frac{a}{g}$$

From the pendulum diagram (Fig. 16):

$$\sin \phi = \frac{\text{opposite}}{\text{hypotenuse}}$$

so,
$$-\frac{a}{g} = \frac{x}{l}$$

$$a = -\frac{g}{l} x$$

Since g and l are constant for a particular pendulum, $a \propto -x$; this is SHM. By comparison with the general equation, we can predict the period of the pendulum.

Comparing
$$a = -\frac{g}{l} x$$

with $a = -(2\pi f)^2 x$

we find that $(2\pi f)^2 = \dfrac{g}{l}$

or $f = \dfrac{1}{2\pi} \sqrt{\dfrac{g}{l}}$

We can now get the time period from:

$$T = \frac{1}{f}$$

$$= \frac{2\pi}{\sqrt{g/l}}$$

$$T = 2\pi \sqrt{\frac{l}{g}}$$

For small angles $(\phi < 8°)$ the period does not depend on the amplitude. Nor does the period depend on the mass of the bob.

15 A clock pendulum has a period of oscillation of 2 seconds. What is its length?

16 What would its period of oscillation be
a on the Moon ($g \approx 1.6$ N kg^{-1})?
b on board an orbiting spacecraft?

A car on its suspension can be thought of as a mass on a spring. The oscillations of the car as it goes over bumps in the road will approximate to SHM.

This force causes acceleration $F = ma$, giving:

$$ma = -kx$$

so, $$a = -\frac{k}{m}x$$

From $$a = -(2\pi f)^2 x \text{ (the general S.H.M. equation)}$$

we get $$2\pi f = \sqrt{k/m}$$

Finally, $$T = 1/f$$

$$T = 2\pi\sqrt{\frac{m}{k}}$$

The period of a horizontal mass–spring system

A car bouncing on its suspension, an ultrasound horn, even atoms vibrating in a solid, are all like mass–spring systems. Suppose you have a spring fixed to a trolley of mass m (Fig. 17). If the mass is displaced, the spring will exert a force which tries to restore it to the resting position. Springs obey Hooke's law: $F = -kx$, where k is the spring constant (in N m^{-1}).

17 What factors influence the period of oscillation of a mass on a horizontal spring? Give physical explanations for each effect.

18 The same mass on the same spring is now hung vertically. How do you think this will affect the period of oscillation?

19 If you doubled the spring constant, how would the following be affected:
a frequency
b energy of oscillation
c maximum speed?

Fig. 17 Restoring force on a mass and spring

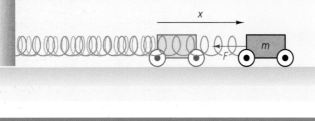

Fig. 18 Period of a vertical mass–spring system

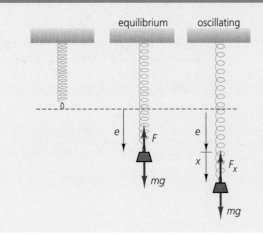

equilibrium   oscillating

This analysis is similar to that for the horizontal spring. The extra forces due to the weight mg make no difference to the period of oscillation. The net effect is only to shift the equilibrium position.
At equilibrium, F must balance mg. From Hooke's Law, $F = ke$, so $ke = mg$.
When oscillating, $F_x = k(e + x)$. The net force acting in the direction of the displacement is $(mg - F_x)$.

So $$ma = mg - F_x \quad \text{(from Newton's second law)}$$
$$ma = ke - k(e + x)$$
$$ma = -kx$$
$$a = -\frac{k}{m}x$$

Comparing with the equation for simple harmonic motion, this gives
$$T = 2\pi\sqrt{m/k}$$

Mixing the mayonnaise

An ultrasonic horn is being developed for emulsifying oil to make mayonnaise. Standard horns don't work well, but a spherical tip to the horn may be more efficient at transmitting energy uniformly through the viscous fluid.

The design of the ultrasonic horn is a small spherical tip of mass 5 g on the end of a rod of length 4 cm and diameter 5 mm (Fig. 19). It is necessary to estimate the natural frequency of oscillation of the horn. If we use simple SHM theory for a mass–spring system the spherical tip can be modelled as the 'mass' and the rod as the 'spring'. Using data about the elastic properties of the rod, we can work out its 'spring constant'.

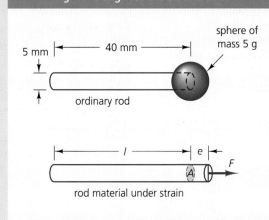

Fig. 19 Design for the oil emulsifier

5 mm

40 mm

sphere of mass 5 g

ordinary rod

l e F

A

rod material under strain

The spring constant, k, is the force per unit extension: $k = F/e$. The metal rod has a Young modulus, E, of 200 GPa.

$$E = \frac{\text{tensile stress}}{\text{tensile strain}}$$

$$= \frac{F/A}{e/l} = \frac{Fl}{eA} = k\frac{l}{A}$$

or, $k = E\frac{A}{l}$

$A = \pi r^2 = \pi(0.0025 \text{ m})^2$
   $= 1.96 \times 10^{-5} \text{ m}^2$
$l = 0.04 \text{ m}$
$E = 200 \times 10^9 \text{ Pa}$

So, $k = 200 \times 10^9 \text{ Pa} \times \dfrac{1.96 \times 10^{-5} \text{ m}^2}{0.04 \text{ m}}$

   $= 9.8 \times 10^7 \text{ N m}^{-1}$

We can then use the formula for SHM of a spring to find the period and frequency:

$T = 2\pi \sqrt{m/k}$

   $= 2\pi \sqrt{0.005 \text{ kg}/9.8 \times 10^7 \text{ N m}^{-1}}$

   $= 4.5 \times 10^{-5} \text{ s}$

and $f = \dfrac{1}{T} = \dfrac{1}{4.5 \times 10^{-5} \text{ s}} = 22 \text{ kHz}$

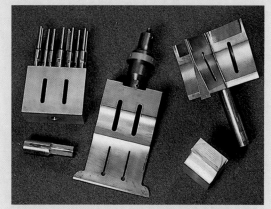

The shape of the horn can focus vibrations for specific uses – from welding the front onto a video recorder to cutting pizzas.

Unfortunately, the horn would be unsuitable for use in an environment with people. A metal rod of this size would have a significant mass, so the effective mass of the probe tip would be greater. This would bring down the natural frequency into the audible range.

20 How could you modify the design to make sure that the horn has a higher natural frequency?

■ A mass–spring system performs SHM with period

$T = 2\pi\sqrt{m/k}$

■ A pendulum performs approximate SHM at small amplitudes with period

$T = 2\pi\sqrt{l/g}$

1.7 Resonance, free and forced vibrations

A child on a swing will oscillate at a certain frequency that depends only on the length of the swing; the oscillating frequency of a guitar string depends on its length, mass and the tension in the string. These oscillations are known as free vibrations and occur at the natural frequency of the system.

Free vibrations

A pendulum or spring that is pulled from its equilibrium position and released will oscillate at its **natural frequency**. These are **free vibrations**, where the system is not subject to any external, varying force.

In some situations, like a child on a swing being repeatedly pushed by a doting parent, there is an external force that varies with its own frequency, referred to as the **driving frequency** (see Fig. 20).

The transfer of energy is most efficient when the driving frequency matches the natural frequency. In an ultrasonic system it is vital that there is a close match between the driving frequency of the transducer and the natural frequency of the horn. Attaching the wrong horn can destroy the transducer. This is because the horn has its own natural frequency of oscillation. If you try to 'drive' it at any other frequency, large and unpredictable forces arise. If the driving frequency is the same as the natural frequency, the horn will continue to accept energy from the transducer, allowing oscillations to increase in amplitude. This build-up of oscillation is an example of **resonance** (Fig. 20).

Resonance

The term 'resonance' originates from the study of sound. You probably know of rooms that have odd acoustics: some musical notes or certain voices seem to 'boom' or echo in these rooms. The room is 're-sounding' or resonating. The driving frequency of the note or voice just happens to match the room's natural frequency.

In many systems, resonance can be a nuisance:

- Machinery rattles and vibrates at certain operating speeds; e.g. in cars, padding is fixed to panels to absorb the energy of vibration.

- High-frequency and relatively large-amplitude vibrations in helicopters cause resonance of the human skull, leading to loss of accurate vision: pilots can fail to see small objects such as overhead power lines.

- Structures can be damaged or destroyed by oscillations at the natural frequency. Bridges are particularly vulnerable when swirling air patterns act as a driving oscillation which can cause resonance.

Fig. 20 Using resonance

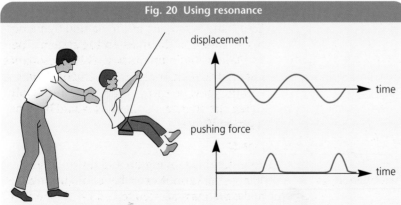

To increase the amplitude of the swing, you need to push it repeatedly.
For effective energy transfer at resonance, the driving oscillation is quarter of a cycle ahead of the driven oscillation. We say that there is a phase difference of a quarter of a cycle – or 90 degrees – between oscillations.

The collapse of the Tacoma Narrows Bridge in 1940 was caused by a mild crosswind. The bridge structure created eddies in the wind of just the right frequency.

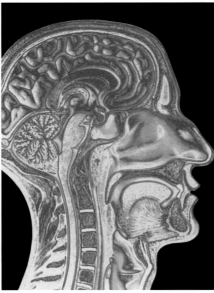

Over 200 French infantrymen died on a bridge in 1850. The regular driving oscillation of their footsteps caused resonance and the bridge tore itself apart and collapsed. Soldiers are now told to break step when crossing a bridge.

However, resonance has many practical applications:

- Many musical wind instruments rely on the resonance of a column of air.

- Digital watches and clocks use resonant vibrations of a quartz crystal as the basis of their accurate time-keeping.

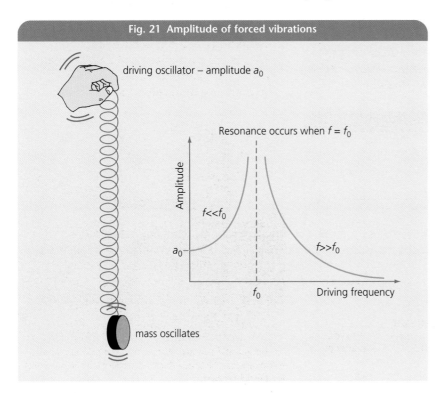

Fig. 21 Amplitude of forced vibrations

driving oscillator – amplitude a_0

Resonance occurs when $f = f_0$

Amplitude

$f \ll f_0$

a_0

$f \gg f_0$

f_0

Driving frequency

mass oscillates

- Radios and televisions are 'tuned' to the right frequency by a resonant electrical (capacitor–inductor) circuit.

- Magnetic resonance imaging (MRI), used in medical diagnosis, relies on identifying the radio waves emitted by the resonant oscillations of certain molecules.

- In microwave ovens, the frequency of the microwaves matches the natural frequency of vibration of water molecules. Food containing water will absorb energy from the microwaves. Glass and plastic dishes do not contain molecules that vibrate at this frequency, so the microwaves pass through these materials without transferring energy.

Forced vibration

An object resonates when the driving frequency matches the natural frequency. But what happens at other frequencies? What if there is a lot of friction? In the case of ultrasonic welding or cutting systems, the idea is to transfer energy to material as heat, not to make the whole object vibrate!

The effects of forced vibration can be predicted by thinking about a simple mechanical system. Suppose you put a mass on the end of a spring and hold the top of the spring. The mass would naturally oscillate at a frequency f_0. You can provide the driving oscillation by raising and lowering the spring by a small amount, A_0, at fixed frequency, f.

Consider (or better still, try) three cases:

$f \ll f_0$:

You raise and lower the spring very slowly. The whole spring–mass system just follows your hand up and down, so $A = A_0$.

$f = f_0$:

Your hand is moving at the natural frequency of oscillation of the mass–spring system. The oscillations build up quickly. This is resonance – soon, the oscillations are destructively large and the mass bounces around uncontrollably. Given the chance, oscillations would become infinitely large: $A \rightarrow \infty$.

$f \gg f_0$:

Your hand is moving up and down rapidly. The spring cannot exert big enough forces to make the mass accelerate and decelerate that quickly. The mass stays almost still: $A \rightarrow 0$.

From this, you can sketch a curve showing how driving frequency affects the amplitude of driven oscillations (Fig. 21).

Damping

In real systems, the amplitude of oscillation cannot rise to infinity. There will always be some resistance to the oscillations and this resistance often increases with amplitude. For example, air resistance damps the motion of a pendulum; the effect is greater when the pendulum is moving faster at large amplitudes. Such resistive forces tend to 'damp down' the oscillations. This loss in the energy of vibration is called **damping.**

In ultrasonic mixing and cleaning systems, the liquid's viscosity will cause damping of the horn. This is beneficial; the idea is to transfer vibrational energy to the liquid, not just to make the horn vibrate in ever-increasing oscillations.

Damping reduces the effects of resonance. The larger the damping, the lower the resonance peak. The resonance peak also shifts to a slightly lower frequency, just below the natural frequency of the driven system.

Heavy and critical damping

If damping is light, oscillations die away gradually. If resistive forces are very high (heavy damping) the system may not oscillate at all (Fig. 23). Visualise a pendulum swinging in a sea of treacle. Once displaced, the bob would very slowly return to equilibrium without overshooting. Oscillation is prevented.

Heavily damped systems respond slowly to changes. With critical damping, the resistive forces are just enough to prevent oscillation. The object returns to equilibrium in the minimum possible time. Critical damping is the ideal state for many mechanical systems:

- Fire doors need to close as quickly as possible, but it could be dangerous if they swung past equilibrium.

- Moving-coil meters need to move swiftly to the new meter reading without oscillating (Fig. 23).

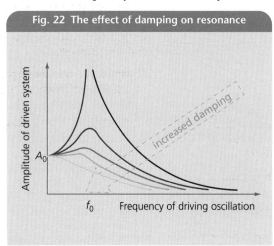

Fig. 22 The effect of damping on resonance

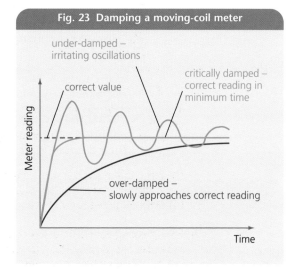

Fig. 23 Damping a moving-coil meter

21 An ultrasonic horn is a resonant oscillator. If the horn is for use in liquids, why would it be unwise to 'tune' the horn (i.e. set the oscillator to the correct frequency) with the horn in air?

1 A helical spring has a spring constant, k. The spring is suspended vertically with a mass of 0.200 kg attached to its lower end. When the mass is given a small vertical displacement and released, it performs *simple harmonic motion* with a time period of 1.26 s. The time period is independent of the *amplitude*.

a Calculate k. (2)

b Define the following terms.

(i) simple harmonic motion

(ii) amplitude (3)

(NEAB PH02 March 1998 Q5)

2 a

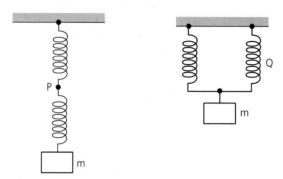

The diagram shows two mass–spring systems each constructed from identical springs, each with a spring constant k, of negligible mass supporting a mass, m.

(i) Write down expressions for the time periods, T_p and T_Q, for the oscillators.
(ii) Determine the ratio of the time periods $T_p : T_Q$. (3)

b Four passengers whose combined mass is 320 kg are observed to compress the springs of a motor car by 50 mm when they enter it. The combined mass of the car and passengers supported by the springs is 1200 kg, find the period of vertical vibration of the loaded car. (3)

(NEAB PH02 June 1997 Q3)

3 a Explain the meanings of the following terms:

(i) free vibration

(i) forced vibration

(i) resonance (3)

b

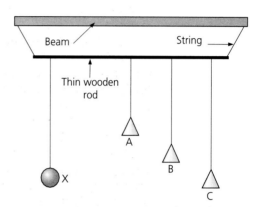

A, B and C are three pendulums, each with a light paper cone for a bob. X is another pendulum with a heavy metal bob. Pendulum X is displaced perpendicular to the plane containing the bobs at rest and then released.

Compare the motions of pendulums A, B and C to that of X, with reference to period and amplitude. (3)

(NEAB PH02 June 1997 Q4)

2 Waves

On May 22, 1960, the largest earthquake ever recorded scientifically, occurred in southern Chile. Fifteen hours later a huge seismic sea wave, known as a tsunami, arrived in Hawaii, 6600 miles away from the earthquake's epicentre. The wave reached a maximum height of 10.7 m and travelled at a speed of over 13 m s^{-1} (30 mph). The wave destroyed over 500 buildings and killed 61 people.

Tsunamis can be extremely destructive but they are strangely difficult to detect. Out in the deep ocean they may be only half a metre high, though they travel at speeds of up to 800 km h^{-1}. As a tsunami reaches the shallower water near a coast, it slows down and grows, reaching a height of up to 20 or even 30 m.

Wave damage in Hawaii following the 1960 Chilean Earthquake.

But these seismic waves would be dwarfed by the tsunami that scientists are predicting for the North Atlantic. Landslides also cause tsunamis and a particularly large landslide could be imminent in the Canary Islands. A large landslide into the water could push a huge wave before it, perhaps as high as 500 m. The wave would travel at a speed of around 800 kilometres per hour across the Atlantic. As the wave spread out, some of its energy would be dissipated but the wave could still be around 50 m high when it struck the coastline of North America. The energy transferred by such a wave would be devastating.

A large piece of the volcanic island of La Palma is unstable; half a trillion tonnes of rock could slip into the sea at any time.

Some of the properties of waves, especially reflection and diffraction, are discussed in *AS Physics*, Chapter 4. You may find it useful, though not essential, to refer to that chapter.

2.1 Progressive waves

Water waves on the surface of the ocean are an example of progressive waves. Progressive waves transfer energy but they do not transfer any matter. Sound waves, waves on strings and the seismic waves that are caused by earthquakes, are all examples of **progressive waves**. In each case energy is transferred by oscillating particles. As a wave passes through the material, particles vibrate about their equilibrium position. When the wave has passed, the particles return to their original positions so that the passage of a wave leaves the material itself undisturbed.

Large ocean waves transfer energy as they break on the shore, but there is no net movement of water across the ocean.

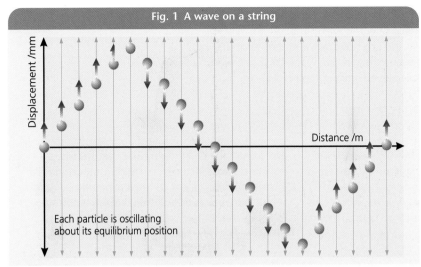

Fig. 1 A wave on a string

Displacement /mm

Distance /m

Each particle is oscillating about its equilibrium position

All the progressive waves in Table 1 are mechanical waves. They transfer energy through a material by a series of vibrations. The material that carries the vibrations is known as the **medium**.

Table 1 Some examples of mechanical waves		
Wave	**Medium**	**Cause**
Sea surface wave	Water	Wind, major disturbances to the water surface (landslides, earthquakes), tides
Waves on strings, e.g. musical instruments	Nylon or metal strings	Plucking the string (as in a guitar), scraping a bow across it (violin) or striking the string (piano)
Seismic waves	Rocks in Earth's lithosphere and mantle	Earthquakes, explosions
Sound waves	Often air, but can be liquid or solid	Vibrations of molecules in the air, caused by a vibrating object

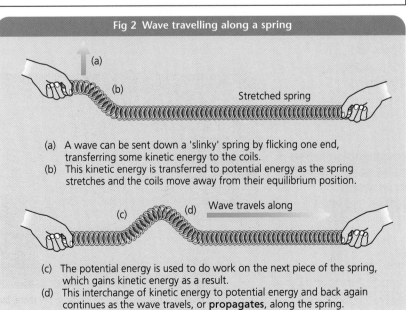

Fig 2 Wave travelling along a spring

Stretched spring

(a) A wave can be sent down a 'slinky' spring by flicking one end, transferring some kinetic energy to the coils.
(b) This kinetic energy is transferred to potential energy as the spring stretches and the coils move away from their equilibrium position.

Wave travels along

(c) The potential energy is used to do work on the next piece of the spring, which gains kinetic energy as a result.
(d) This interchange of kinetic energy to potential energy and back again continues as the wave travels, or **propagates**, along the spring.

1 During your AS Physics course you will have learnt that light can be treated as a wave. Why is light (or any other electromagnetic wave) not included in Table 1?

2 Look again at Table 1. Think of a different example of a wave motion, which is not included in the table. Use your example to add another row to Table 1.

Displacement–distance graphs and wavelength

Progressive waves can be drawn frozen in time (Fig. 3). Such a 'snapshot' shows how the displacement of the particles depends on distance at a certain time.

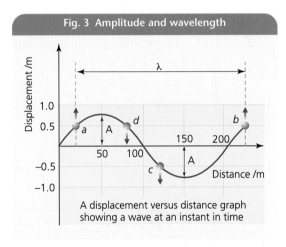

Fig. 3 Amplitude and wavelength

A displacement versus distance graph showing a wave at an instant in time

The maximum displacement caused by the wave is known as the **amplitude**, A. The amplitude is measured as the maximum displacement from the equilibrium position and may be either positive or negative. The amount of energy transferred by a wave depends on the amplitude.

The distance between any two identical points on a wave is referred to as the **wavelength**, λ. The wavelength is measured in metres.

If we concentrate on two points on the wave that are exactly one wavelength apart (such as a and b in Fig. 3), we would see that they are oscillating in time with each other. These points are said to be **in phase**. Points on the wave which are half a wavelength apart reach the opposite extremes of their oscillation at the same time, like points a and c in Fig. 3. These points are in **antiphase**, i.e. completely out of phase with each other. Other points on the wave, like a and d, have a **phase difference** that depends on what fraction of a wavelength lies between them.

3 Two seagulls are 150 m apart on the surface of the sea. They are bobbing up and down as waves pass them. When one of the seagulls is at the crest of a wave, the other is in a trough. When this happens there is one wave crest between the seagulls. What is the wavelength of the waves?

APPLICATION

Phase difference

The phase difference between two waves, or between two points on a wave, is expressed as an angle. One whole wave, or one cycle (see Fig. 4), represents an angle of 360°. Two points with a phase difference of 360° are in phase, and so a whole number of wavelengths apart. Two points with a phase difference of 180° are exactly out of phase. This corresponds to a path difference that is equal to an odd number of half wavelengths. Points on the same wave that have a phase difference of 90° are at least $\frac{1}{4}\lambda$ apart, though they could be $1\frac{1}{4}\lambda$, $2\frac{1}{4}\lambda$, $3\frac{1}{4}\lambda$, etc. apart.

are 2π radians in a whole circle. 2π radians is equivalent to 360°, which means that one radian is an angle equivalent to approximately 57.3°. A phase difference of 2π is the same as 360°, and it refers to two points which are a whole number of wavelengths apart.

4

a Sketch a displacement versus distance graph for a wave with a wavelength of 5 m and an amplitude of 1 m.

b Mark a point at the top of the first wave crest and label it A. Now mark, and label, a point that has a phase difference, compared to A, of

  i $\pi/2$ (label it B)
  ii π (label it C)
  iii 2π (label it D)

5 Two points on a wave have a phase difference of $\pi/6$ radians. Express this phase difference in degrees. If the wavelength of the wave is 3 m, what is the smallest possible distance between these points?

Fig. 4 Phase difference as an angle

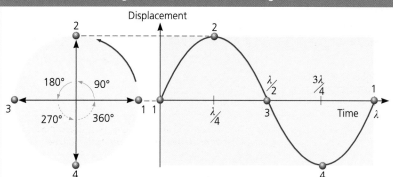

As the particle moves around the circle, its displacement above and below the *x*–axis traces out a sine wave

Phase difference is sometimes expressed in **radians** rather than in degrees. A radian is defined in terms of a circle. One radian is the angle turned through at the centre of the circle when a distance of one radius is travelled around the circumference (see Fig. 5). Since the circumference of a circle of radius *r* is $2\pi r$, there

Fig. 5 The radian

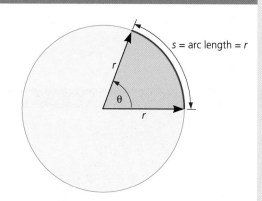

A radian is defined as the angle at the centre of a circle that is subtended by an arc that is the same length as the radius.

The angle θ is defined as $\theta = \dfrac{\text{arc length}}{\text{radius}} = \dfrac{s}{r}$ in radians

This is often written as $s = r\theta$. When $s = r$, $\theta = 1$ radian

---

Table 2 Path differences and the corresponding phase differences		
Path difference	**Phase difference (degrees)**	**Phase difference (radians)**
1λ, 2λ, 3λ, . . .,	360°, 720°, 1080°, . . ., etc.	2π, 4π, 6π, . . ., etc.
$\lambda/2$, $3\lambda/2$, $5\lambda/2$, . . .,	180°, 540°, 900°, . . ., etc.	π, 3π, 5π, . . ., etc.
$\lambda/4$, $5\lambda/4$, $9\lambda/4$, . . .,	90°, 450°, 810°, . . ., etc.	$\pi/2$, $5\pi/2$, $9\pi/2$, . . ., etc.
$\lambda/3$, $4\lambda/3$, $7\lambda/3$, . . .,	120°, 480°, 840°, . . ., etc.	$2\pi/3$, $8\pi/3$, $14\pi/3$, . . ., etc.

Displacement–time graphs and frequency

Rather than sketch a wave at a point in time, we can concentrate on one point and sketch how its displacement varies with time (Fig. 6). The graph looks very similar to Fig. 3, but in this graph two identical points are separated by a certain time, rather than by a certain distance. The time taken for one complete wave to pass by is known as the **period**, T, of the wave, and it is measured in seconds.

The period of wind-driven ocean surface waves is typically around 10 seconds. That means that there is $1/10$ of a wave every second. In other words the **frequency** of the waves is $1/10 = 0.1$ Hz. This inverse relationship between the period of a wave and its frequency can be written as

$$f = \frac{1}{T} \quad \text{or} \quad T = \frac{1}{f}$$

6 A tuning fork gives out a note of frequency 256 Hz. What is the period of these sound waves?

7 One of the unusual features of a tsunami is its long period, typically about 1 hour. What is the frequency of such a tsunami?

Table 3 Speed of sound

Material	Speed of sound (m s^{-1})
Iron	5000
Water (at 25°C)	1498
Air (at 0°C)	331.3

Wave speed

The speed of a mechanical wave depends on the properties of the medium. In particular the wave speed depends on:

- The size of the forces between each vibrating particle, that is the **elasticity** of the medium.

- The **inertia** of the vibrating particles, i.e. how difficult it is to accelerate each particle (see Fig. 7).

For example, sound travels much more quickly through a solid than through a liquid or a gas (see Table 3), because the forces between adjacent particles are so much stronger.

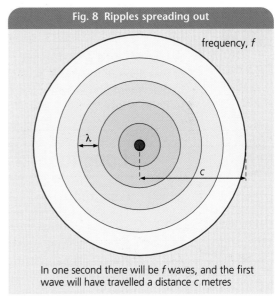

Fig. 8 Ripples spreading out

frequency, f

λ

c

In one second there will be f waves, and the first wave will have travelled a distance c metres

The speed of a wave, c, is connected to its wavelength, λ, and its frequency, f. Think about the ripples that spread out when you dip your finger in and out of the water of a lake (see Fig. 8). If the circular waves that spread out have a speed c, then after 1 second the first wave will have travelled c metres from your finger. If the frequency at which you tap is f, then after 1 second there are f waves occupying a distance c. The length of each wave, λ, is therefore

$$\lambda = \frac{c}{f}$$

This relationship is true for all waves and is usually written:

$$c = f \lambda$$

The equation can be used to calculate the speed of a wave, if its wavelength and frequency are known. For example a wind-driven ocean wave has a frequency of around 0.1 Hz and a wavelength of around 100 m.

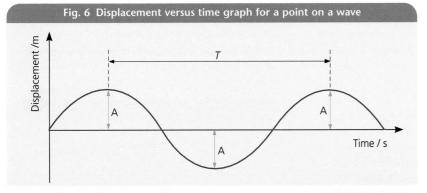

Fig. 6 Displacement versus time graph for a point on a wave

Displacement /m

T

A

A

A

Time / s

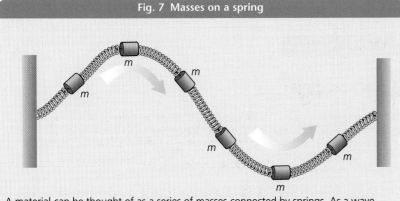

Fig. 7 Masses on a spring

m m m m m m

A material can be thought of as a series of masses connected by springs. As a wave progresses through the material, the springs stretch and exert forces on the masses. A wave would travel relatively slowly through a system of weak springs and large masses

This gives a wave speed of:

$$c = 100 \text{ m} \times 0.1 \text{ Hz} = 10 \text{ m s}^{-1}$$

Compare this with the speed of a tsunami that has a low frequency of 2.7×10^{-4} Hz, but a long wavelength of up to 500 km in the open sea. This gives a wave speed for the tsunami of

$$c = 2.7 \times 10^{-4} \text{ Hz} \times 500\,000 \text{ m} = 140 \text{ m s}^{-1}$$

or about 500 km h^{-1}.

8 The speed of sound in air is about 330 m s^{-1}. Calculate the wavelength of a sound wave that has a frequency of 256 Hz.

9 The BBC transmits Radio 4 on the long-wave band at a wavelength of 1500 m. The speed of radio waves in air is approximately 3×10^8 m s^{-1}. Calculate the frequency of these radio waves.

2.2 Longitudinal and transverse waves

Longitudinal waves

The seismic waves that arise from earthquakes are of two distinct types. The first wave to arrive is known as the primary or **P-wave**. P-waves are an example of *longitudinal* waves (Fig. 9). Longitudinal waves have oscillations that vibrate in a direction parallel to the wave's velocity.

Sound waves are another example of longitudinal waves. Sound waves emanate from a vibrating source, like the strings of a musical instrument or the cone of a loudspeaker, which repeatedly push the air. The sound waves travel through the air in a series of **compressions** and **rarefactions**.

A compression is a region of relatively high pressure and density where the air molecules are closer together than their average position. In a rarefaction the air molecules have moved further apart than usual; this leads to a region of lower density and pressure. These variations can be plotted on a graph as in Fig. 10.

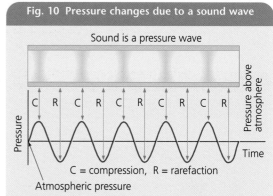

Fig. 10 Pressure changes due to a sound wave

Sound is a pressure wave

C = compression, R = rarefaction

The pressure of a sound wave is greatest at a compression and lowest at a rarefaction. Even for a very loud sound the pressure changes are small when compared to atmospheric pressure, typically 20 to 30 Pa compared to air pressure of 100 000 Pa.

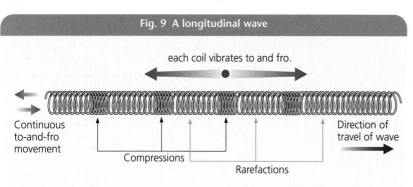

Fig. 9 A longitudinal wave

each coil vibrates to and fro.

Continuous to-and-fro movement

Compressions

Rarefactions

Direction of travel of wave

A long spring (slinky) can be used to show the passage of longitudinal wave.

The P-wave component of seismic waves travels relatively quickly, typically 7500 m s^{-1}, and is the first to arrive after an earthquake. The jolt from the P-wave rarely causes any damage to buildings, which tend to be strong in the vertical direction. The P-wave is just the herald of worse problems to come. It is the slightly slower moving **S-waves** that cause much of the damage.

> **10** Figure 11 shows how the displacement of an air molecule varies with time as a sound wave passes by.
> **a** Calculate the frequency of the sound wave.
> **b** Use the graph to plot a velocity versus time graph for the air molecule.

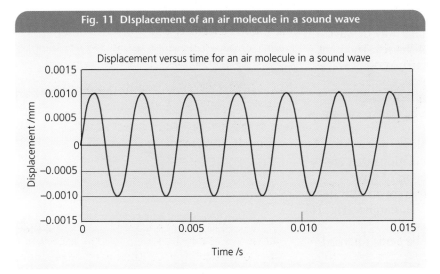

Fig. 11 DIsplacement of an air molecule in a sound wave

Displacement versus time for an air molecule in a sound wave

Transverse waves

S-waves vibrate the Earth in a totally different way to P-waves. An S-wave is an example of a *transverse* wave (Fig. 12). In a transverse wave the vibrations are at right angles to the direction of propagation of the wave. This is

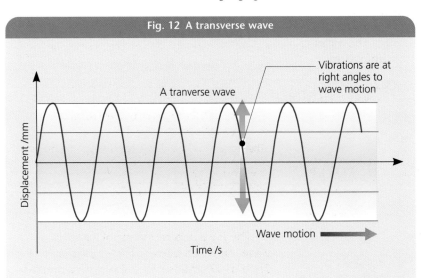

Fig. 12 A transverse wave

why S-waves are so much more destructive than P-waves: the side-to-side shaking of the ground is much harder for buildings to withstand.

Electromagnetic radiation, like light and radio, is a transverse wave motion similar to simple waves on a string. However, there is an important difference. Electromagnetic (EM) waves do not require a medium in which to travel. All the waves in the electromagnetic spectrum can travel through empty space, indeed they all travel at the same speed in a vacuum of around 2.997×10^8 m s^{-1}. If EM waves can travel through empty space, what exactly is it that oscillates?

The answer is that EM waves are actually linked electric and magnetic fields (see Chapter 7). These electric and magnetic fields vary in time and in space. As the electric field changes, it induces a change in a magnetic field at right angles to it. Similarly, as the magnetic field varies, it leads to a change in the associated electric field. This periodic fluctuation propagates through space as a self-perpetuating wave.

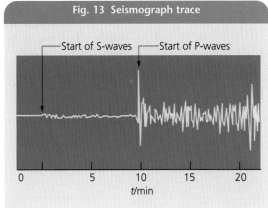

Fig. 13 Seismograph trace

> **11** The trace from a seismograph in Fig. 13 shows the delay between the arrival of the P-wave and the S-waves. This P-S interval can be used to estimate the distance from the earthquake's epicentre. If P-waves travel at 7500 m s^{-1} and S-waves travel at 4000 m s^{-1}, estimate how far away this seismograph reading was from the epicentre.

> **12** It takes at least three readings from different seismograph stations to identify the position of the earthquake's epicentre. Why is this?

Although we cannot see directly that light is a transverse wave motion, there is clear evidence

Fig. 14 Water wave

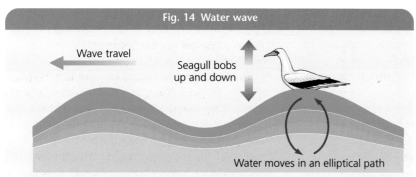

Wave travel

Seagull bobs
up and down

Water moves in an elliptical path

A surface water wave is not a true transverse wave. The water particles are not merely displaced up and down by the wave, they move in roughly elliptical paths; in the direction of the wave motion at a crest, and in the opposite direction in a trough.

that light behaves in a similar way to waves on strings or on the surface of the sea. The light can be reflected and refracted, as other waves are (see Chapter 4 *AS Physics*).

Light can also be **polarised**, which is a phenomenon only shown by transverse waves.

Polarisation

Transverse waves have oscillations that are perpendicular to the direction of wave propagation. However, there are an infinite number of ways that this can happen (Fig. 16).

If the oscillations are confined to just one plane, the wave is said to be *plane polarised*.

Polarisation and radio waves

Television and radio aerials must be fixed in the correct orientation. Radio waves are transverse electromagnetic waves which are transmitted with certain polarisation. If the direction of the electric field vector of the wave fails to match the aerial direction, the signal received will be weak (Fig. 18).

Alignment of an aerial, however, is not exactly critical. An aerial at an angle to the wave will still pick up a component of the wave's displacement vector (Fig. 19).

Fig. 15 An electromagnetic wave

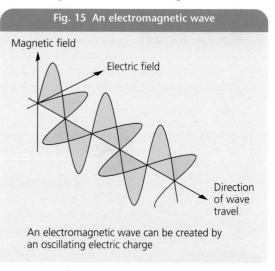

Magnetic field

Electric field

Direction of wave travel

An electromagnetic wave can be created by an oscillating electric charge

Fig. 16 Planes of polarisation

The electric vector can take many different orientations

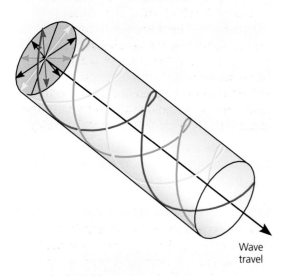

Wave travel

An unpolarised wave has vibrations that move in any direction perpendicular to the wave motion. Ordinary light is unpolarised because photons are emitted with their electric field vectors randomly orientated.

Fig. 17 Polarising filters

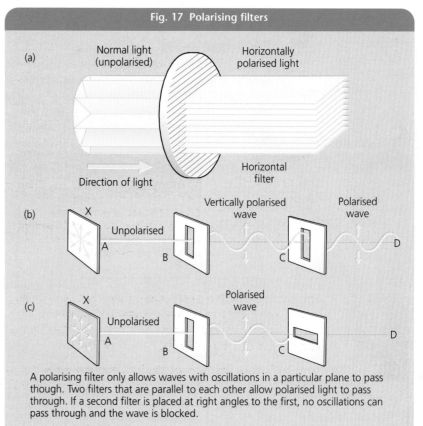

(a)

Normal light (unpolarised)

Horizontally polarised light

Direction of light

Horizontal filter

(b)

X

Unpolarised

A

B

Vertically polarised wave

C

Polarised wave

D

(c)

X

Unpolarised

A

B

Polarised wave

C

D

A polarising filter only allows waves with oscillations in a particular plane to pass though. Two filters that are parallel to each other allow polarised light to pass through. If a second filter is placed at right angles to the first, no oscillations can pass through and the wave is blocked.

Fig. 18 Signal strength and wave polarisation

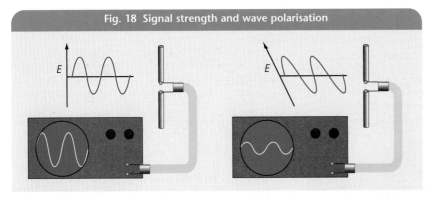

Polarisation and light

Ordinary visible light is not polarised because photons are emitted with random orientations. Polarisation can take place when light is reflected from a transparent material. The 'glare' from reflections on glass and water is therefore partly plane polarised and can be greatly reduced by using a polarising filter. 'Polaroid' is the trade name for a filter material consisting of long molecules which work in the same way as the metal bars in the microwave experiment described above.

Polaroid sunglasses are not suitable for driving because they pick out strange patterns

Fig. 19 Picking up a component of a wave

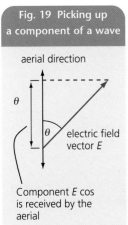

aerial direction

θ

θ electric field vector E

Component $E \cos \theta$ is received by the aerial

Polarisation provides the most convincing evidence for the transverse nature of electromagnetic waves. The electric vector of the wave interacts most strongly with matter, because the electric field causes charges to oscillate. Normally, this results in absorption of the wave. This can be demonstrated using a microwave beam with a set of parallel metal bars. If the bars are parallel to the electric field vector, the wave makes a current flow in the bars, which absorbs the energy of the wave. Not much of the wave gets through. With the bars at right angles to the electric field vector, there is little absorption (Fig. 20).

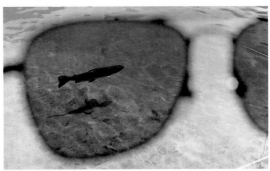

Polaroid lenses reduce the glare from the surface of water by using a polarising filter.

Fig. 20 Microwave polarisation

absorption

E

I

transmission

E

E

Polarised light can be used to visualise residual stress in some types of plastic. In this photograph, an engineer is measuring the width of a stress pattern in a thin polymer film.

in windscreens. These patterns arise from stresses which are 'frozen' into the glass. Stressed areas of some materials can cause rotation of the plane of polarisation. This effect is used by engineers to find concentrations of stress in proposed designs for structures.

Materials which affect the plane of polarisation of light are called 'optically active'. Some sugar molecules, for example, cause rotation of the plane of polarisation. Some materials will rotate the plane of polarisation in the presence of an electric field. This is technologically important: the effect is the basis of 'liquid crystal' displays.

KEY FACTS

- Transverse waves have oscillations that move at right angles to the direction of wave travel. Examples include electromagnetic waves, waves on strings and the S-wave component of seismic waves.

- Longitudinal waves have oscillations that move parallel to the direction of wave travel. Examples include sound waves and the P-waves from earthquakes.

- Transverse waves can be polarised: the direction of the displacement vector is relevant. For electromagnetic waves, the electric field vector is chosen as the direction of the plane of polarisation.

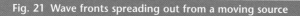

EXTENSION Waves from a moving source

The Doppler effect
As a pebble is dropped into the surface of a lake, the ripples spread out evenly in all directions. A circular wave is propagated. However, if the source of the waves moves, then the waves get crowded together in one direction, and spread out in the other (see Fig. 21). As the moving wave source comes towards you the wavelength is artificially shortened and the frequency rises. Behind the wave source, as it moves away from you, the waves are stretched out and the apparent frequency drops.

Any moving source of waves, from a train blowing a whistle, to a distant galaxy emitting light, will lead to the same phenomenon. The **Doppler** shift, as this effect is called, depends on the relative velocity of the source and observer, as compared to the speed of the waves. The faster the source moves the larger the Doppler shift. This effect is important in modern cosmology – you will learn more about it if you study astrophysics as your optional module.

The sound from the train's whistle appears to increase in frequency (pitch) as it approaches you and then decrease as the train goes past.

The police use the Doppler shift of reflected radio waves to measure the speed of passing cars.

Fig. 21 Wave fronts spreading out from a moving source

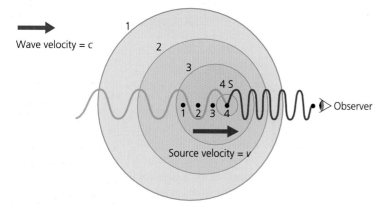

Wave velocity = c

Source velocity = v

Observer

A moving wave source (or a moving observer) changes the wave frequency that the observer will measure. The apparent frequency increases if the source is coming towards you, but it decreases when the wave goes away.

Fig. 22 A shock wave

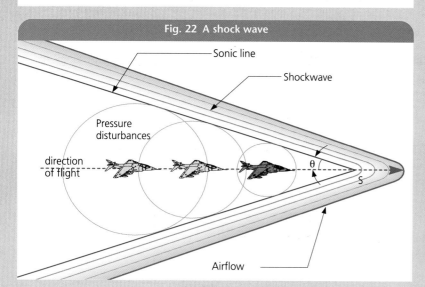

Sonic line

Shockwave

Pressure disturbances

direction of flight

θ

S

Airflow

Shock waves
When a wave source moves as fast as, or faster than, the speed of the waves themselves, the waves pile up and become a shock wave. This ability of waves to add together into a larger wave is known as **superposition** (see Section 2.3).

The bow wave is a shock wave, caused because the boat's speed is greater than the speed of the waves.

Concorde is the world's only supersonic passenger aircraft. Because Concorde moves faster than sound through the air, the sound waves pile up in front of it causing a sound shock wave. It is this that rattles the windows as Concorde flies over.

Radioactive isotopes from nuclear power stations are kept under water after use to cool down (see Chapter 9). Some of the particles that are emitted travel faster than the speed of light in water. This gives rise to a light 'shock wave' known as Cerenkov radiation.

2.2 Superposition of waves

The constant noise from a helicopter rotor is stressful for the pilot and makes communication difficult. Pilots wear 'active headphones' to reduce the noise by playing a reverse copy of the noise back into the pilot's ears.

It seems remarkable but it is possible to add two sounds together and produce silence. Active noise control works on this principle. A reverse copy of the noise is played through small loudspeakers. This 'antinoise' adds to the original noise to produce a much quieter sound (Fig. 23).

This sound 'cancellation' is possible because of what happens to waves when they are added together. When two similar waves, e.g. two sound waves or two water waves, meet, the total displacement is the *vector* sum of the two individual displacements. The vector sum means that we need to take account of whether the displacement was positive or negative. For example, if two water waves meet with their crests together, the result will be an extra-high crest. If a crest meets a trough, the resulting displacement of the water would be zero (see Fig. 24). This is known as the **principle of superposition**.

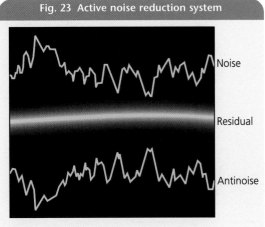

Fig. 23 Active noise reduction system

Noise

Residual

Antinoise

Adding extra noise that is out of phase with the original noise reduces the sound level.

13 The two highly unlikely wave pulses shown in Fig. 25 are heading towards each other on a stretched string. Sketch the displacement of the string after 0.1, 0.2 and 0.3.

Stationary waves

Stationary, or standing, waves are formed by two waves of the same frequency travelling in opposite directions (Fig. 26, page 30). The two waves add together, in accordance with the principle of superposition, in such a way that there are some points on the wave which do not vibrate at all. These points are called **nodes**. At other points along the wave there are places where the amplitude goes from zero

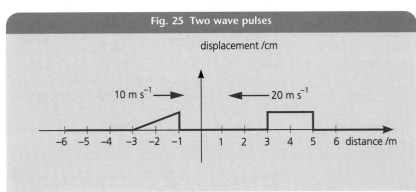

Fig. 25 Two wave pulses

displacement /cm

$10 \text{ m s}^{-1} \longrightarrow$ $\longleftarrow 20 \text{ m s}^{-1}$

−6 −5 −4 −3 −2 −1 1 2 3 4 5 6 distance /m

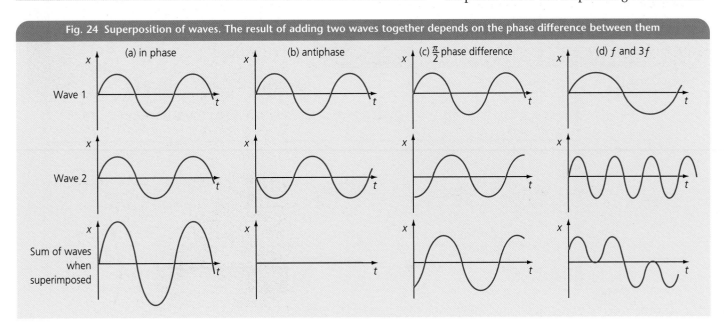

Fig. 24 Superposition of waves. The result of adding two waves together depends on the phase difference between them

(a) in phase (b) antiphase (c) $\frac{\pi}{2}$ phase difference (d) f and $3f$

Wave 1

Wave 2

Sum of waves when superimposed

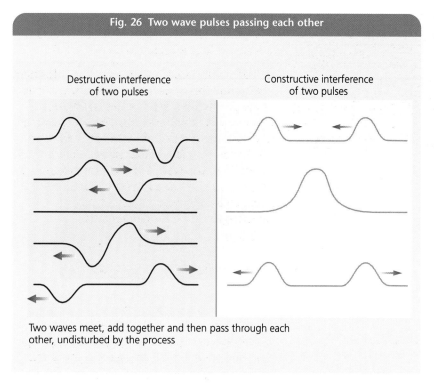

Fig. 26 Two wave pulses passing each other

Destructive interference of two pulses

Constructive interference of two pulses

Two waves meet, add together and then pass through each other, undisturbed by the process

by the wave. In a stationary wave the nodes and antinodes are both fixed and no energy is transferred along the wave. This is because a stationary wave is formed in systems that have boundaries. Progressive waves are reflected at these boundaries and a stationary wave is caused by the superposition of these reflected waves. The energy is not transferred beyond the boundaries of the system and becomes stored in the standing wave.

There is another difference between progressive and standing waves. On a progressive wave there is always a phase difference between adjacent points. In a standing wave all the points between consecutive nodes are vibrating in phase. All these points reach their maximum displacement at the same time, but each point has a different amplitude. Points on a progressive wave all have the same amplitude, but reached at different times.

Waves on strings

The standing wave on the string of a musical instrument is set up because of the superposition of the waves that reflect from the fixed ends of the string. This phenomenon can be investigated using the apparatus shown in Fig. 28. The vibration generator causes a wave to be sent along the string. At certain frequencies a standing wave

to a maximum; these are called **antinodes**. If the frequency of the wave stays fixed, the positions of the nodes and antinodes do not change; there is always a distance of half a wavelength between two successive nodes, or antinodes (see Fig. 27).

Progressive waves have crests that move at the speed of the wave and energy is transferred

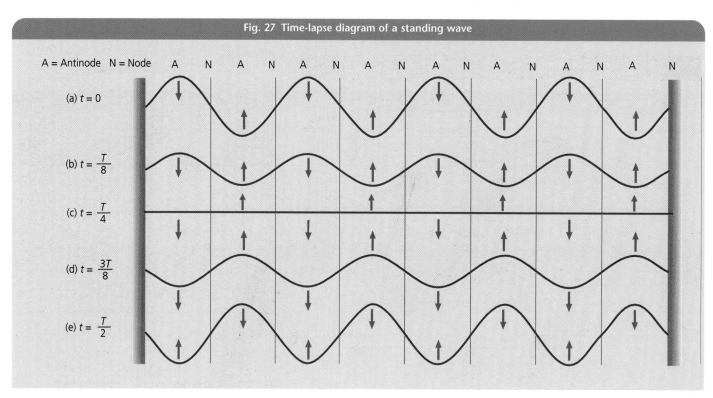

Fig. 27 Time-lapse diagram of a standing wave

A = Antinode   N = Node

(a) $t = 0$

(b) $t = \dfrac{T}{8}$

(c) $t = \dfrac{T}{4}$

(d) $t = \dfrac{3T}{8}$

(e) $t = \dfrac{T}{2}$

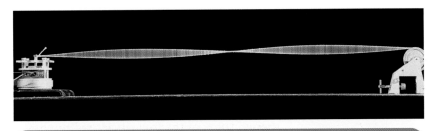

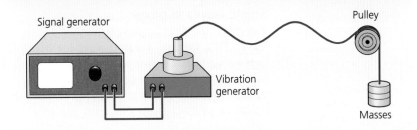

Fig. 28 Apparatus for Melde's experiment

Signal generator
Vibration generator
Pulley
Masses

The driving frequency of the oscillator is varied until it matches the natural frequency of vibration of the string. This is an example of *resonance* (see Chapter 1). The string can be made to resonate at its fundamental frequency, or at the frequency of the harmonics.

is set up. These frequencies are known as **harmonics**. The frequencies at which these harmonics occur depend on several factors:

• The tension in the string. In the experiment adding extra masses to the end of the string will increase the tension.

• The mass per unit length of the string. Thicker, heavier strings vibrate more slowly and the harmonics occur at lower frequencies.

• The length of the string. A shorter string has shorter wavelength vibrations, which leads to higher frequencies.

For a string that is fixed at both ends, there can be no vibrations at the ends of the string. These points are always nodes. The lowest frequency at which a standing wave is formed is known as the **fundamental** frequency or first harmonic. This standing wave has a single antinode in the centre of the string (Table 4). There is one half of a full wavelength on the string so for a string of length *l*, the wavelength of the fundamental is:

$$\lambda = 2l$$

and since $f = \frac{c}{\lambda}$

$$f_0 = \frac{c}{2l}$$

where f_0 is the fundamental frequency.

The second harmonic, also known as the first overtone, is formed with a node in the centre of the string. In this case there is a whole wavelength on the string so

$$\lambda = t \quad \text{or} \quad f_1 = \frac{c}{l} = 2f_0$$

The second harmonic has twice the frequency of the fundamental. A similar argument shows that for a vibrating string all the overtones have frequencies that are integral multiples of the fundamental frequency.

Table 4 Modes of vibrations of a string		
Harmonic	**Standing wave pattern**	**Frequency**
First harmonic (Fundamental)	Antinode	$f_0 = \frac{c}{2l}$
Second harmonic (1st overtone)	Node	$f_0 = \frac{c}{l}$
Third harmonic (2nd overtone)	Node Node	$f_0 = \frac{3c}{2l}$
Fourth harmonic (3rd overtone)	Node Node Node	$f_0 = \frac{2c}{l}$

Musical instruments rely on stationary waves to produce notes.

The vibrations on a real string, on a guitar or violin for example, are much more complex. Many of the harmonics can be present at the same time, though the

Fig. 29 Addition of harmonics to form complex wave

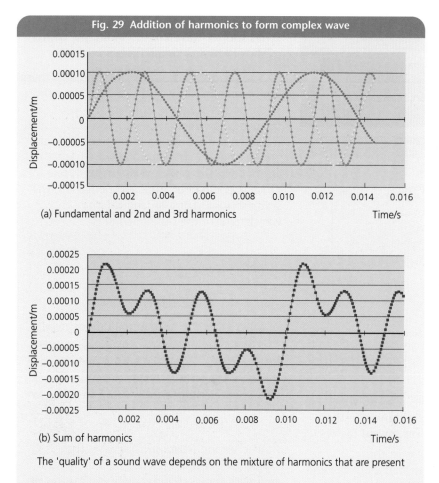

(a) Fundamental and 2nd and 3rd harmonics

Time/s

(b) Sum of harmonics

Time/s

The 'quality' of a sound wave depends on the mixture of harmonics that are present

amplitude of the higher overtones is usually smaller. As the string vibrates it sets a progressive sound wave in motion in the air around it, amplified by the sound box that is the body of the instrument. The sound wave will vibrate with the same mixture of frequencies that the string vibrated with, though some of the frequencies are amplified more than others by the sound box.

Sound waves in pipes

It is possible to set up longitudinal standing waves, by reflecting a sound wave for example.

The air in the tubes and pipes of musical instruments like organs and oboes can be made to vibrate as a stationary wave. Sound waves can reflect from the open end of a pipe, as well as the closed end, so that standing waves can be set up in both kinds of pipe. There is always a node at a closed end of the pipe, and an antinode at an open end. That means that different modes of vibration occur in pipes that are closed at one end, like an oboe, or open at both ends, like a flute. In an open pipe all the harmonics can exist, f_0, $2f_0$, $3f_0$, etc., whereas a closed pipe will only support the odd harmonics, f_0, $3f_0$, $5f_0$, etc. The fundamental note of a closed pipe is always at a lower pitch, half the frequency, of an open pipe of the same length.

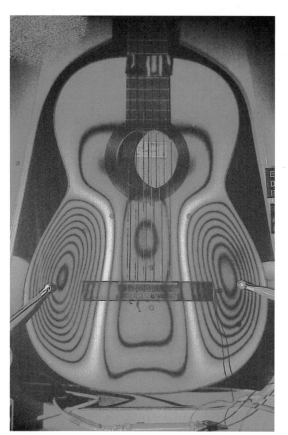

Holograms are used to show two-dimensional standing waves on the front plate of a guitar. These patterns are used to help in the design of better guitars.

Fig. 30 Apparatus for setting up a standing sound wave

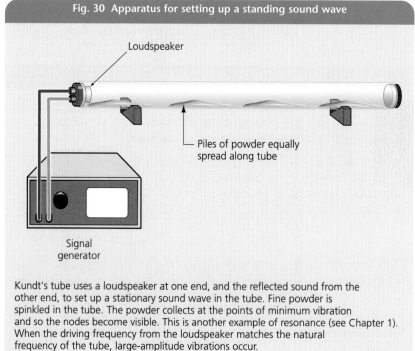

Loudspeaker

Piles of powder equally spread along tube

Signal generator

Kundt's tube uses a loudspeaker at one end, and the reflected sound from the other end, to set up a stationary sound wave in the tube. Fine powder is sprinkled in the tube. The powder collects at the points of minimum vibration and so the nodes become visible. This is another example of resonance (see Chapter 1). When the driving frequency from the loudspeaker matches the natural frequency of the tube, large-amplitude vibrations occur.

Fig. 31 Vibrations in open and closed pipes

Closed pipe

length = l

1/4 λ

Fundamental f_0
$\lambda = 4l$, $f_0 = \dfrac{c}{4l}$

3/4 λ

1st overtone f_1
$\lambda = \dfrac{4}{3}l$, $f_1 = \dfrac{3c}{4l} = 3f_0$

5/4 λ

2nd overtone f_2
$\lambda = \dfrac{4}{5}l$, $f_2 = \dfrac{5c}{4l} = 5f_0$

Open pipe

$\lambda/2$

Fundamental
$\lambda = 2l$, $f_0 = \dfrac{c}{2l}$

λ

1st overtone
$\lambda = l$, $f_1 = \dfrac{c}{l} = 2f_0$

3/2 λ

2nd overtone
$\lambda = \dfrac{2}{3}l$, $f_2 = \dfrac{3c}{2l} = 3f_0$

Although the sound wave is a longitudinal wave, it can be drawn as a tranverse wave, plotting pressure changes on the y-axis as a function of position on the x-axis

14 The air in a pipe that is open at each end is made to vibrate. If the pipe is 30 cm long, what frequency would the fundamental note be? How would the fundamental frequency change if the pipe were then closed at one end (speed of sound in air = 330 m s^{-1})?

15 Sketch the standing wave pattern for the fifth harmonic for a wave on a string. Sketch the same harmonic for a sound wave in a pipe closed at one end.

In a trumpet the length of the vibrating air column can be altered by use of valves, but the real skill of the trumpeter is in blowing in the right way to excite the required harmonics.

KEY FACTS

- The principle of superposition says that when two waves meet, the resulting disturbance at any point is the vector sum of the two individual disturbances.

- Stationary waves are formed by the superposition of two waves of the same frequency and amplitude that are travelling in opposite directions.

- Stationary waves have points of zero amplitude called nodes that are half a wavelength apart.

- Stationary waves do not transfer energy as a progressive wave does.

APPLICATION

Standing waves made from light

Stationary waves occur on vibrating strings, stationary sound waves in columns of air, and it is even possible to create stationary light waves by reflecting light. A standing light wave can be formed by reflecting a laser beam back on itself. This standing wave can be used to direct a stream of atoms to a high degree of precision.

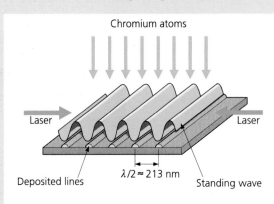

Chromium atoms are directed down onto a surface, typically silicon, where they are deposited. Just before the atoms hit the surface, they are deflected by the standing wave of laser light rather like raindrops falling on a corrugated iron roof. The atoms collect into lines and so form an array of narrow lines on the surface.

Scanning Atomic Force Microscope (AFM) image of chromium lines deposited on a silicon surface. A standing wave of laser light acts as an array of microcylindrical lenses, focusing the atoms into an array of parallel lines. The standing wave is tuned to the deep-blue atomic resonance at 425.43 nanometres. The spacing between the nodes is therefore half of that, or 212.78 nm. Thus each trough acts like a conventional cylindrical lens but only 0.2 microns across. This lens then focuses the atoms to much smaller lines, perhaps as small as 10 nm.

EXAMINATION QUESTIONS

1 a Graph A shows the displacement at time $t = 0$ at different points on a progressive wave. Graph B shows the situation at $t = 0.10$ s.

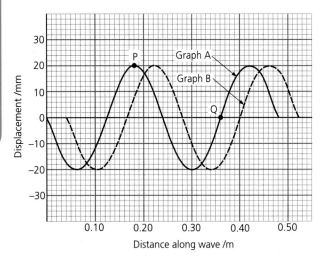

Use graphs A and B to determine, for the wave,
  (i) the wavelength,
  (ii) the amplitude,
  (iii) the wave speed,
  (iv) the frequency of the wave,
  (v) the phase difference between points P and Q marked on graph A. (6)

b Using the grid below, sketch a graph to show the variation with time of the displacement of point P on the graph in part (a), showing numerical scales on both axes. (3)

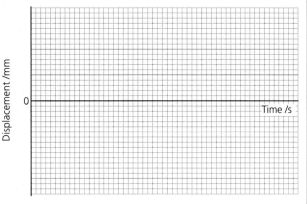

c When a stone is thrown into a still pond, circular ripples spread out. How could you tell, from observations of the ripples, whether or not they were travelling at constant speed? Explain your answer. (2)

d Describe an experiment to demonstrate that light waves are transverse. (4)

(PH02 June 1998)

2 a Graph A below shows the variation, at time $t = 0$, of displacement with distance along the path of a progressive transverse wave of constant amplitude. The wave is travelling in the direction of the arrow at 0.40 m s⁻¹.

(i) For the wave shown, determine
The amplitude,
The wavelength,
The frequency of the vibrations.

(ii) On the same axes as graph A, show the position of the wave at $t = 0.05$ s.

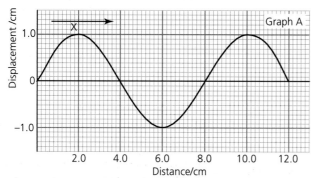

Graph A

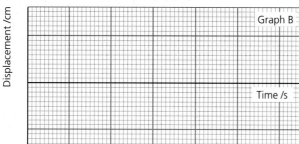

Graph B

(iii) On the set of axes labelled graph B, sketch a graph showing displacement against time for the particle whose position at $t = 0$ is shown by X on graph A, starting at $t = 0$ and showing scales on both axes.

(iv) On the appropriate graph, show the positions of two particles, P and Q, which differ in phase by π radians. (7)

b Graph C below shows the variation of displacement with distance along a stationary transverse wave at time $t = 0$ when the displacement of the particles is the greatest. The period of the vibrations causing the wave is 0.10 s.

(i) Draw, on the same axes, the appearance of the wave at $t = 0.025$ s, labelling this graph D, and the appearance of the wave at $t = 0.050$ s, labelling this graph E.

(ii) Compare the frequency, amplitude and phase of the particles whose positions at $t = 0$ are shown by V, W and Z.

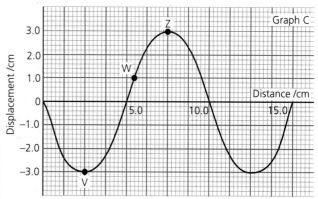

Graph C

(iii) State the two conditions necessary for the production of a stationary wave. (8)

(PH02 June 2000)

3 a Explain what is meant by

(i) unpolarised light,

(i) plane polarised light. (2)

b

A light source appears bright when viewed through two pieces of polaroid, as shown. Describe what is seen when B is slowly rotated through 180° in its own plane. (2)

c (i) Tick which of the following categories of waves can be polarised.

radio	
ultrasonic	
microwaves	
ultraviolet	

(ii) State your criterion for deciding which to pick. (2)

(PH02 June 2000)

3   Diffraction and interference

The Constellation of Ursa Major (The Plough).

Ursa Major, or The Plough as it is better known, is one of the most easily recognised constellations in the sky. It is less easy to see that the second star in the 'handle' of the plough, Mizar, is in fact a double star. Arab astronomers named Mizar's companion star Al-Jat, the passenger, and we now know it as Alcor. It is traditionally a test of good eyesight to be able to distinguish Mizar and Alcor. Through a small telescope further details become apparent: Mizar is itself a double star.

But why is it that we need a telescope to help us to distinguish these stars? The reason lies in the wave nature of light. Because light is a wave it tends to spread out as it passes through an aperture, like the pupil of your eye or a telescope lens. This spreading, or *diffraction*, is what limits our ability to resolve separate objects. The light from each of the stars overlaps and becomes indistinguishable. The effects of diffraction are less with larger apertures; that is why a telescope with a large-diameter lens is needed to take high-

resolution photographs of the sky.

It is impractical to build telescopes with larger and larger lenses or mirrors and this limits our ability to see detail in the sky. However, another property of light may well come to the rescue. Because light is a wave, two light waves add together according to the principle of superposition. If the position of two telescopes is very accurately known, and the time at each telescope is measured with high precision, the light from the telescopes can be added together. This technique, which is called optical interferometry, simulates an aperture as big as the distance between the telescopes. Modern computing techniques are used to generate high-resolution images. Optical interferometry is now being used to measure the diameter of stars and to study binary star systems.

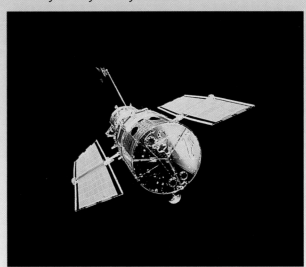

The large aperture of the Hubble Space Telescope improves its resolving power.

These images of Capella were taken on September 13 and September 28 1995 at Cambridge University. The images clearly show the rotation of this binary star over a 15-day period.

This unconventional looking telescope is the optical interferometer at Cambridge University that is now being used to take high-resolution pictures of stars.

3.1 Interference

It is the interference of two light waves that leads to the coloured fringes in soap bubbles and oil films.

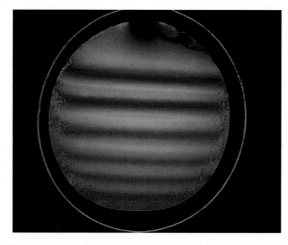

Fig. 1 Superposition of waves

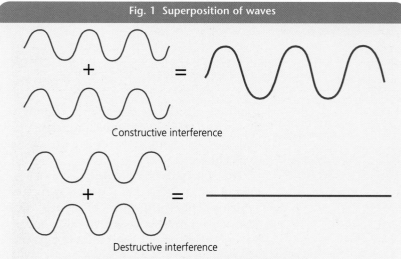

Constructive interference

Destructive interference

Two similar waves may add together (reinforce) to make a double-height wave, or add together so as to cancel each other out.

Fig. 2 Interference between two waves

The waves at **A** have travelled equal distances, AP and AQ, so they *must* be in phase. They will add together, giving twice the signal strength. Waves at **B** have a path difference of BQ – BP = 1 wavelength. These two waves will be in phase, so the signal will increase in strength. Waves at **C** don't fit this simple rule. **CP** is 3.5 wavelengths and CQ is 4 wavelengths. There is a half-wavelength difference, so the waves will be in antiphase. That means they will cancel out. The antenna at **C** would receive a very weak signal. A, B and C are three points in space. Performing the same calculations for other points shows that there are lines along which the signal is stronger (constructive interference) and lines of almost complete cancellation (destructive interference).

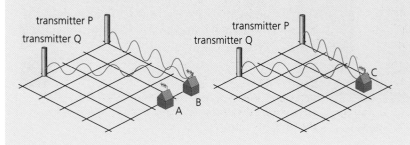

When people talk about **interference**, they usually mean the unwanted noise on a radio receiver, or some crackling on a mobile phone. In physics, the word interference has a much more precise meaning. Interference is the effect produced when two sets of identical waves are added together.

Interference is a particular example of the **principle of superposition** (see page 29 of Chapter 2) of waves. This principle says that the overall displacement caused when two waves meet is equal to the sum of the displacements from each individual wave (Fig. 1). The principle applies to all electromagnetic waves. It also works for mechanical waves in a medium which obeys Hooke's law. Waves can be added together at any point in space, even though they may have come from different directions. Superposition even works when the waves are of different frequencies, but interference effects only become noticeable when the waves are of the same frequency.

Suppose that you live in a village that is between two television transmitters which are broadcasting at the same frequency. The total signal strength that you receive is the sum of the two separate waves. If the waves arrive **in phase**, you will receive a stronger signal. If the waves arrive out of phase, you will receive a weaker signal. Although the waves may be in phase when they leave the transmitter, the phase difference between them when they arrive at your house depends on how far each wave has travelled. In particular the total signal strength will depend on the **path difference** between the waves, that is the difference in the distance travelled by each wave (see Fig. 2).

When the path difference is a whole number of wavelengths, λ, 2λ, 3λ, 4λ, ..., $n\lambda$, the waves will be exactly in phase and will add together to give a larger wave. This is **constructive interference**.

Destructive interference occurs when the path difference is an odd number of half wavelengths, $\frac{1}{2}\lambda$, $\frac{3}{2}\lambda$, ..., $(n + \frac{1}{2})\lambda$, where n = 0, 1, 2, ..., since the waves will arrive in antiphase.

It would be inconvenient to have strips of the country where there was very poor TV or radio reception because of destructive

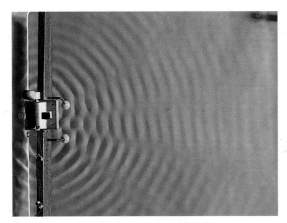

Interference between ripples on a water tank.

interference. Therefore, adjacent transmitters ensure that the waves cannot interfere by using either different frequencies or different polarisations.

Fig. 3 Interference bands

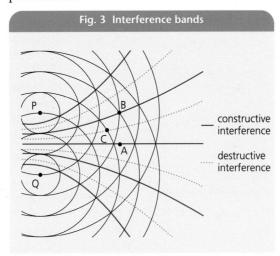

— constructive interference

···· destructive interference

Interference and sound

Sound waves are added together according to the principle of superposition, but we don't get persistent interference patterns except in special circumstances. We need to have two loudspeakers playing identical sounds, notes of the same frequency and the same

Sound is often played through two identical loudspeakers, but we don't get parts of the room where the sound is very quiet and other parts where it is extra loud.

Fig. 4 Apparatus for observing interference between sound waves

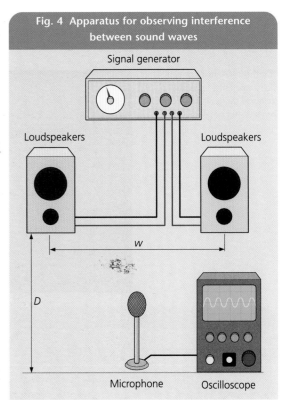

amplitude, before we can observe regions of silence and of louder sound. Sound sources that produce identical waves like this are said to be **coherent**.

The apparatus in Fig. 4 will produce an interference pattern that can be observed with a microphone, with regions of silence where destructive interference is cancelling out the waves. The distance between these regions, s, will depend on:

- The wavelength of the sound wave, λ
- The distance between the speakers, w
- The distance between the speakers and the microphone, D.

It can be shown (Fig. 8) that the separation of two adjacent interference minima (or between two adjacent maxima) is

$$s = \frac{\lambda D}{w}$$

If we had two loudspeakers placed 2 m apart, each playing a sound wave of frequency 400 Hz, how far apart would the interference maxima be? The wavelength of the sound waves is

$$\lambda = \frac{c}{f}$$

where c is the speed of sound, say 340 m s^{-1}.

$$\lambda = \frac{340 \text{ m s}^{-1}}{400 \text{ s}^{-1}} = 0.85 \text{ m}$$

If we observe the interference pattern at a distance of 5 m from the speakers, the fringes will be:

$$s = \frac{\lambda D}{w} = 0.85 \times \frac{5}{2} \text{ m} = 2.13 \text{ m apart}$$

1 Two loudspeakers are placed so that they face each other at a distance of 10 m apart. The loudspeakers are playing identical notes of wavelength 1 m. A microphone is moved along a line from one loudspeaker to the other. What would the microphone detect? Explain your answer.

2 An interference pattern is created by loudspeakers placed 3 m apart. An observer, 5 m away from the loudspeakers (see Fig. 5) detects quiet regions that are 50 cm apart. What frequency note are the loudspeakers playing?
Suggest three changes that could be made to the situation that would make the quiet regions further apart.

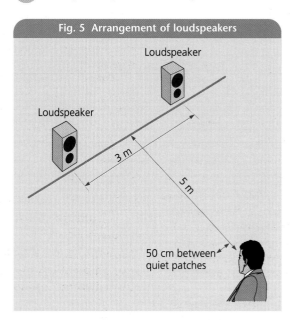

Fig. 5 Arrangement of loudspeakers

Loudspeaker

Loudspeaker

3 m

5 m

50 cm between quiet patches

Interference and the nature of light

It seems strange to suggest that adding two beams of light together can lead to darkness, and yet under some circumstances this is possible. The interference of light is one of the main pieces of evidence for the wave theory of light.

This theory has not always been accepted. Isaac Newton suggested that light was made up of tiny solid particles which he called corpuscles. His theory was an educated guess,

and one that he didn't defend strongly, though he used it to explain the reflection and refraction of light.

The case for the wave nature of light was first put convincingly by Thomas Young (1773–1829). He demonstrated that light could show an interference pattern by putting hairs or silk threads in front of an illuminated slit. Supporters of the corpuscle theory could not explain this interference pattern. The Young's slits experiment is still used to demonstrate the wave nature of light. The experiment also allows you to calculate the wavelength of the light.

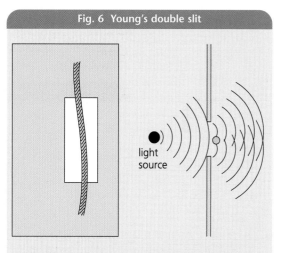

Fig. 6 Young's double slit

light source

Thomas Young effectively created two slits when he stretched a fibre in front of an illuminated slit. Waves from each side of the fibre overlapped and caused interference.

We now know that neither the particle model nor the wave model is completely correct. Both are models. Models help us to understand something that is not directly observable, by comparing it with things we *can* see. Our most recent model of light is that it consists of **photons**. Photons can be thought of as little packets of electromagnetic waves, each lasting about a nanosecond.

It is normally very difficult to make white light show interference effects because:

- The wavelength is so small (about 500 nm on average). This means that the interference bands are too close together to be discernible.

- The range of colours in white light hides the interference effects. Destructive interference for one colour is masked by the presence of other colours.

- Different photons are not necessarily in phase and have random polarisations.

To show any stable and detectable interference effect, the wave sources need to be **coherent**. They need to be:

- the same frequency;
- in a constant phase relationship;
- polarised in the same plane;
- of roughly the same amplitude.

Coherence can be achieved by using **monochromatic** light, light of a single frequency. The constant phase relationship is achieved by using two different parts of the same wave, perhaps by allowing the wave to pass through two slits (see Fig. 7). **Diffraction** will ensure that these two waves overlap and so interfere with each other. Diffraction is where waves spread out after passing through a narrow gap.

Fig. 7 Two-slit interference

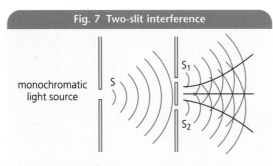

Waves emerging from S_1 and S_2 are coherent, so produce observable interference.

Each slit acts as a point source of waves: the resulting interference system is the same as that for two point sources in a ripple tank of water, or the sound waves from two loudspeakers. You cannot see the ripples in an electromagnetic field, but you can detect the effect when the waves hit a screen. Constructive interference produces a bright area, while destructive interference produces a dark area. These observed patterns are called interference fringes.

The formula which relates wavelength to the fringe spacing is just the same as for sound waves (see Fig. 8 for derivation):

$$\frac{\text{fringe separation}}{\text{wavelength}} = \frac{\text{distance to screen}}{\text{slit separation}}$$

$$\frac{s}{\lambda} = \frac{D}{w}$$

For example, with the screen at a distance $D = 1$ m, a slit separation of 1 mm would produce two fringes per millimetre for yellow light of 500 nm wavelength.

Fig. 8 Deriving the Young's slits equation

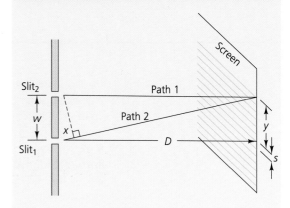

Paths 1 and 2 differ by a few wavelengths of light in a total distance of around a metre.

We can say to within less than a thousandth of a percent error that: path 1 = path 2 = D.

The tiny difference between path 1 and path 2 (shown as x on the diagram) must be a whole number of wavelengths for constructive interference to occur.

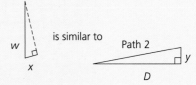

There are two similar triangles on the diagram. For similar triangles, the ratio of sides is the same, so:

$$\frac{x}{w} = \frac{y}{\text{path 2}} \approx \frac{y}{D}$$

If we now move up to the next bright fringe, x increases by one wavelength, λ, and y increases by the fringe separation, s.

Therefore $\dfrac{x}{w} = \dfrac{y}{D}$

gives: $\dfrac{(x + \lambda)}{w} = \dfrac{(y + s)}{D}$

and so: $\dfrac{\lambda}{w} = \dfrac{s}{D}$ or $\dfrac{s}{\lambda} = \dfrac{D}{w}$

The equation is valid whenever there is two-source interference with $D \gg \lambda$.

Coherent sources can now be produced easily using **lasers**. Laser light differs from other sources in that photons are released by a process of 'stimulated emission'. The monochromatic light from the laser is effectively one long wave train, with constant phase over long time periods. Lasers are therefore ideal for showing interference effects with visible light.

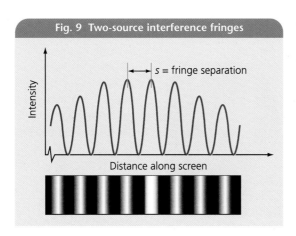
Fig. 9 Two-source interference fringes

s = fringe separation

Intensity

Distance along screen

3 All electromagnetic waves show the same sort of pattern of two-source interference (Fig. 9), but the spacing of fringes varies enormously. Why?

4 Suggest two ways of increasing fringe separation for the same colour of light.

5 Two radio transmitters are 1 km apart. Both transmit a 3 MHz radio wave. The waves are coherent. If a car moves along a road parallel to the line joining the transmitters, how will the received signal change? If the road is 10 km from the transmitters, how far apart will positions of maximum reception be?

APPLICATION

Interference and standing waves

Portable televisions often work well in one part of a room, but the signal is much weaker in other places. The signal can change when people walk around the room or cars drive past. These problems occur because of interference between the incoming wave and its reflections, from people or from walls. The problem is much greater when there is a metal surface nearby, such as a car body, which acts as a good reflector. When the incoming wave and the reflected wave travel along the same line, the interference can set up a **standing wave** (Fig. 10).

Antinodes are positions of constructive interference, separated by a distance $\lambda/2$. **Nodes** are positions of destructive interference, also separated by $\lambda/2$. At a reflecting surface, there must always be a displacement node.

For television transmissions, the wavelength is of the order of 0.6 m. Moving a portable television set 15 cm could therefore take it from an antinode to a node. The signal intensity is very weak at a node, so the picture will degenerate.

More distant reflectors can give rise to another television problem: *ghosting*. Ghosting shows on the screen as a faint second image, slightly offset from the first. It arises from the time delay between receiving the wave from the transmitter and the reflected wave. A large building 300 m away would give rise to a time delay of about 2 μs, during which time the dot has moved about a centimetre across a typical screen.

6 Explain why a mobile phone conversation sometimes fades as you walk around the house.

7 Television aerials have a reflector a short distance from their active aerial element (Fig. 11). Suggest two reasons for this.

8 A television with an outdoor aerial is found to suffer from a fluctuating signal when an aircraft flies over. Explain why this happens.

Fig. 10 Reflections interfering to create a standing wave
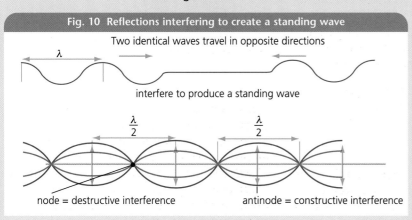
Two identical waves travel in opposite directions

λ

interfere to produce a standing wave

$\frac{\lambda}{2}$ $\frac{\lambda}{2}$

node = destructive interference   antinode = constructive interference

Fig. 11 Yagi television aerial
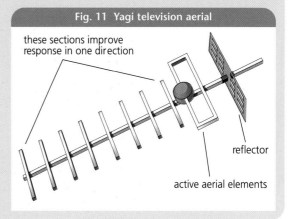
these sections improve response in one direction

reflector

active aerial elements

Getting rid of reflections

Lenses can be coated with an anti-reflective coating that prevents light being reflected from the lens.

About 5% of the light that hits a transparent glass surface is reflected. This can be reduced by coating the lens with a thin layer of a material such as magnesium fluoride or a metal oxide.

This gives rise to a second reflection from the lens, one from the coating and one from the glass. It is destructive interference between these two reflected waves that reduces the amount of reflected light.

Suppose that the lens is coated with a thin layer of magnesium fluoride that has a **refractive index** (see *AS Physics*, page 64) of

1.38. The lens itself is made of glass that has a refractive index of about 1.50. It is not possible to make a coating that is the correct thickness for all wavelengths of light. If we choose to make the lens non-reflective in the middle of the optical range, say 550 nm (yellow), the wavelength in the coating will be less:

$$\lambda = \frac{550}{1.38} \ nm = 399 \ nm$$

The path difference needs to be a half-wavelength, but this is there and back through the film, so $2t = 399/2$. The thickness needs to be 100 nm.

This only works exactly for this particular wavelength and some wavelengths will still be reflected. If the incident light is 'white', the reflected light will be deficient in yellow and will be richer in red and blue light. The lens will look purple.

Anti-reflective coatings prevent light being reflected from the lens. Since less is reflected, more light is transmitted through the lens.

Fig. 12 Thin-film interference

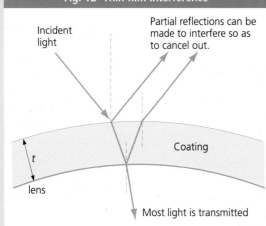

Incident light

Partial reflections can be made to interfere so as to cancel out.

Coating

t

lens

Most light is transmitted

The path difference between two reflected rays is approximately 2t. If 2t is equal to half a wavelength, then the two waves will be out of phase and the waves will interfere destructively so that no light is reflected.

9 Oil films on water appear coloured when viewed in 'white' light. This is due to constructive interference. Explain, with the help of a diagram, why the coloured fringes appear.

- Superposition is the vector addition of waves. Coherent waves are needed for an observable interference pattern.

- Coherent waves have a constant phase relationship. For complete cancellation the waves also need to have the same amplitude, the same frequency and the same polarisation.

- Two sources with the same phase will interfere constructively if the path difference is a whole number of wavelengths. Destructive interference will occur for an odd number of half-wavelengths.

- Two-source interference (e.g. Young's slits experiment) fits the equation: $\lambda = ws/D$.

3.2 Diffraction

Microwave transmitter.

We use an enormous range of radio wavelengths in our modern communication systems. The wavelength of the VLF (very low frequency) radio waves that are used for maritime distress signals and AM radio can be as long as 100 kilometres. The wavelength of the EHF (extremely high frequency) radio waves used for high-speed digital communications links with satellites is only 1 millimetre. The wavelength of these waves affects their range and the way they are transmitted.

The longest waves are not very directional: the waves spread out in all directions and they are able to spread quite effectively around obstacles, such as hills and buildings, because of their long wavelength. This spreading of waves is known as **diffraction** (see *Physics AS*, page 61) and is more pronounced for longer waves. It is diffraction that allows mobile telephones to work even when there is no line-of-sight transmission path between the mobile phone and the base station. The short wavelength – microwave – end of the radio spectrum is less prone to diffraction. Microwave links, used by TV companies for outside broadcasts for example, have to have 'line of sight' between transmitter and receiver.

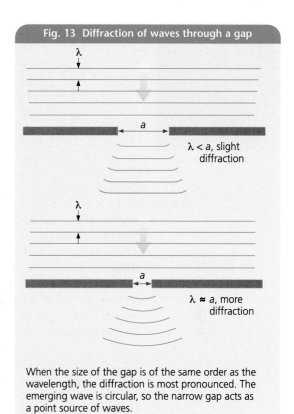

Fig. 13 Diffraction of waves through a gap

$\lambda < a$, slight diffraction

$\lambda \approx a$, more diffraction

When the size of the gap is of the same order as the wavelength, the diffraction is most pronounced. The emerging wave is circular, so the narrow gap acts as a point source of waves.

A way of explaining the diffraction of waves is known as Huygens' principle. Huygens suggested that each point on a wavefront could be thought of as a point source of a new wave. Each of these new waves, called **secondary wavelets**, spreads out and overlaps with other secondary wavelets. The new wavefront is formed by the

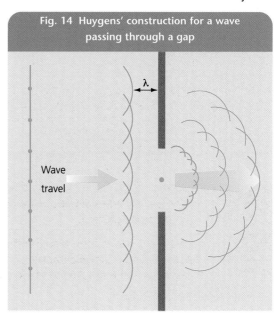

Fig. 14 Huygens' construction for a wave passing through a gap

Wave travel

43

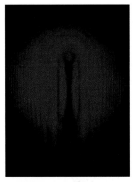

Light waves are diffracted so that light passes into the region of geometric shadow. This is only noticeable for small objects like this eye of a needle.

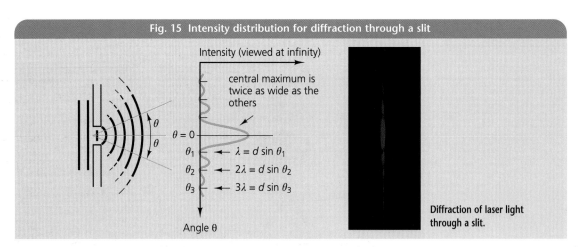

Fig. 15 Intensity distribution for diffraction through a slit

Intensity (viewed at infinity)

central maximum is twice as wide as the others

$\theta = 0$

θ_1 ← $\lambda = d \sin \theta_1$

θ_2 ← $2\lambda = d \sin \theta_2$

θ_3 ← $3\lambda = d \sin \theta_3$

Angle θ

Diffraction of laser light through a slit.

constructive interference of all the secondary wavelets. (Strictly speaking there is also constructive interference in the reverse direction but this would indicate a wave that was travelling backwards and so this part of the construction is ignored.) As a plane wave passes through an aperture, the spreading of new wavelets causes diffraction.

10 One of the ways in which people can tell the direction of a sound wave is because of the shadowing effect of the head; the ear that is further from the sound is effectively blocked by the head. This method is much more successful at high frequencies: people find it more difficult to locate the source of low-frequency sounds. Explain why this is.

11 Why is it that houses in the shadow of a hill get poor TV reception but can still get good radio reception? (TV transmission is typically at 600 MHz, whilst medium-wave radio is transmitted at a frequency of around 1000 kHz.)

Diffraction of light

Light waves can also be diffracted, yet the effects are not noticeable in everyday situations because the wavelength of light is so small, between 400 and 700 nm. It is only when the obstacles or apertures are almost as small as the wavelength that diffraction effects become apparent. When light is allowed to pass through a small slit, we can see the light spreading out into the region where we would expect to see only shadow. But this is not the only effect. A series of light and dark fringes becomes visible. These are similar to the interference fringes discussed above, but here there is only one source of light. What is causing the interference?

The answer is that light from the slit is interfering with itself. Secondary wavelets from different parts of the slit are able to interfere with each other. In some directions they add together constructively, and a bright fringe is formed. In other directions the secondary wavelets are out of phase and the net effect is a dark fringe (see Fig. 16).

For a slit of width d, and light of wavelength λ, the minima occur at angles given by

$$\sin \phi = \frac{n\lambda}{d} \quad \text{where } n = 0, \pm1, \pm2, \pm3, ..., \text{etc.}$$

This diffraction through a slit has important consequences. It sets a limit on the amount of detail that can be seen in an image. If you look at two light sources that

Fig. 16 Self-interference of light

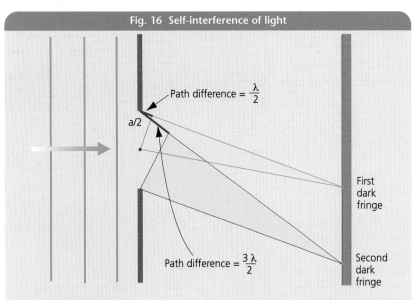

Path difference = $\frac{\lambda}{2}$

a/2

First dark fringe

Path difference = $\frac{3\lambda}{2}$

Second dark fringe

At the first dark fringe the path difference between a secondary wavelet from the top of the slit and the one from the middle of the slit is half a wavelength. In this way all the wavelets from the top half of the slit are cancelled out by the wavelets from the bottom half of the slit.

are sufficiently close together so that their diffraction patterns overlap on your retina, it is not possible for you to tell them apart and we say that the objects are not resolved. The way to see greater detail is to use a telescope with a large lens or mirror, so that diffraction is less of a problem. (You will consider this topic further if you study the optional module 'Astrophysics'.)

12 Why do radio telescopes need to be so much larger than optical telescopes?

13 In the apparatus shown in Fig. 17 a microwave transmitter operating at a frequency of 10 GHz is aimed at a gap between two metal plates. The plates are originally 30 cm apart.

a Describe what you would detect with a microwave probe moved along the line XY.

b The plates are moved closer together until the gap is only 3 cm. What would the microwave probe detect now?

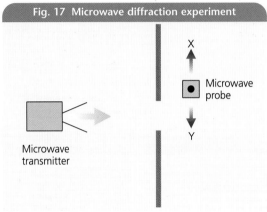

Fig. 17 Microwave diffraction experiment

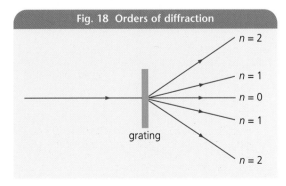

3.2 Diffraction gratings

The spectrum of light from a star tells us how hot it is, what it is made of and how fast it is moving.

Much of our understanding of the structure of stars and galaxies is based on measurements of the light that they emit. Different atoms and molecules emit and absorb different frequencies of light. By studying the light emitted from a star we can compare its spectrum with the spectrum from laboratory light sources. This tells us what elements are present in the star. The strength of different spectral lines gives us information on the star's temperature. If the spectral lines are slightly shifted compared to laboratory light sources, we can infer that the star is moving

and we can work out its velocity (see Chapter 2, page 25). All this is done by using a **diffraction grating** to produce a spectrum.

A diffraction grating is simply a set of parallel slits. As light waves pass through the grating, each slit causes diffraction. The waves from each slit overlap and interfere to give areas of constructive and destructive interference. In most directions there is complete destructive interference and no light is transmitted. Constructive interference takes place in a few directions. In these directions diffracted light beams occur. These beams are called the 'orders' of diffraction (Fig. 18).

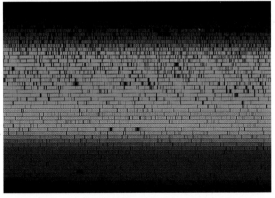

Fig. 18 Orders of diffraction

$n = 2$
$n = 1$
$n = 0$
$n = 1$
grating
$n = 2$

Fig. 19 Using Huygens' construction to illustrate the occurrence of constructive interference

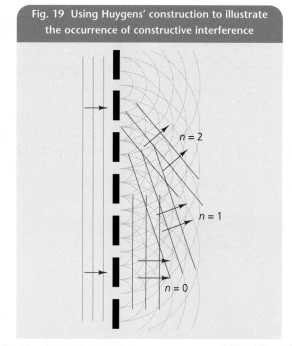

The central beam is zero order, the adjacent beams on either side are first order, and subsequent beams are numbered accordingly.

The direction of the diffracted beams is related to the spacing of the slits and the wavelength. This can be demonstrated using Huygens' construction (Fig. 19).

Suppose that we use a diffraction grating with 400 000 lines per metre. We can use the expression $n\lambda = d \sin \theta$ to calculate the wavelength of light that gives a second-order beam at an angle of 25° (see Fig. 21).

The grating spacing, d, is found by dividing:

$$d = \frac{1}{\text{number of lines per metre}}$$

In this case

$$d = \frac{1}{400\,000 \text{ m}^{-1}} = 2.5 \times 10^{-6} \text{ m}$$

Using $n\lambda = d \sin \theta$,

$$2\lambda = 2.5 \times 10^{-6} \times \sin 25° \text{ m}$$

This gives:

$$\lambda = 5.28 \times 10^{-7} \text{ m} = 528 \text{ nm}$$

From this result we can calculate how many diffracted beams would be visible. Sin θ cannot be bigger than 1, so the maximum value of n is given by $n\lambda = d$:

$$n \le \frac{d}{\lambda} = \frac{2.5 \times 10^{-6} \text{ m}}{5.28 \times 10^{-7} \text{ m}} = 4.73$$

The fourth-order beam will be the last possible beam. The total number of visible beams is therefore $4 + 4 + 1 = 9$.

Beams of X-rays reflecting off planes of atoms in a crystal behave in the same way as light at a diffraction grating. Measurements of X-ray diffraction patterns are used to give information about the structure of crystalline materials.

Fig. 20 Spectrometer

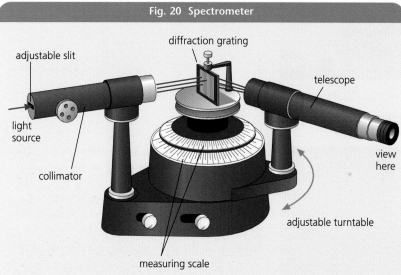

adjustable slit

diffraction grating

telescope

light source

collimator

view here

measuring scale

adjustable turntable

A spectrometer is an optical instrument which allows us to measure the angles at which light comes out of the diffraction grating. From these angle measurements, we can calculate the wavelengths of the light.

Fig. 21 Relating n, d, λ and θ

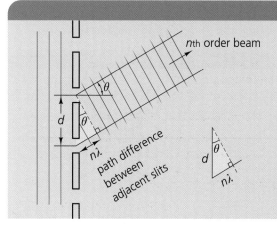

nth order beam

θ

d

$n\lambda$

path difference between adjacent slits

d

θ

$n\lambda$

The straight-through beam, $\theta = 0°$, is formed from light from each slit arriving exactly in phase; there is no path difference at all and every wavelength will arrive in phase.

The first-order beam is formed in the direction in which adjacent slits have a path difference of a whole wavelength, λ. These waves are therefore back in phase. The second-order beam is in a direction in which light from adjacent slits is two wavelengths out of phase, 2λ.

In general the nth order beam is at an angle θ to the original wavefront direction. Along this beam, waves from adjacent slits have a path difference of $n\lambda$.

We can relate this path difference to the distance between each slit, d, by looking at the central (shaded) triangle of the diagram left.

Using

$$\sin\theta = \frac{\text{opposite}}{\text{hypotenuse}} = \frac{n\lambda}{d}$$

this can be written

$$n\lambda = d \sin \theta$$

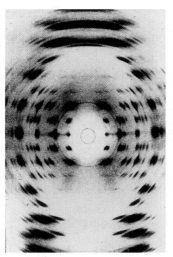
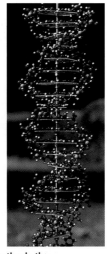

X-ray diffraction pictures gave vital information in the determination of the structure of DNA.

14 If white light passes through a diffraction grating, most of the orders of diffraction split the light into different colours. The central, zero-order beam is always white. Explain why this is so.

15 A diffraction grating has 200 000 lines per metre. How many diffracted beams will be visible if red light, λ = 600 nm, is used to illuminate the grating?

EXAMINATION QUESTIONS

1 The diagram shows two identical loudspeakers, A and B, placed at 0.75 m apart. Each loudspeaker emits sound of frequency 2000 Hz.

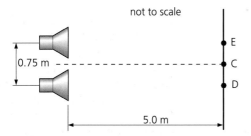

Point C is on a line midway between the speakers and 5.0 m away from the line joining the speakers. A listener at C hears a maximum intensity of sound. If the listener then moves from C to E or D, the sound intensity heard decreases to a minimum. Further movement in the same direction results in the repeated increase and decrease in the sound intensity. Speed of sound in air = 330 m s⁻¹

a Explain why the sound intensity

  (i) is a maximum at C,
  (ii) is a minimum at D or E.   (4)

b Calculate

  (i) the wavelength of the sound,
  (ii) the distance CE.   (4)

(NEAB PH02 June 1999 Q5)

2 The diagram shows two small loudspeakers positioned a few metres apart with a small microphone, M, connected to an oscilloscope, positioned exactly midway between them. The loudspeakers are connected in parallel to a signal generator producing oscillations at a frequency of 3300 Hz.

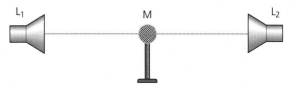

a Calculate the wavelength of the sound waves produced.
Speed of sound waves in air = 330 m s⁻¹.   (1)

b The microphone is now moved slowly to the right.

  (i) Describe and explain how the trace height on the oscilloscope will change as the position of the microphone is changed.
  (ii) Explain why this occurs.   (4)

(NEAB PH02 June 1998 Q7)

3 The diagram for this question is drawn to scale and 1 mm on the diagram represents an actual distance of 8.8 mm.

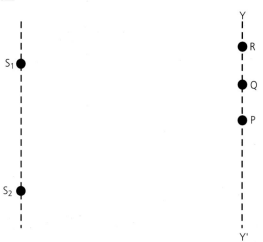

S_1 and S_2 are identical *coherent* transmitters emitting, in phase, microwaves with a wavelength of 25 mm. They are positioned 250 mm apart on a horizontal surface and a detector can be placed anywhere along the line YY', which is in the same plane as the transmitters and parallel to the line containing S_1 and S_2.

a Explain what is meant by *coherent*. (2)

b By making measurements on the diagram and using the scale, determine the number of wavelengths in the path

(i) S_1R,

(ii) S_2R.

(iii) Use your answers to (i) and (ii) to determine whether or not you expect the signal received by a detector placed at R to be a maximum. Explain your answer. (5)

c Describe how you would expect the signal strength to vary as the detector is moved from R to P via Q. (2)

d Calculate the frequency of the microwaves. (1)

(NEAB PH02 March 1999 Q5)

4 a

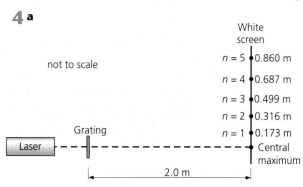

In a laboratory experiment, monochromatic light of wavelength 633 nm from a laser is incident normal to a diffraction grating. The diffracted waves are received on a white screen which is parallel to the plane of the grating and 2.0 m from it. The above diagram shows the positions of the diffraction maxima with distances measured from the central maximum.
By means of a graphical method, use all these measurements to determine a mean value for the number of rulings per unit length of the grating.

(6)

b Describe and explain the effect, if any, on the appearance of the diffraction pattern of

(i) using a grating which has more rulings per unit length,

(ii) using a laser source which has a shorter wavelength,

(iii) increasing the distance between the grating and the screen. (6)

c The diagram below shows the diffracted waves from four narrow slits of a diffraction grating similar to the one described in part (a). The slit separation AB = BC = CD = DE = d and EQ is a line drawn at a tangent to several wavefronts and which makes an angle θ with the grating.

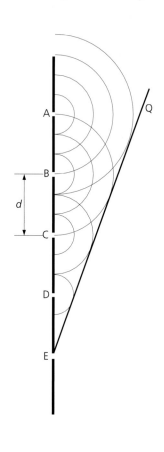

(i) Explain why the waves advancing perpendicular to EQ will reinforce if superposed.

(ii) Show that this will happen when $\sin\theta = \lambda/d$.

(3)

(NEAB PH02 June 1999 Q3)

5 a A student carried out an experiment to determine the grating spacing, *d*, of a diffraction grating by determining the diffraction angle in the second order for several special lines of known wavelength. These results are given in the table.

wavelength/nm	435	521	589	652
second-order angle (degrees)	20.4	24.6	28.1	31.4

Use these results to obtain the values needed to plot a straight line graph. Draw the graph and used it to determine a value for *d*.

b Three diffraction gratings, illustrated below, are available for observing line spectra. The grating width and the total number of vertical rulings on the grating are given for each one. Determine which of the three gratings will give the largest diffraction angle in the first order with a given spectral line.

(3)

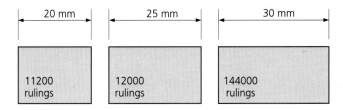

(NEAB PH02 June 1998 Q4)

6 a

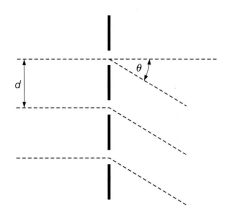

The diagram shows a plan view of part of a diffraction grating of spacing *d*. Plane monochromatic waves of wavelength λ are incident normally on the diffraction grating. The diffracted waves make an angle θ with the normal. Derive from first principles the diffraction equation

$n\lambda = d\sin\theta$.

(You may draw on the diagram if it assists your derivation.)

(4)

b A diffraction grating is illuminated with light of wavelength 577 nm. The second-order maximum is formed at an angle of 41.25° to the normal. Calculate the total number of lines on the grating if it is 30 mm wide.

(3)

7 a (i) Describe and explain, with the aid of a labelled diagram, the double-slit arrangements which you would set up in order to produce and observe Young's interference fringes using monochromatic light.

(ii) Suggest approximate values for the slit separation and the distance from slits to screen.

(6)

b (i) Describe **two** features of the interference fringes.

(ii) Describe and explain one change in the appearance of the fringes if the slit separation is reduced.

(4)

c (i) State the measurements you would make in order to determine the wavelength of the light used.

(ii) Calculate the fringe separation which would result, using the approximate values which you gave in part (a) (ii), assuming that the wavelength of light used is 600 nm.

(4)

(NEAB PH02 Feb 1996/PH02 June 2000)

4 Capacitors

John collapsed at work on Monday morning. While he could still speak, he complained of severe chest pains. In the ambulance, his heart stopped and he lost consciousness. He was lucky: the paramedic in the ambulance had a defibrillator. John survived his heart attack.

A healthy heart is a tremendously reliable pump, operating at seventy or so beats per minute; that's a staggering two and a half billion beats in the course of a lifetime. The heart has its own pacemaker, the sino-atrial node, which fires electrical signals 60 to 100 times per minute (Fig. 1). Most heart muscle cells can generate electrical pulses on their own. The pulse from the sinoatrial node keeps them all beating in the right sequence.

Heart attacks kill one in four people in wealthy industrialised countries. Fatty foods, lack of exercise and smoking all contribute to death or illness related to the heart. Fatty deposits build up on the walls of coronary arteries, blocking them and reducing the

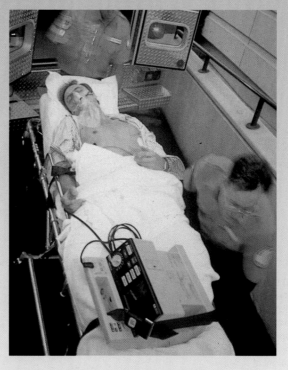

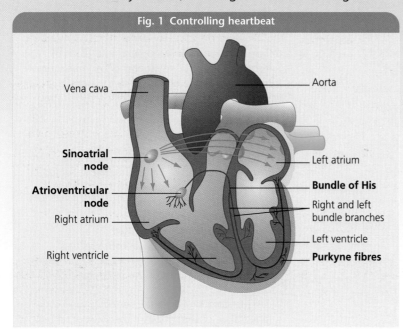

Fig. 1 Controlling heartbeat

Vena cava

Aorta

Sinoatrial node

Left atrium

Atrioventricular node

Bundle of His

Right atrium

Right and left bundle branches

Left ventricle

Right ventricle

Purkyne fibres

blood supply to the heart. Small regions of heart muscle can die, making the heart prone to electrical disturbances that upset the normal pumping rhythm. In the worst case, *ventricular fibrillation* starts: the heart's muscles contract randomly and therefore don't squeeze the ventricles, and the flow of blood stops.

The defibrillator that saved John's life delivered a carefully controlled shock to his heart. This stopped the fibrillation and started his regular heart rhythm again. A defibrillator needs to transfer a precise amount of energy to the patient. Too little energy and the shock won't be effective; but too much energy could kill the patient. The best way to control the amount of electrical energy transferred is to use a **capacitor**.

4.1 Capacitance

A capacitor is a component that is able to store electrical charge. It behaves a bit like a rechargeable battery, except that the energy is stored in electric fields instead of chemical reactions. The simplest capacitor consists of just two parallel plates (Fig. 2), though others rely on an electrolytic reaction to store charge.

A capacitor can be charged by connecting it to a source of d.c. voltage, like a battery. Negative charges, electrons, flow off one plate and onto the other (see Fig. 3), resulting in a charge difference between the plates. A positive charge of $+Q$ is stored on one plate and a negative charge of $-Q$ is stored on the other. The amount of charge stored is

(c)

(b)

(a)

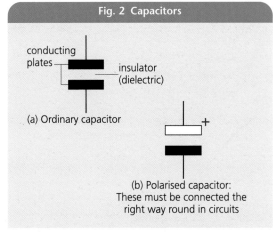

Fig. 2 Capacitors

conducting plates — insulator (dielectric)

(a) Ordinary capacitor

+

(b) Polarised capacitor: These must be connected the right way round in circuits

(a) Paper, ceramic and mica are all used as the non-conductor (dielectric) between the conducting plates. These capacitors are cheap but they can only store a limited amount of charge. Their capacitance values are rarely above a few microfarads.
(b) Electrolytic capacitors have larger capacitances and can be charged to higher potentials. Unlike other capacitors they have a definite polarity and must be connected the right way round.
(c) Air capacitors are two sets of interleaved, parallel metal plates. One set of plates can be moved so that it overlaps the other set and this varies the capacitance.

proportional to the potential difference (voltage) across the plates;

$$Q \propto V$$

In fact,

$$Q = CV$$

where C is the **capacitance** of the capacitor.

To put this another way, the capacitance is the charge stored per unit potential difference. In SI units charge is measured in coulombs and potential difference is measured in volts.

The SI unit of capacitance, the farad, is therefore defined as the amount of charge in coulombs stored by a capacitor, for every volt of potential difference placed across it.

It is difficult to manufacture capacitors with a large capacitance. Most capacitors have a capacitance of less than one hundredth of a

farad. Many electrical circuits use capacitors that have capacitances between one picofarad (1 pF $=10^{-12}$ F) and one nanofarad (1 nF = 10^{-9} F). A capacitor also has a maximum potential difference to which it can be charged. This represents the voltage at which breakdown will occur between the plates, when the insulator begins to conduct.

1. All insulators allow some current to flow. How do you think this affects the charge on a capacitor?

2. A capacitor is marked 10 pF, 0.1 V. Explain what these markings mean.

3. How much charge could be stored on a 1 microfarad capacitor with an applied potential difference of 10 V? How much charge could be stored if the applied potential is increased to 100 V? What limits the charge that can be stored on any particular capacitor?

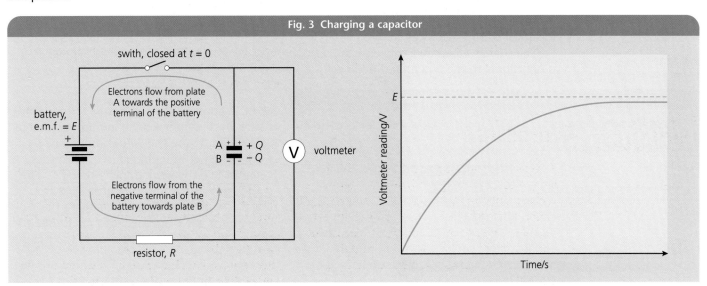

Fig. 3 Charging a capacitor

swith, closed at $t = 0$

Electrons flow from plate A towards the positive terminal of the battery

battery, e.m.f. = E

A $+Q$
B $-Q$

V voltmeter

Electrons flow from the negative terminal of the battery towards plate B

resistor, R

E

Voltmeter reading/V

Time/s

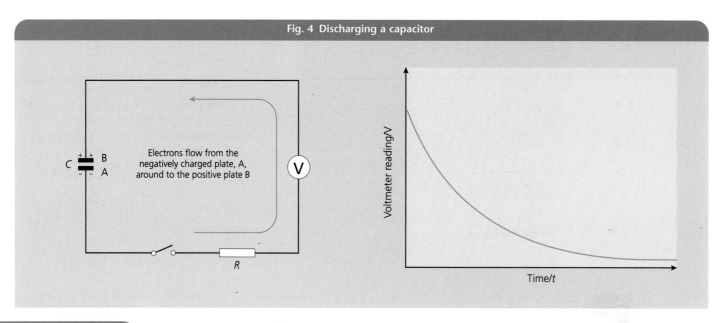

Fig. 4 Discharging a capacitor

Electrons flow from the negatively charged plate, A, around to the positive plate B

Voltmeter reading/V

Time/t

4.2 Energy storage

Electric fields

An **electric field** is a region of space where charged particles experience a force. There is a strong electric field in the region between a capacitor's plates. The field is uniform between the plates, which means that the lines of force are parallel to each other. The strength of this electric field is often expressed in terms of the potential difference per metre. In the same way that an object in a gravitational field will experience a force, any charged particle in the space between the plates will experience an electrostatic force.

Energy is needed to set up the electric field when charge is stored on the plates of a capacitor. If the charge is allowed to flow through an external circuit, the stored energy is transferred to the circuit. Capacitors are a means of storing electrical energy.

The charge stored by a capacitor is proportional to the potential difference,

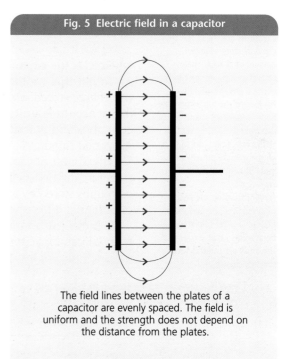

Fig. 5 Electric field in a capacitor

The field lines between the plates of a capacitor are evenly spaced. The field is uniform and the strength does not depend on the distance from the plates.

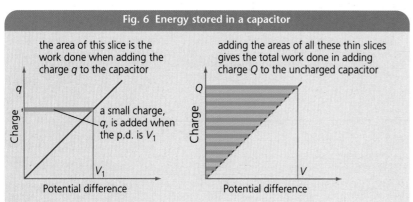

Fig. 6 Energy stored in a capacitor

the area of this slice is the work done when adding the charge q to the capacitor

a small charge, q, is added when the p.d. is V_1

Charge

Potential difference

adding the areas of all these thin slices gives the total work done in adding charge Q to the uncharged capacitor

Charge

Potential difference

$Q = CV$. Suppose the p.d. across the capacitor is already V_1 when a small amount of charge, q, is added. Using the definition of p.d. = work done per unit charge (see AS Physics Chapter 11), the work done is $W = qV_1$. This is the same as the area of a little slice in Fig. 6. The total work done charging the capacitor is the combined area of all the little slices. These add up to the area of the triangle ($\frac{1}{2} \times$ base $\times$ height). Therefore:

energy stored = total work done = $\frac{1}{2}QV$

Thunderclouds can generate potential differences of 100 MV or more, creating electric field strengths high enough to make air conduct.

It is rare that the charge, Q, is measured directly, so it is more useful to substitute $Q = CV$ into the equation, giving:

$$\text{energy stored} = E = \tfrac{1}{2}CV^2$$

The energy stored in a capacitor can give someone a nasty shock. For a 1000 µF capacitor charged to a potential difference of 100 V, the energy stored would be:

$$E = \tfrac{1}{2}CV^2 = \tfrac{1}{2} \times 1000 \times 10^{-6} \times (100)^2 = 5\ \text{J}$$

APPLICATION

The defibrillator

In using a defibrillator, a doctor needs to be able to transfer different amounts of energy to different patients. A patient with an irregular heart rhythm can be given a small electric shock before the condition of the heart deteriorates. If fibrillation has started, a much larger shock is required to restart normal contractions. Designers of defibrillators need to be able to relate the amount of energy stored to the capacitance of the defibrillator capacitors and the p.d. across the plates.

Small irregularities in heart rhythm can be corrected by transferring around 10 J of energy to the patient. Stopping fibrillation needs much more energy: in adults, about 200 J at the first attempt and 360 J for subsequent attempts. This energy is delivered as a pulse of short duration; somewhere between 3 and 9 milliseconds is typical. The Hewlett Packard Codemaster defibrillator and monitor, pictured on the left, uses a 12 V, 4 Ah battery. Only 10% of the battery's stored energy is used to charge the capacitor. How many times could it be used at the 360 J setting?

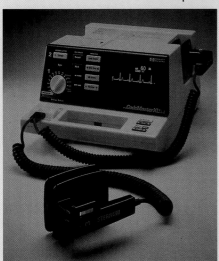

The total charge, Q, that can be delivered by the battery is:

$$Q = It = 4\ \text{Ah} = 4\ \text{A} \times 3600\ \text{s} = 14\ 400\ \text{C}$$

Energy supplied by the battery:

$$QV = 14\ 400\ \text{C} \times 12\ \text{V} = 172\ 800\ \text{J}$$

But only 10% is available for charging, so $E = 17\ 280$ J. At 360 J per discharge, the maximum number available is:

$$\frac{17\ 280\ \text{J}}{360\ \text{J}} = 48\ \text{discharges}$$

4 Human skin has quite a high resistance. Would it be better to build a defibrillator using a small capacitance charged to a large p.d. or a large capacitance charged to a small p.d.? Explain your answer.

5 The manufacturing limit for portable high-voltage capacitors is about 100 mF. Show that a charging p.d. of 2700 V would be needed to store 360 J.

Potential differences of around 2700 V are difficult to achieve on portable equipment, particularly as the operator needs the capacitor to recharge rapidly for further shocks. Doctors need a recharge time of 5 seconds. What charging current is required?

At 2700 V, charge stored on a 100 µF capacitor is:

$$Q = CV$$
$$= 100 \times 10^{-6}\ \text{F} \times 2700\ \text{V}$$
$$= 0.27\ \text{C}$$

To deliver this in 5 seconds needs a mean charging current, I, of:

$$I = \frac{Q}{t} = \frac{0.27\ \text{C}}{5\ \text{s}} = 0.054\ \text{A}$$

This may seem small, but the mean charging power would be:

$$P = \frac{E}{t} = \frac{360\ \text{J}}{5\ \text{s}} = 72\ \text{W}$$

Most defibrillators use a small sealed lead–acid battery to meet this power requirement.

- Capacitors store charge.

- Capacitance (C) is the charge stored (Q) per volt (V):

$$C = \frac{Q}{V}$$

- Capacitance is measured in farads, F. A capacitor of 1 farad will store one coulomb of charge for every volt across it.

- The charge on a capacitor creates an electric field. Energy is stored in the field between the plates of a capacitor:

$$E = \tfrac{1}{2}QV = \tfrac{1}{2}CV^2$$

4.3 Charging and discharging capacitors

Capacitors are often used in circuits to block a d.c. current. Once a capacitor is fully charged, no more current will flow. However, when an uncharged capacitor is placed in a circuit, and the circuit is first switched on, charge will flow for a short while. Then, as charge builds up on the capacitor it becomes more difficult for further charge to flow, and the current in the circuit drops. Eventually the potential across the capacitor matches that of the supply and no more current flows.

The current in the circuit is highest at first, since there is no potential difference across the capacitor to oppose it. The potential difference of the cell, V, will cause an initial current, I_0, to flow in the circuit. Initially the size of this current is equal to V/R. As the current charges up the capacitor, the potential across the resistor decreases and the current drops (see Fig. 7).

There is a similar effect when a charged capacitor in a circuit is allowed to discharge through a resistor (Fig. 8). Initially there is a potential difference, V_0, across the capacitor. This potential difference is equal to Q_0/C, where Q_0 is the initial charge on the capacitor.

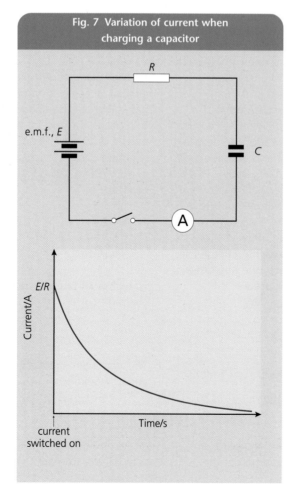

Fig. 7 Variation of current when charging a capacitor

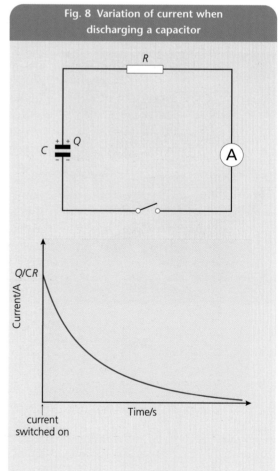

Fig. 8 Variation of current when discharging a capacitor

As the current flows, the charge on the capacitor falls to zero. That means that the potential difference driving the current falls, and so the current itself drops to zero.

The charge, Q, left on the capacitor at time t seconds after the switch has been closed is given by:

$$Q = Q_0 e^{-t/RC}$$

Like water leaking from a tank or bucket, the charge flowing from a capacitor acts to reduce the force that is driving it. The flow rate drops exponentially.

The steepness of the exponential decay, and therefore the time taken to discharge a capacitor, depends on two factors:

- The capacitance, C, since a larger capacitor will hold more charge and take longer to discharge.

- The resistance, R, of the circuit through which it discharges.
  A larger resistor will limit the current and increase the discharge time.

The product of these two factors, RC, is known as the *time constant* of the circuit. The time constant represents the time it takes for the charge on a capacitor to drop to $1/e$ of its previous value.

Since $Q = Q_0 e^{-t/RC}$

when $t = RC$

$$Q = Q_0 e^{-RC/RC}$$

So $Q = Q_0 e^{-1}$

or $\dfrac{Q}{Q_0} = \dfrac{1}{e} = 0.368$ (to 3 s.f.)

After two time constants, $t = 2RC$, the charge will drop to $1/e^2$, or 0.135, of its initial value. After three time constants, the charge will be only $1/e^3$, or 0.05 of its initial value, and so on.

The product RC must have units of seconds, if the equations above are to make sense. We can show that this is true by considering alternative ways of writing resistance and capacitance:

$$R = \dfrac{V}{I} \quad \text{and} \quad C = \dfrac{Q}{V}$$

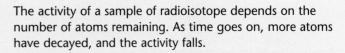

Fig. 9 Discharging a capacitor compared to radioactive decay

The discharge of a capacitor is rather like decay of atoms in radioactivity (see Chapter 10). Both these situations give rise to an exponential decay curve.

	Quantity	Rate of change	Equation	Solution
Radioactivity	Number of atoms, N	Activity, A $A = \Delta N/\Delta t$	$A \propto N$ or $-(\Delta N/\Delta t) \propto N$	$N = N_0 e^{-\lambda t}$
Capacitor discharge	Charge, Q	Current, I $I = \Delta Q/\Delta t$	$I \propto Q$ or $-(\Delta Q/\Delta t) \propto Q$	$Q = Q_0 e^{-t/RC}$

The current flowing depends on the amount of charge remaining. As time goes on, the charge drops and so the current falls.

The activity of a sample of radioisotope depends on the number of atoms remaining. As time goes on, more atoms have decayed, and the activity falls.

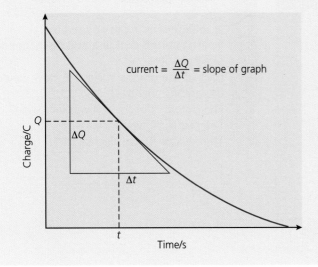

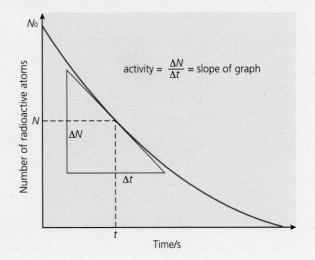

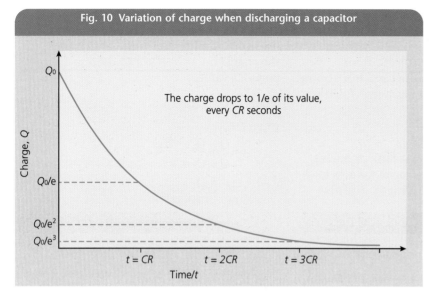

Fig. 10 Variation of charge when discharging a capacitor

The charge drops to 1/e of its value, every CR seconds

This gives

$$RC = \frac{Q \times V}{I \times V} = \frac{Q}{I}$$

Since charge = current × time, we can substitute $Q = It$ into this equation:

$$RC = \frac{I \times t}{I} = t$$

Therefore RC has the same units as time, and can be written in seconds.

6 Show that it takes 7 time constants for the charge on a discharging capacitor to drop to less than 0.1% of its original value.

7 Figure 11 shows a 1000 μF capacitor discharging through a resistance. Use the graph to estimate the time constant and hence the resistance of the circuit.

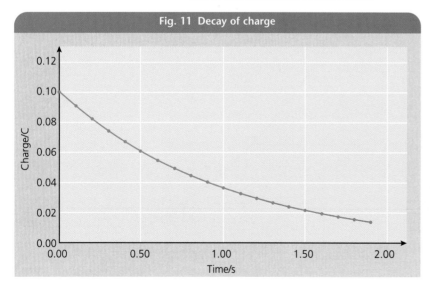

Fig. 11 Decay of charge

Suppose a 1000 μF capacitor is charged to a potential of 100 V and then discharged through a 100 kΩ resistor. How long will it take for the potential to drop to less than 10 V?

Since $Q = CV$, and C is constant, the potential difference across a discharging capacitor follows the same exponential decay curve that charge does:

$$V = V_0 e^{-t/RC}$$

So $\quad \dfrac{10}{100} = e^{-t/RC}$

To find the time we need to take natural logs of both sides of this equation:

$$\ln(0.1) = \frac{-t}{RC}$$
$$= -2.30$$

For this circuit:

$$RC = (100 \times 10^3) \times (1000 \times 10^{-6}) = 100 \text{ s}$$

Therefore,

$$t = (-100) \times (-2.30) = 230 \text{ s}$$

or almost 4 minutes.

A capacitor like this could act as a short-term backup to maintain a voltage in case of a power failure.

8 A 1000 nF capacitor is charged to a potential of 6 V and then discharged through a circuit of resistance 1 MΩ.
a Calculate the initial charge on the capacitor.
b Calculate the time constant of the circuit.
c Sketch a graph showing how the charge on the capacitor varies with time.
d Calculate the charge on the capacitor after 1 s.
e Use this value to calculate the potential across the capacitor, and hence the current through the resistor, after 1 second.

9 A voltage sensor can be used to investigate the charging and discharging of a capacitor.
Look at the graphs in Fig. 12. How would the graphs change if:
a The potential of the cell was increased?
b The resistor R_1 was increased?
c The resistor R_2 was decreased?

10 The graphs in Fig. 12 show how the charge varies on a capacitor as it is being charged and as it is being discharged. Sketch graphs to show how the following quantities change with time during charging and discharging:

a the current through the resistor;

b the potential difference across the capacitor.

11 Suppose that you were going to use the circuit in Fig. 12 to investigate charging a capacitor of capacitance 10 μF. If the circuit has a resistance of 10 kΩ and your datalogger has a memory of 1000 readings, which of these sampling rates would you choose for the datalogger to take readings from the voltage sensor? once every millisecond; or once every 100 milliseconds; or once every second.

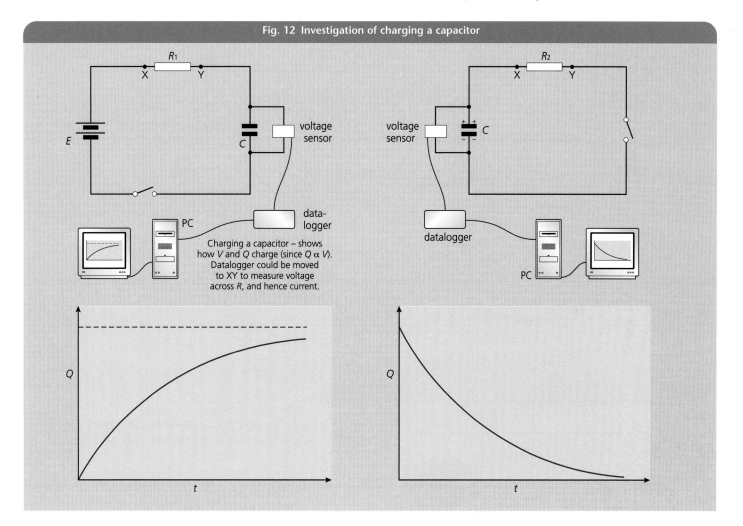

Fig. 12 Investigation of charging a capacitor

Charging a capacitor – shows how V and Q charge (since Q α V). Datalogger could be moved to XY to measure voltage across R, and hence current.

Using calculus to derive the discharge equation

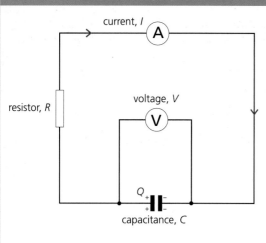

Fig. 13 Simple discharge circuit

If you are studying A-level mathematics and you are familiar with the process of integration, you might like to look further at the equation for the discharge of a capacitor, which can be derived using integration.

The current in the circuit at any time, I, depends on the potential difference across the plates of the capacitor:

$$I = \frac{V}{R}$$

The potential V depends on how much charge there is on the capacitor: $V = Q/C$, so

$$I = \frac{Q}{CR}$$

But I is the rate of change of charge, $I = -dQ/dt$ (the negative sign is there because Q decreases as time increases). So:

$$\frac{dQ}{dt} = -\frac{Q}{CR} \quad \text{or} \quad \frac{dt}{CR} = -\frac{dQ}{Q}$$

Both sides of this equation can be integrated, between time $t = 0$ when charge $= Q_0$, and time t, when charge $= Q$:

$$\int_0^t \frac{dt}{CR} = -\int_{Q_0}^{Q} \frac{dQ}{Q} = \int_Q^{Q_0} \frac{dQ}{Q}$$

This becomes:

$$\frac{t}{CR} = \ln\left(\frac{Q_0}{Q}\right)$$

So: $Q = Q_0 e^{-t/CR}$

Making and combining capacitors

Making capacitors

A defibrillator needs to use a capacitor with a maximum capacitance of 100 µF and must operate at several thousand volts. How easy is this to achieve in practice?

Capacitors store charge on plates, so doubling the area, A, would be like having two storage areas. The dimensions of a capacitor affect its capacitance:

capacitance ∝ area

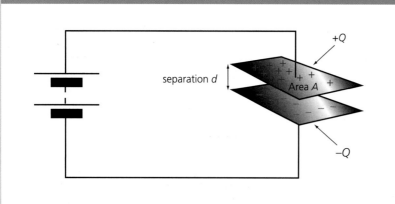

Fig. 14 Factors affecting capacitance

The distance, d, between the plates is also important. There are opposite charges on the plates. When the plates are closer, these opposite charges attract more. This makes it

easier to charge the capacitor. Its capacitance rises. For parallel plates, the capacitance is:

$$\text{capacitance} = \frac{1}{\text{distance}}$$

so: $C \propto \dfrac{\text{area}}{\text{distance}}$

If the plates are separated by a vacuum, the constant of proportionality is ε_0 ('epsilon-nought'):

$$C = \varepsilon_0 \frac{A}{d}$$

where A = area of one plate
  d = distance between the plates
  ε_0 is a constant called the permittivity of free space:
  $\varepsilon_0 = 8.85 \times 10^{-12}$ F m⁻¹

Ambulance crews need defibrillators that are small enough to be portable. Size restrictions mean that the maximum area for the capacitor plates is about 10 cm by 12 cm. Suppose the capacitor were made of two metal plates 1 mm apart. Would this give a big enough capacitance?

$$C = \varepsilon_0 \frac{A}{d}$$

$$= \frac{8.85 \times 10^{-12} \, \text{F m}^{-1} \times 0.10 \, \text{m} \times 0.12 \, \text{m}}{0.001 \, \text{m}}$$

$$= 1.06 \times 10^{-10} \, \text{F}$$

This is much less than the 100 μF needed. Commercial capacitors use several methods for making capacitance bigger:

- Increase the area – many square metres of very thin metal foil can be wound into a capacitor body (below).

- Decrease the distance the two plates are held apart using a very thin film of insulating material.

- Use an insulator called a dielectric. The molecules of the dielectric are polarised in the electric field between the plates. This gives rise to an opposing electric field which lowers the potential difference across the capacitor. More charge is therefore required on the plates to match the applied (charging) p.d. (Fig. 15).

Fig. 15 The action of a dielectric

with no electric field there is an even charge distribution	an electric field distorts electron orbits, leaving molecules polarised	these negative charges reduce the potential of the top plate, so the capacitance is increased

---

The factor by which capacitance increases when using dielectrics is called relative permittivity. For example, mica has a relative permittivity of 5. Parallel plates separated by mica would have five times the capacitance of a vacuum-filled capacitor of the same size.

High voltages across a capacitor can cause electrical breakdown, where electrons are torn from the atoms in the dielectric. The dielectric then conducts. In air, about 3000 V mm^{-1} will cause conduction. Mica can withstand 150 000 V mm^{-1} before it starts to conduct.

A medical defibrillator needs a capacitor with a capacitance of about 100 μF which will withstand a p.d. of about 3000 V. The minimum thickness, d, of mica you would be able to use is:

$$\frac{3000\ V}{150\,000\ V\ mm^{-1}} = 0.02\ mm$$

Mica has a relative permittivity of 5, so its capacitance is:

$$C = 5\varepsilon_0\frac{A}{d}$$

The area of plates needed will therefore be:

$$A = \frac{Cd}{5\varepsilon_0}$$

$$= \frac{100 \times 10^{-6}\ F \times 0.02\ m \times 10^{-3}\ m}{5 \times 8.85 \times 10^{-12}\ F\ m^{-1}}$$

$$= 45\ m^2$$

Unfortunately, this is too large for a single capacitor as mica is brittle and difficult to work with over such a large area. In addition, the total volume of insulator needed would be too large. Clearly the capacitor needs a different dielectric.

Capacitance can be increased by a factor of more than 300 using strontium titanate as a dielectric. Thin, even films can be deposited on capacitor plates by electrolysis. This gives a very high capacitance in a small volume.

12 Why is it difficult to make high-voltage capacitors with a high capacitance?

Combining capacitors

Another way of increasing capacitance at high voltages involves wiring smaller capacitors in series and parallel combinations. Instead of using one high-capacitance capacitor for a defibrillator, it is possible to use a combination of smaller capacitors to achieve the required capacitance.

A capacitor with high capacitance can be made by wiring several smaller capacitors in parallel (Fig. 16). The p.d. across each capacitor will be the same, so each capacitor needs to be able to withstand the 'operating' voltage. This is several kilovolts in a defibrillator.

The combined capacitance of two or more capacitors connected in series is *less* than the individual capacitors (Fig. 17). This seems to

Fig. 16 Capacitors in parallel

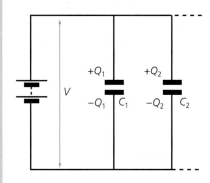

The p.d. across each capacitor is the same. The total charge stored is:
$$Q = Q_1 + Q_2 + Q_3 + \ldots$$

The combined capacitance is therefore:

$$C = \frac{Q}{V} = \frac{(Q_1 + Q_2 + Q_3 + \ldots)}{V}$$

$$= \frac{Q_1}{V} + \frac{Q_2}{V} + \frac{Q_3}{V} + \cdots = C_1 + C_2 + C_3 + \ldots$$

$$C = C_1 + C_2 + C_3 + \ldots$$

Fig. 17 Capacitors in series

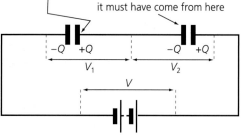

if charge ^+Q has been induced here

it must have come from here

Each capacitor holds the same charge $+Q$ on its positive plate. The p.d. across the whole series is the sum of the p.d.s across each capacitor.

$$V = V_1 + V_2$$

So,
$$\frac{Q}{C} = \frac{Q}{C_1} + \frac{Q}{C_2}$$

Dividing by Q gives
$$\frac{1}{C} = \frac{1}{C_1} + \frac{1}{C_2}$$

be a 'waste' of capacitance, but an advantage of this arrangement is that the p.d. across each capacitor is reduced. You could therefore build a capacitor with a high operating voltage using capacitors with lower operating voltages.

The equations for resistor and capacitor combinations are similar, except *series* and *parallel* are swapped; i.e. resistors in series add up, capacitors in parallel add up.

13 Suppose you connected a 60 μF capacitor and a 40 μF capacitor in series across a 1000 V supply. What would be the combined capacitance and the p.d. across each capacitor?

14 How could you make a 100 μF capacitor with a working voltage of 3000 V for a defibrillator using 50 μF capacitors with a working voltage of 1000 V?

EXAMINATION QUESTIONS

1 a A capacitor of capacitance C is charged so that the potential difference between its terminals is V. Show that the energy stored by the capacitor is given by:

energy = $\frac{1}{2}CV^2$ (3)

b A capacitor whose capacitance can be varied is set to its maximum value of 500pF and connected to a 12 V battery so that it becomes fully charged. The capacitor is now removed from the battery and its terminals are isolated.

1 pF = 10^{-12} F

  (i) Calculate the charge stored by the capacitor. The capacitance is now charged to a value of 250 pF. If no charge leaves the capacitor in the process, calculate:

  (ii) the change in potential difference across the capacitor.

  (iii) the change in energy stored by the capacitor.

                (6)

            (PH01 June 1998 Q6)

2 a A 1.0 F capacitor is used as a battery back up in a calculator. If the capacitor has been fully charged so that there is a potential difference of 6.0 V across its terminals, how much energy does it store?   (2)

b The fully charged capacitor is removed from the voltage source and connected across a 1.0 kΩ resistor. Calculate

  (i) the initial current through the resistor

  (ii) the current at which the capacitor has lost 75% of its stored energy.   (6)

c Give **one** disadvantage of using this charged capacitor as a battery replacement in an electric circuit.   (1)

           (PH01 February 1996 Q7)

3

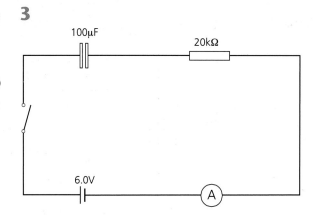

a In the circuit shown, the switch is closed and sometime later the ammeter reads 210 μA. Calculate for that instant

  (i) the p.d. across the resistor

  (ii) the p.d. across the capacitor.   (2)

b When the capacitor has become fully charged, calculate

  (i) the energy stored in the capacitor,

  (ii) the total energy taken from the battery.   (4)

          (PH01 February 1997 Q7)

5 Circular motion

The latest theme park rides use a combination of very high accelerations and near collisions to produce a thrilling experience. The 90-second ride on Nemesis at Alton Towers takes you through an 80 km per hour barrel roll and a 'zero-*g*' turn where you experience four seconds of space-style weightlessness. You then go through a vertical loop at four times the acceleration due to gravity.

Oblivion, at Alton Towers, is the world's first vertical-drop roller coaster. As if falling down a 60 m vertical drop isn't exciting enough, in the Oblivion ride you are actually accelerated down at 4.5*g*; that is 4.5 times the acceleration due to gravity.

Nemesis; Alton Towers' £10 million white-knuckle ride.

The intense competition between theme parks for the most exciting, yet safe, 'white-knuckle' experience is pushing rides to the limits of human endurance. The physics of circular motion can have unpleasant effects on the human body. High accelerations caused by sudden changes in direction have already proved fatal to a number of jet-fighter pilots.

5.1 Moving in circles

Angular frequency

RAF scientists at the Institute of Aviation Medicine at Farnborough study the effects of high accelerations on jet pilots. The pilots are strapped in a capsule at the end of a long rotor arm and are whirled round in the 'human centrifuge'.

When the centrifuge rotates at a constant rate, the pilot moves at a steady speed. Even so, the pilot is still accelerating. Acceleration is the rate of change of **velocity** (see *AS Physics*, page 89). Velocity is a vector quantity, so acceleration can arise from a change in either magnitude or direction. The direction of the pilot's motion is constantly changing, so the pilot is accelerating.

At any instant, the direction of the pilot's motion is along the tangent to the circle

'Spin-drying' the pilot. The size of the pilot's acceleration can be varied by changing the speed of rotation.

(Fig. 1). If the restraining straps broke, the pilot would move in a straight line along a tangent, in accordance with Newton's first law.

The size of a pilot's acceleration depends on how quickly the centrifuge spins. The time for one rotation is known as the period, T. The number of rotations in a given time is called the angular frequency, f. In SI units, the angular frequency is measured in rotations per second, or Hz.

$$f = \frac{1}{T}$$

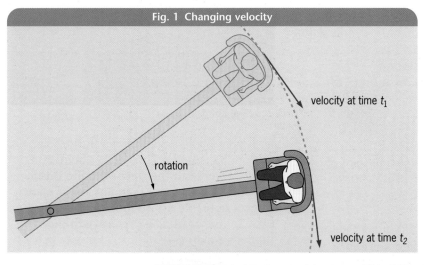

Fig. 1 Changing velocity

velocity at time t_1

rotation

velocity at time t_2

The London Eye revolves once every 30 minutes. In other words its period T is 30 minutes or 1800 s. The frequency of rotation is $1/T = 1/1800 = 5.55 \times 10^{-4}$ Hz.

1 What is the angular frequency of the Earth as it rotates about its axis?

2 An audio compact disc spins at between 200 and 500 times per minute, depending on which track is being played. Find the period of rotation for each of these speeds.

Angular velocity

The rate of turning in car engines or washing machines is measured in revolutions per minute (r.p.m.). For example, the typical 'speed' of a spin drier is 1000 r.p.m. However, physicists use angular velocity to measure how quickly something rotates. Angular velocity is the angle turned through in one second.

The angle turned through could be measured in degrees. An alternative unit, preferred by physicists, is the **radian** (Fig. 2).

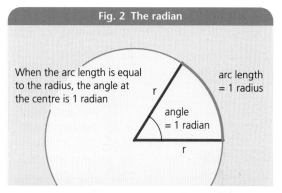

Fig. 2 The radian

When the arc length is equal to the radius, the angle at the centre is 1 radian

arc length = 1 radius

r

angle = 1 radian

r

If you ride on a fairground roundabout of radius 4 m, you turn through one radian each time you travel 4 m round the circumference of the circle.

One radian is defined as the angle subtended at the centre of a circle by an arc whose length is equal to the radius.

We can find the size of an angle in radians using the ratio:

$$\text{angle (radians)} = \frac{\text{distance on circumference}}{\text{radius of circle}}$$

$$\theta = \frac{s}{r}$$

This can be rewritten to allow us to calculate the distance travelled round a circle, $s = r\theta$.

For one full rotation, the arc length is equal to the circumference, $s = 2\pi r$. The angle you have turned through is therefore:

$$\theta = \frac{2\pi r}{r} = 2\pi \text{ radians}$$

This is equivalent to 360°, so:

$$1 \text{ radian} = \frac{360°}{2\pi} = 57.3° \text{ (to 3 s.f.)}$$

The abbreviation for radian is rad.

$$\text{one degree} = \frac{2\pi}{360} = 0.017 \text{ rad}$$

The angular velocity, ω, is the angle turned through per second. It has units of radians per second. Since a full rotation is equivalent to 2π radians, the angular velocity is $2\pi \times$ the number of rotations per second.

The London Eye takes 30 minutes to revolve once. Its angular velocity is therefore:

$$\omega = \frac{2\pi}{T} = \frac{2\pi}{1800} = 0.0035 \text{ rad s}^{-1}$$

3 A pilot is in a centrifuge that spins at 10 r.p.m. What is the pilot's angular velocity in rad s^{-1}?

4 What is the angular velocity of the Earth due to its annual orbit of the Sun?

Angular velocity and linear speed

An object moving at a steady angular velocity has a constant speed. The magnitude of the speed depends on the radius. The link between angular velocity and speed can be deduced from the definition of the radian:

$$\text{angle turned through, } \theta = \frac{s}{r}$$

If this takes t seconds:

$$\text{angular velocity, } \omega = \frac{\theta}{t} = \frac{s/r}{t}$$

$$= \frac{s}{tr} = \frac{\text{speed}}{r}$$

The symbol v is used for the *magnitude* of the linear velocity, i.e. the speed:

$$\omega = \frac{v}{r} \quad \text{or} \quad v = r\omega$$

Jupiter has the shortest day of any planet in the Solar System.

Jupiter is the largest planet in the solar system. Its radius is 71 000 km, about 11 times bigger than the Earth. Despite this, it spins on its axis faster than any other planet: it takes only 9 hours 50 minutes to spin on its axis. To find the linear velocity of a point on Jupiter's equator we need to calculate its angular velocity, ω:

$$\omega = \frac{2\pi}{T} = \frac{2\pi}{35\,400 \text{ s}} = 1.77 \times 10^{-4} \text{rad s}^{-1}$$

The linear velocity is:

$$v = r\omega$$
$$= 71\,000 \times 10^3 \text{ m} \times 1.77 \times 10^{-4} \text{ m s}^{-1}$$
$$= 12.6 \text{ km s}^{-1}$$

5 The United States Air Force uses a centrifuge with a 5 m radius to train their pilots. If the centrifuge has a period of 3 seconds,
a what is the pilot's angular velocity?
b what is his speed?

6 What is the Earth's speed in its orbit around the Sun? (Mean Earth–Sun distance = 14.9 × 10^{10} m.)

KEY FACTS

- An object moving at constant speed in a circle is accelerating. Its instantaneous velocity is along the tangent to the circle.

- Angular frequency = 1/period. $f = 1/T$.

- Angles can be measured in radians; there are 2π radians in a whole circle. 2π rad = 360°.

- Angular velocity, $\omega = 2\pi f$, and is measured in radians per second.

- Linear speed depends on radius and angular velocity, $v = r\omega$.

Centripetal acceleration

Whenever an object changes direction it is accelerating. The magnitude of a jet-fighter's acceleration when cornering at high speed is crucial to the safety of the pilot. Above $4g$ (g is the acceleration due to gravity: 9.8 m s^{-2}), the physical symptoms leading to a black-out begin to occur. Theme park rides usually keep the accelerations below $3g$, though they sometimes touch $4g$ for short periods. The size of the acceleration depends on two factors:

• How sharp the turn is, i.e. the radius of curvature, r, of the circle. The tighter the curve, the smaller the radius of curvature.

• How quickly the plane is travelling.

For an object moving in a circle the change of velocity, Δv, is always towards the centre of the circle (Fig. 3). Therefore, the acceleration is also towards the centre of the circle. For a small time interval, Δt, the acceleration is given by:

$$a = \frac{\Delta v}{\Delta t}$$

Note The bold symbol $\boldsymbol{v}$ represents the velocity *vector*. It is used when both the magnitude and the direction of velocity are important. The symbol v is just the magnitude of the velocity, i.e. the speed.

Study the vector triangle in Fig. 3. If the time interval is very small, θ will be a small angle and the vector $\Delta \boldsymbol{v}$ will be almost the same length as the arc AB. Because the object is moving at constant speed, $\boldsymbol{v}_1$ and $\boldsymbol{v}_2$ have the same magnitude, which we write as v. The angle θ, in radians, is therefore given by:

$$\theta = \frac{s}{r} = \frac{\Delta v}{v}$$

giving $\Delta v = \theta \times v$

The magnitude of the acceleration is:

$$a = \frac{\Delta v}{\Delta t} = \frac{\theta \times v}{\Delta t}$$

If the object has an angular velocity ω, where

$$\omega = \frac{\theta}{\Delta t}$$

$$\theta = \omega \times \Delta t$$

so $\quad a = \dfrac{\omega \times \Delta t \times v}{\Delta t}$

or $\quad a = \omega \times v$

We can eliminate either the speed or the angular velocity from this equation using the expression:

$$v = r \times \omega$$

to give either $\quad a = r\omega^2 \quad$ or $\quad a = \dfrac{v^2}{r}$

This acceleration is always directed towards the centre of the circle and is known as **centripetal acceleration**.

Fig. 3 Accelerating towards the centre

$\theta = \dfrac{s}{r}$

v = magnitude of $\boldsymbol{v}_1$ and $\boldsymbol{v}_2$

$\theta \approx \dfrac{\Delta v}{v}$

In a short time interval, Δt, the plane moves through a small angle, θ

7 The Thunderlooper was a white-knuckle ride at Alton Towers. It took passengers hurtling round a 23 m radius vertical loop at speeds of up to 60 mph (26 m s^{-1}). What is their centripetal acceleration?

8 Imagine you are standing on the equator. What is your centripetal acceleration due to the Earth's rotation about its axis? (The Earth's radius is 6×10^6 m.)

9 A modern passenger airliner makes a turn of radius 3 km. Calculate the speed at which it can make this turn if it is to keep the acceleration below $3g$.

APPLICATION

Surviving *g*-forces

Modern fighter planes can travel at speeds over 1500 km h^{-1} (400 m s^{-1}). If a pilot wants to turn at this speed, and keep the acceleration below 3*g*, the radius of the turn will have to be quite large. The smallest possible radius of curvature, *r*, would be:

$$r = \frac{v^2}{a}$$

$$= \frac{(400 \text{ m s}^{-1})^2}{30 \text{ m s}^{-2}} \approx 5 \text{ km}$$

Pilots need to manoeuvre through sharper turns than this. Modern aircraft are built to withstand accelerations of up to 12*g*, far higher than the human body can tolerate. How can pilots fly such planes?

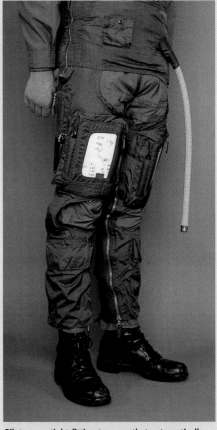

Pilots wear tight-fitting trousers that automatically inflate when high accelerations occur. These squeeze the blood out of the legs and abdomen, back towards the brain.

Fighter pilots can experience severe effects when high acceleration causes poor blood flow to the brain. When pilots turn their aircraft so that the cockpit is on the inside of the curve, blood drains from the head and accumulates in the lower body and legs. The brain then becomes starved of oxygen.

At relatively low acceleration, the body can adapt. The heart rate can increase to raise the blood pressure, and this ensures that the brain gets an adequate supply of oxygenated blood.

At high acceleration, the brain's oxygen reserves can last for periods of up to 5 seconds only. Any longer than this, and the pilot is likely to experience visual blackout and then G-LOC (gravity-induced loss of consciousness). A centrifuge is used to train pilots to cope with these effects. A combination of anti-*g* straining manoeuvres and breathing techniques can raise the blood pressure in the upper body and brain.

10 The human body can withstand prolonged accelerations of up to 3*g* (30 m s^{-2}). If a jet fighter makes a turn whilst travelling at a speed of 1000 km h^{-1}, calculate the minimum radius of the turn, if the centripetal acceleration is to stay below 3*g*.

Fig. 4 Effects of sustained *g*-forces

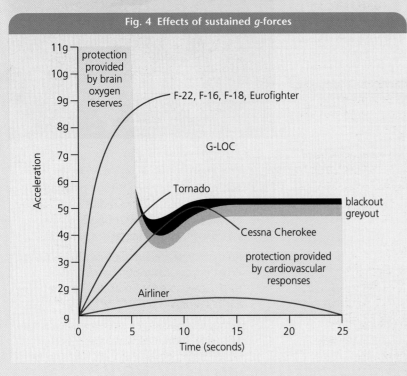

Forces in circular motion

Any object moving in a circular path accelerates towards the centre of the circle. Newton's second law says that a force is needed to cause this acceleration. This is sometimes referred to as the centripetal force. The centripetal force is not an extra force that arises due to the circular motion; it is the **resultant** of all the real forces acting on the body (Fig. 5).

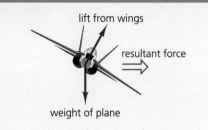

Fig. 5 The forces leading to a centripetal force on a turning aircraft

lift from wings

resultant force

weight of plane

A centrally directed (centripetal) force has to be supplied in order to move in a circle.

For an object of constant mass, the force is given by $F = ma$. We know that for an object moving in a circle $a = v^2/r$. The resultant force must be:

$$F = \frac{mv^2}{r} \quad \text{or} \quad F = mr\omega^2$$

When the Thunderlooper train (see Question 7) is fully loaded, it has a mass of about 7000 kg. The track has to exert a force of over 200 000 N to accelerate the train around the loop.

When a car drives round a roundabout it is the friction of the road acting on the tyres that pushes the car around the corners. Without friction, as in icy conditions, the car would keep going in a straight line.

Fig. 6 Source of centripetal force on a turning car

contact force of road on car

resultant force

frictional force on car tyres

weight of car

The resultant force is towards the centre of the circle.

11 Identify the force or forces which are causing the following objects to move in a circle.
a The Moon in its orbit around the Earth
b A pair of wet Y-fronts in a spin drier
c A train taking a corner

12 Estimate the size of the frictional force necessary to make a family car drive round a large traffic island.

13 Imagine you are standing on some bathroom scales at the equator. Would they show the same reading if you stood on them at the North Pole?

Centrifugal effect

If a high-speed aircraft pilot was to turn with the cockpit on the outside of the curve, he would experience a huge flow of blood to his head. The pilot would literally 'see red' and feel as if his head was going to explode. The force that the pilot *feels* pushing his body towards the cockpit roof is often referred to as

Fig. 7 Points of view

The child feels the centrifugal effect as a real force tugging her off the roundabout.

The adult sees that the child is in an accelerating frame of reference. She has to hold on – pull inwards – to stay on the roundabout.

Fig. 8 How a satellite really stays up

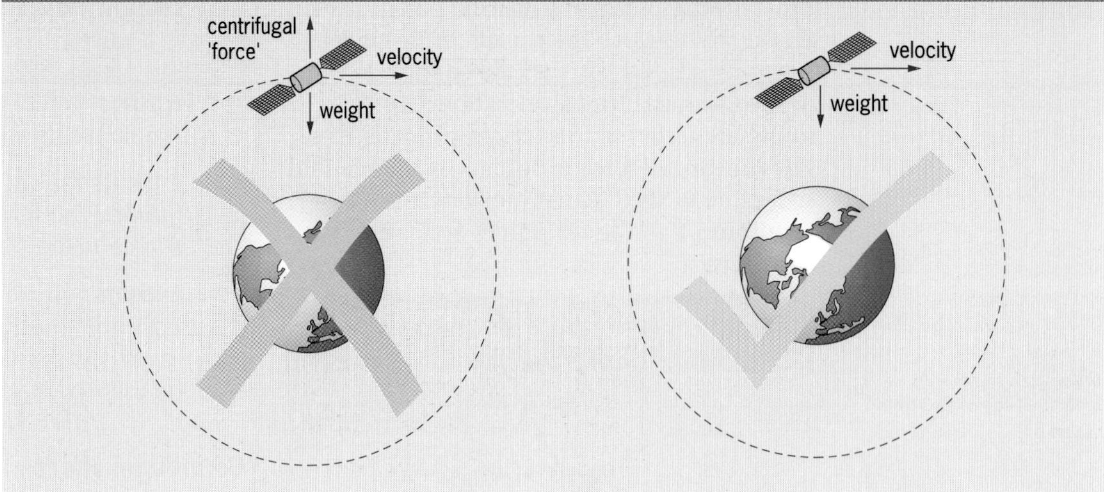

the centrifugal force. In fact, the centrifugal force does not exist. There isn't really a force pulling the pilot away from the centre of the circle. The pilot is just obeying Newton's first law. He would continue to move in a straight line at constant speed, but the force exerted by his restraining straps pulls him round in a circular path.

Consider a satellite in a circular orbit above the Earth's atmosphere (Fig. 8). It stays at the same height above the Earth's surface and travels at constant speed. The only significant force acting on the satellite is the pull of the Earth's gravity, i.e. the satellite's weight.

Therefore there is a resultant force on the satellite. This force acts towards the centre of the Earth. It would be wrong to say that the satellite is in equilibrium; it is constantly accelerating towards the centre of the Earth.

14 'A hammer thrower whirls round in a circle, gaining speed until the centrifugal force is great enough to carry the hammer a long way.' Rewrite this explanation correctly.

15 Explain, using the correct terms, how a spin-drier helps to dry clothes.

KEY FACTS

■ An object moving in a circular path is not in equilibrium; it is accelerating towards the centre of the circle.

■ The resultant force on the object acts towards the centre of the circle. This centripetal force is the resultant of the real forces acting on the object.

■ The size of the centripetal force is

$$F = \frac{mv^2}{r} = mr\omega^2$$

Horizontal circles

The riders on the swinging chairs move in a large circle. As the ride speeds up, the chairs swing further out. At top-speed, the riders move in a horizontal circle, with the chains at a large angle from the vertical.

To build an exciting but safe ride, designers need to know the maximum centripetal acceleration that passengers will experience. We can draw a diagram to represent the forces acting on the chair and passenger (Fig. 9). The tension in the chain can be resolved into horizontal and vertical components.

Once the ride has reached a steady speed the chair moves horizontally. This means that the vertical forces must balance:

$$T \cos \theta = W = mg$$

Horizontally, the chair is not in equilibrium; there is a resultant centripetal force, $T \sin \theta$:

$$T \sin \theta = \frac{mv^2}{r}$$

If we divide these equations we get:

$$\frac{T \sin \theta}{T \cos \theta} = \frac{mv^2/r}{mg}$$

so, $\tan \theta = \dfrac{v^2}{gr}$

where $\sin \theta / \cos \theta = \tan \theta$

This equation tells us that the angle, θ, does not depend on the mass of the chair and rider. If the circle has a radius of 10 m and the riders hang at a maximum angle of 60° to the vertical, the top speed will be:

$$v^2 = gr \tan \theta$$
$$= 9.8 \text{ m s}^{-2} \times 10 \text{ m} \times \tan 60° = 170$$
$$v = \sqrt{170} = 13.0 \text{ m s}^{-1}$$

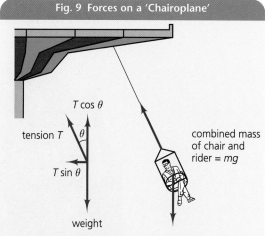

Fig. 9 Forces on a 'Chairoplane'

tension T

$T \cos \theta$

$T \sin \theta$

weight

combined mass of chair and rider = mg

The resultant force, $T \sin \theta$, provides the centripetal force.

The centripetal acceleration is

$$a = \frac{v^2}{r}$$
$$= \frac{170 \text{ m}^2 \text{ s}^{-2}}{10 \text{ m}}$$
$$= 17.0 \text{ m s}^{-2} \text{ (about } 1.7g)$$

16 There is very little frictional force on the ice track of a bob-sleigh run. Explain, using a forces diagram, how a bob-sleigh is able to corner.

17 Suppose that the bob-sleigh is taking a corner with a radius of curvature of 20 m and the maximum angle of the track is 45° to the vertical. Calculate the highest speed at which the corner can be taken.

■ For an object moving in a horizontal circle, the vertical forces balance. The resultant horizontal force causes a centripetal acceleration.

Vertical circles

The 'Corkscrew' ride at Alton Towers takes its victims through two complete 360° vertical turns and reaches speeds of up to 65 km h⁻¹ along its 750 m track.

Fig. 10 Forces around the loop

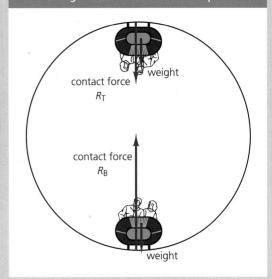

It is more difficult to apply ideas about circular motion when an object is moving in a vertical circle. (Motion in vertical circles is therefore beyond the specification at A2 level.) Motion in vertical circles is more complicated because the force of gravity acts towards the centre of the circle at the top of the circular motion, and away from the centre at the bottom. That means that the magnitude of other forces will change as the object goes around the circle.

It is the contact force between a passenger and the seat that varies as the car goes around the Corkscrew's vertical circle.

At the bottom of the loop, the contact force, R_B, acts in the opposite direction to the weight. The resultant force has to provide the centripetal acceleration upwards, towards the centre of the circle.

$$R_B - W = \frac{mv^2}{r} \quad \text{or} \quad R_B = W + \frac{mv^2}{r}$$

The contact force is greater than the passenger's weight, so the passengers feel pushed into their seats (Fig. 10).

At the top of the loop, the contact force, R_T, is in the same direction as the weight. Together these forces provide the centripetal acceleration downwards, towards the centre of the circle.

$$R_T + W = \frac{mv^2}{r} \quad \text{or} \quad R_T = \frac{mv^2}{r} - W$$

The contact force depends on the speed. Suppose that the speed stays constant during the loop. For a passenger of mass 50 kg travelling at a velocity of 18 m s⁻¹ around a loop with a radius of about 11 m:

$$R_T = \frac{50 \text{ kg} \times (18 \text{ ms}^{-1})^2}{11 \text{ m}} - 500 \text{ N}$$
$$= 970 \text{ N}$$

The passenger feels pushed upwards into the seat with a force equal to about twice her weight. If the speed was reduced, the contact force would decrease. There is a critical value of the speed at which the contact force drops to zero, and an unrestrained passenger would begin to fall out of the ride:

$$R_T = 0 = \frac{mv^2}{r} - W$$
$$\frac{mv^2}{r} = W = mg$$
$$v^2 = gr$$

The critical velocity is independent of the passenger's mass. For the example above:

$$v = \sqrt{gr} = 10.4 \text{ ms}^{-1}$$

18 Suppose that you whirl a 1 kg mass on the end of a spring balance at a steady speed in a vertical circle. If you spin it just quickly enough to prevent the mass falling on your head, explain how you would expect the balance reading to vary during one revolution.

19 If a stunt pilot flew in a vertical circle of radius 500 m, what is the minimum speed that she would need to maintain to stay in her seat at the top of the loop?

20 If the pilot flew that same loop at 100 m s⁻¹, what would her acceleration be? If she had a mass of 60 kg what would the resultant force on her be:
a at the top of the loop?
b at the bottom of the loop?

1 **a** A stone of mass 0.10 kg is attached to a piece of string and whirled at a constant rate in a horizontal radius of 0.75 m. The stone completes 2.5 revolutions each second.
Calculate

   (i) the angular velocity of the stone.
   (ii) the orbital speed of the stone. (4)

 b In order to move in a circle the stone must be subjected to a centripetal force.

   (i) Calculate the magnitude of the centripetal force acting on the stone in (a).
   (ii) State what provides this centripetal force. (3)
   (PH01 February 1996 Q4)

2 A communications satellite of mass 550 kg performs a circular orbit above the equator with a period of 24 hours. The radius of the orbit of the satellite is 4.2×10^7 m.

 a Calculate the angular speed of the satellite. (2)

 b Calculate the magnitude of the force needed to keep the satellite in the circular orbit and state its direction. (3)

   (PH01 February 2001 Q2)

3 A satellite of mass 50 kg travelling in a circular orbit round the Earth at a height of 300 km above the surface takes 90 minutes to make one complete orbit.

 a Calculate its angular speed around the centre of the Earth. (1)

 b Using the value of the Earth's radius given in the data section, calculate

   (i) The acceleration of the satellite,
   (ii) The centripetal force acting on it. (3)

 c For the satellite in the course of one complete orbit, state and explain what changes, if any, occur to

   (i) the momentum,
   (ii) the kinetic energy. (4)
   (PH01 June 1995 Q5)

6 Gravity

On April 13th 1970, Apollo 13 astronauts Jim Lovell, Jack Swigert and Fred Haise were four-fifths of the way to the Moon when disaster struck. Swigert radioed to NASA Mission Control in Houston to report, 'We seem to have a problem here.' The problem was serious. The main oxygen supply was leaking into space. Two of the spacecraft's three fuel cells had stopped working and the other one was failing fast.

With only 14 minutes of oxygen left in the main spacecraft, the three astronauts scrambled into the Lunar Excursion Module (LEM). Though originally designed for the last leg of the astronauts' journey to the Moon's surface, the LEM, with its own oxygen supply, would now have to serve as a life-boat.

There were two options open to Mission Control. They could fire Apollo's engines to reverse the spacecraft's direction, and bring it back to Earth as rapidly as possible. This was a high-risk strategy as there might not be enough fuel left for the final course adjustments needed to get them home safely.

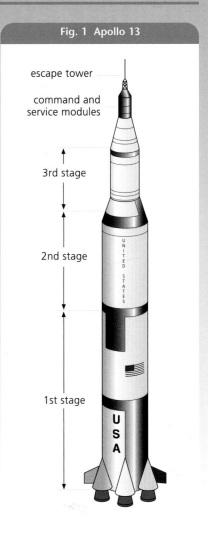

Fig. 1 Apollo 13

escape tower

command and service modules

3rd stage

2nd stage

1st stage

USA

A second option was for the astronauts to continue to the Moon and use its gravity to swing the spacecraft round, like a slingshot, back to Earth. This plan was preferred by the astronauts. At least the spacecraft would definitely return to Earth.

The crew of Apollo 13 examine a model of the lunar module.

6.1 Newton's law of gravitation

Pictures of 'floating' astronauts mislead many people into thinking that there is no gravity acting in space. Newton understood gravity to be a universal force of attraction which acts between all objects. He suggested that the force that pulls objects like apples down to the ground also extends out into space and holds the Moon in its orbit around the Earth. For two objects, the size of the gravitational attraction between them is:

- proportional to the product of their masses, $m_1 m_2$;
- inversely proportional to the square of the distance, r, between them (Fig. 2).

$$F \propto m_1 m_2 \quad \text{and} \quad F \propto \frac{1}{r^2}$$

$$\text{or,} \quad F = -\frac{G m_1 m_2}{r^2}$$

The constant G is known as the universal constant of gravitation. In SI units, G is measured in N m^2 kg^{-2}.

Fig. 2 Force of gravity

Force and displacement are vector quantities. They are in opposite directions, so there is a negative sign in the equation.

$$F = -G \frac{m_1 m_2}{r^2}$$

m_1

m_2

F = force

displacement
r

The period of the Moon's orbit

Newton didn't know the size of the universal constant, G, so he was unable to check his theory by direct measurement. Instead, he tested his hypothesis by using it to predict the orbital period of the Moon (Fig. 3).

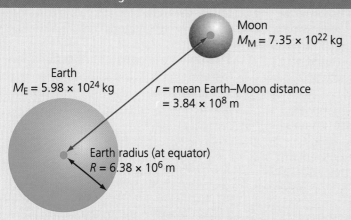

Fig. 3 Earth and Moon

Moon
$M_M = 7.35 \times 10^{22}$ kg

Earth
$M_E = 5.98 \times 10^{24}$ kg

r = mean Earth–Moon distance
$= 3.84 \times 10^8$ m

Earth radius (at equator)
$R = 6.38 \times 10^6$ m

According to Newton's law, the force of gravity on an object of mass m at the Earth's surface is:

$$F = -\frac{GmM_E}{R^2}$$

where R is the radius of the Earth and M_E is the Earth's mass. This force would lead to an acceleration, a, of:

$$a = \frac{F}{m} = -\frac{GmM_E}{mR^2}$$

$$= -\frac{GM_E}{R^2}$$

In the same way, the acceleration of the Moon in its orbit due to the Earth's gravity is:

$$a = -\frac{GM_E}{r^2}$$

where r is the radius of the Moon's orbit. The ratio of these accelerations is:

$$\frac{a \text{ at Earth's surface}}{a \text{ at Moon's orbit}} = \frac{-\dfrac{GM_E}{R^2}}{-\dfrac{GM_E}{r^2}}$$

$$= \frac{r^2}{R^2} \quad \text{or,} \quad \left(\frac{r}{R}\right)^2$$

Newton knew that the Moon was about 60 Earth radii away, so he calculated that the acceleration due to the Earth's gravity would be 3600 times greater on the Earth's surface than at the Moon's orbit. At the Earth's surface, the acceleration due to gravity can be measured

directly as 9.8 m s^{-2}. Newton calculated that the acceleration of the Moon, due to Earth's gravity, should be:

$$\frac{9.8 \text{ ms}^{-2}}{3600} = 2.72 \times 10^{-3} \text{ m s}^{-2}$$

He used this figure to predict the time taken by the Moon to orbit the Earth. Assuming the Moon is in a circular orbit around the Earth, its acceleration is $a = v^2/r$ (see Chapter 5). This can be rearranged to give $v = \sqrt{ra}$. Since the Moon is, on average, 3.84×10^8 m away from the Earth:

$$v = \sqrt{3.84 \times 10^8 \text{ m} \times 2.72 \times 10^{-3} \text{ m s}^{-2}}$$

$$= 1022 \text{ m s}^{-1}$$

The time taken for one orbit, T, is therefore:

$$T = \frac{2\pi r}{v}$$

$$= 2.36 \times 10^6 \text{ s} \ (27.3 \text{ days})$$

Newton predicted a period of 27.3 days for the Moon's orbit. The time between full moons is actually 29.5 days. This difference is due to the Earth's motion around the Sun. If we measure the Moon's position relative to the distant stars, it has an orbital period of 27.32 days. Newton's theory worked, and though some modifications were made following Einstein's general theory of relativity, Newton's law was still accurate enough to plan ventures to the Moon.

1 A satellite orbiting the Earth at a height of 700 km falls into a lower orbit of 500 km.
a By what factor does the gravitational force increase?
b What effect will this have on the satellite's speed?
(Remember to take account of the Earth's radius, $r = 6.4 \times 10^6$ m.)

2 Fifty years before Newton, Johannes Kepler published three laws of planetary motion. The third law says that: 'The square of the period of a planet's orbit, T, is proportional to the cube of its mean distance from the Sun, r' (i.e. $T^2 \propto r^3$). Use Newton's law of gravitation to derive Kepler's third law. Assume that the planets move in circular orbits and remember that any object moving in a circle has an acceleration of v^2/r.

3 Pluto is 40 times further from the Sun than we are. How long is a year on Pluto? (Use Kepler's third law.)

6.2 The strength of gravity

Kennedy Space Centre, April 11th, 1970. The successful launch of Apollo 13.

The Saturn V rocket which carried the Apollo 13 astronauts towards the Moon was 110 metres high and had an initial mass of 3000 tonnes. Three different rocket motors, or stages, were used to send it into Earth orbit. Eight seconds before lift-off, the first stage ignited. At lift-off, the clamps holding the rocket to the launch pad were released. By this time the rocket was burning 15 tonnes of fuel per second and exerting a thrust of 33 million newtons against the Earth's gravitational attraction.

The gravitational force acting on less massive objects is much smaller. When you jump in the air, you overcome your gravitational attraction to the entire Earth fairly easily. Two people standing one metre apart exert a gravitational attraction on each other of about 0.2 mN.

Today, physicists believe that there are just four fundamental ways in which matter interacts (Table 1). Gravity is by far the weakest of these forces. In a hydrogen atom, the electrostatic force between the proton and the electron is about 10^{-7} N. The gravitational attraction between them is only about 10^{-47} N, a factor of 10^{-40} times smaller. Despite this, it is gravity that keeps the planets in their orbits and holds our galaxy together.

Electric charges can be positive or negative. This means that electromagnetic forces can cause either attraction or repulsion. On a larger scale, these forces cancel out. However, because particles cannot have negative mass, the force of gravity is always attractive. In space, gravity is the dominant force because the small, attractive forces between particles add together. A consequence of this is that it is not possible to shield against gravity. Unlike electromagnetic forces, the force between two masses is not affected by the material between them.

The universal constant of gravitation

Rearranging Newton's formula shows the significance of G, the universal constant of gravitation:

$$G = -\frac{Fr^2}{m_1 m_2}$$

Suppose $r = 1$ m and both masses are 1 kg, $m_1 = m_2 = 1$ kg. Then $G = -F$. So G is the attractive force between two 1 kilogram masses placed 1 metre apart. This force is extremely small. The first accurate measurement of G was done in 1798 by Henry Cavendish. He used a sensitive torsion balance to measure the turning effect exerted by two masses (Fig. 4).

Fig. 4 Cavendish's apparatus

When the large masses, M and M', are brought up to the small masses, m and m' the beam rotates as a result of the attraction between the masses. The couple exerted by the fibre for a given angular displacement can be measured and G calculated.

fibre

M m' m M'

Modern measurements of G rely on the same principle. They give a value of 6.673×10^{-11} N m² kg⁻². Scientists believe that G has the same value throughout the universe.

 Cavendish's experiment has been called 'weighing the Earth'. Once G was known, the mass of the Earth could be calculated. How?

Table 1 The fundamental forces				
	Gravitational	**Electromagnetic**	**Strong nuclear**	**Weak nuclear**
range	infinite	infinite	within the nucleus < 10^{-12} m	within the nucleus < 10^{-17} m
acts between	all masses	all charges	hadrons (nuclear particles like protons and neutrons)	hadrons and leptons (nucleons and electrons)
effect	holds stars together and planets in their orbits	holds atoms together, keeps electrons in their orbits	holds nuclei together	responsible for radioactivity
relative magnitude	10^{-36}	1	100	0.01

- Newton's law of gravitation states that the gravitational force of attraction, F, between two masses, m_1 and m_2, a distance r apart is given by:

$$F = -\frac{Gm_1m_2}{r^2}$$

- G is the universal gravitational constant = 6.673×10^{-11} N m^2 kg^{-2}.

Work done against gravity

Despite the enormous power of the Saturn V rocket, Apollo 13 took more than 10 seconds to clear the launchpad tower. The first and second stages were jettisoned before the third stage carried the astronauts into Earth orbit, just 11 minutes and 25 seconds after lift-off.

To lift the astronauts into orbit, work had to be done against the gravitational force between the spacecraft and the Earth. For a steady force we can calculate the work done using the formula:

work = force × distance moved

However, the force on the rocket changes as it goes up. This is partly because the mass of the rocket falls as fuel is burned, but also because the gravitational force decreases as the rocket gets further from the Earth.

In order to simplify things, consider an object with a constant mass, m, at a distance x from the centre of the Earth. We can calculate how much work is done in moving the object a small distance, Δx, further away. If Δx is small enough, the force will not change significantly over that distance, so:

$$\text{work done} = F\Delta x = -\frac{GM_E m\Delta x}{x^2}$$

This is the area of one of the strips marked on Fig. 5.

The total work done, W, is the sum of the areas of all such strips, from the Earth's surface to an infinite distance away. However, it can be found more accurately by integrating the expression $F\,dx$ between the Earth's radius, R, and infinity:

$$W = \int_R^\infty F\,dx = -GM_E m\int_R^\infty \frac{1}{x^2}\,dx$$

$$= -GM_E m\left[-\frac{1}{x}\right]_R^\infty = \frac{GM_E m}{R}$$

This is the work done in taking the mass, m, from the Earth's surface to infinity (i.e. completely out of the influence of Earth's gravity).

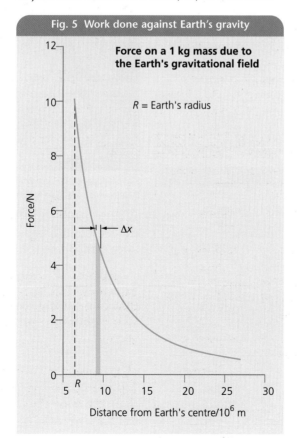

Fig. 5 Work done against Earth's gravity

Force on a 1 kg mass due to the Earth's gravitational field

R = Earth's radius

Δx

Force/N

R

Distance from Earth's centre/10^6 m

5. Apollo 13's command, service and lunar modules had a combined mass, m, of 44 tonnes. Calculate the work done by the Saturn V rocket in lifting them into orbit at a height, h, of 185 km above the Earth (mass = 5.98×10^{24} kg).

6. The ascent stage of the lunar module, mass = 4450 kg, was designed to lift the Apollo astronauts off the surface of the Moon and back into lunar orbit, at a height of about 110 km. How much work does it need to do against the Moon's gravitational field? (Radius of Moon = 1.74×10^6 m, mass of Moon = 7.35×10^{22} kg.)

Escape velocity

'What goes up must come down' is a saying that reflects our everyday experience of the Earth's gravity. But if you could throw an object fast enough, it might never come down. The energy required by the mass to escape the Earth's pull is:

$$W = \frac{GM_E m}{R}$$

If this all comes from the initial kinetic energy of the object then:

$$\frac{1}{2}mv^2 = \frac{GM_E m}{R}$$

$$v = \sqrt{\frac{2GM_E}{R}}$$

This is known as the escape velocity.

The Earth's escape velocity is 11.2×10^3 m s^{-1}, just over 11 km per second. The mass of the object has no effect on v, the escape velocity. If you could throw a projectile at this speed it would never come down. In theory, it would eventually come to rest an infinite distance from Earth, though it would probably come under the gravitational influence of another object in space. A rocket doesn't have to travel at an initial speed of 11 km s^{-1} to escape from the Earth, but its motors will eventually have to provide an equivalent amount of energy.

7 In 1798, the French mathematician Pierre Laplace predicted the existence of objects so dense that their escape velocity would be greater than the speed of light ($c = 3 \times 10^8$ m s^{-1}). Two hundred years later, astronomers are looking for these objects, which they call 'black holes'. How small would you have to crush the Earth before it became a black hole?

6.3 Orbiting the Earth

Newton had foreseen the possibility of orbiting the Earth. He thought that if a large enough cannon could be constructed and placed at the top of a very high mountain it could fire a shell that would never fall back to the Earth's surface (Fig. 6).

At the right speed, the shell becomes a satellite, falling towards the Earth's surface at exactly the rate that the Earth's surface curves

Since 1972, when the final Apollo mission went to the Moon, all manned space flights have been confined to orbiting the Earth.

away. If a satellite, of mass m, moves in a circular orbit, of radius r, the gravitational force on the satellite is:

$$F = \frac{GM_E m}{r^2} = ma$$

Since the satellite is moving in a circle, its acceleration is:

$$a = \frac{v^2}{r}$$

So,

$$\frac{GM_E m}{r^2} = \frac{mv^2}{r}$$

or,

$$v^2 = \frac{GM_E}{r}$$

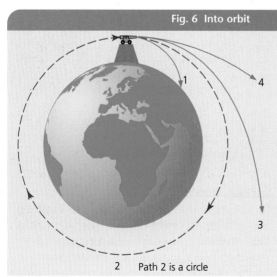

Fig. 6 Into orbit

1. $v^2 < GM_E/r$
The shell falls to Earth (parabolic path)
2. $v^2 = GM_E/r$
The shell becomes a satellite (a circular orbit)
3. $v^2 > GM_E/r$ but v is less than escape velocity. The shell moves in an elliptical orbit
4. $v >$ escape velocity The shell leaves Earth on a hyperbolic trajectory

2   Path 2 is a circle

For a satellite orbiting the Earth, GM_E is a constant, so $v^2 \propto 1/r$. This means that there is a unique velocity for each orbit. The lower the satellite, the faster it must travel to stay in orbit.

The trajectory of the Saturn V rocket was calculated to put the astronauts into the correct orbit. The powerful first stage moved the rocket vertically, taking the shortest path through the densest part of the atmosphere. The rocket then climbed at an angle until it reached Earth orbit. During this phase, stages 1 and 2 were jettisoned. A final firing of the rocket motors brought Apollo's speed up to the correct value for that orbit.

The Apollo spacecraft orbited at a height of about 185 km. To find its orbital radius we must add on the radius of the Earth, which is 6.38×10^6 m. Apollo's orbital speed is given by:

$$v = \sqrt{\frac{GM_E}{r}}$$
$$= \sqrt{\frac{6.67 \times 10^{-11}\ \mathrm{N\,m^2\,kg^{-2}} \times 5.98 \times 10^{24}\ \mathrm{kg}}{6.56 \times 10^6\ \mathrm{m}}}$$
$$= 7800\ \mathrm{m\,s^{-1}}$$

We can also calculate the time it took for the spacecraft to complete one orbit. The period, T, is:

$$T = \frac{\text{orbit circumference}}{\text{speed}}$$
$$= \frac{2\pi r}{v} = \frac{2\pi \times 6.56 \times 10^6\ \mathrm{m}}{7800\ \mathrm{m\,s^{-1}}}$$
$$= 5300 \text{ seconds (about 88 minutes)}$$

Artificial satellites

The space industry now concentrates on putting unmanned satellites into orbit. We use them to send telephone messages and TV

Satellites can give detailed information on a variety of phenomena. The false-colour IR photograph shows the spread of forest fires due to slash and burn farming in Mozambique.

Radar imaging from a satellite over California illustrates the ground displacement following an earthquake.

pictures around the world and to give us detailed information about the weather. Satellites can also be used for navigation. The Global Positioning System uses a network of 20 satellites to tell users exactly where they are, with an uncertainty of only 15 metres.

Communications satellites such as Astra, which broadcasts TV programmes, are often placed in high orbits. The signals are received by small, fixed dish aerials (Fig. 7). This is only possible if the satellite remains at exactly the same position in the sky relative to the receiver. The satellites must therefore be placed in a **geostationary** orbit, an orbit that has a period of exactly 24 hours. As the Earth rotates, the satellite moves to remain above exactly the same position on the Earth's surface.

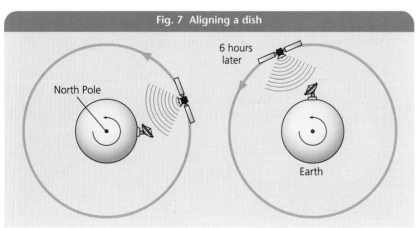

Fig. 7 Aligning a dish

North Pole

6 hours later

Earth

APPLICATION — Weightlessness

Free-fall or weightlessness? A lunch-time drink is not easy in either case.

Astronauts in orbit around the Earth feel weightless. The Russian cosmonaut, Oleg Atkov, had 8 months of weightlessness in Earth orbit, aboard the Russian space station Salyut 7. He had difficulty sleeping because his head floated from the pillow. The organs of balance in his inner-ear did not work properly in 'weightless' conditions and he felt constantly dizzy. Despite regular, vigorous exercise his muscles wasted and his bones lost calcium. When he returned to Earth he could not support his own weight and had to be carried from his spacecraft on a stretcher.

'Weightlessness' is rather a misleading expression. The force of the Earth's gravity on the astronauts is only slightly less than when they were on Earth. What has changed is the contact force between the astronauts and the spacecraft. When we are standing, it is the contact force of the ground which prevents us from accelerating downwards under gravity. This upwards force acting on our feet makes us aware of our weight. When the ground moves beneath you, in a lift for example, you feel as if your weight is changing (Fig. 8). If the lift accelerates upwards you feel heavier, though gravity has not changed. It is simply that the contact force from the lift floor has increased. When the lift accelerates downwards you feel lighter; the contact force is now less than your weight.

If the lift cable breaks and the lift falls freely under gravity, the contact force between you and the floor disappears altogether, you feel weightless. For an astronaut in Earth orbit, the sensation is the same as being in a freely falling lift. The astronaut, the spacecraft and everything in it are falling together, at exactly the same acceleration. This is sometimes called 'weightlessness' or 'zero-gravity', but free-fall is a more accurate term. Later in their voyage the Apollo astronauts experienced a point of true weightlessness. This is where the gravitational attraction of the Earth and Moon cancel out (see page **80**).

The Apollo astronauts did not have to contend with the long-term effects of weightlessness. Several hours after launch, they used the third and final stage of the rocket motors to leave the Earth's orbit and head for the Moon.

Fig. 8 Going up?

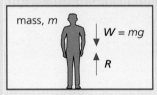

For a stationary lift, or one moving at constant velocity, the person is in equilibrium, $R = W$.

In a lift accelerating upwards, there must be a resultant force on the person, $R - W = ma$ so $R > W$, and the person feels heavier.

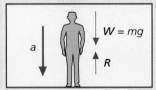

As the lift accelerates downwards there is a resultant force downwards on the person, $W - R = ma$ so $R < W$ and the person feels lighter.

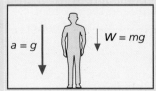

If the lift falls freely $a = g$, $W - R = mg$ but $W = mg$, so $R = 0$. There is no constant force between you and the floor.
The person feels weightless (for a short time at least).

8 Suppose one of the astronauts stood on some bathroom scales during their flight. Explain what the scales would show:
a during the ascent into Earth orbit;
b when the craft was in orbit.

9 It has been suggested that a space station in Earth orbit could spin to simulate the acceleration due to gravity. The space station could be shaped like a doughnut, rotating about an axis through its centre (Fig. 9). If the radius of the space station was 1 km, how fast would it need to turn? Which surface would the astronauts walk on?

Fig. 9 Artificial gravity

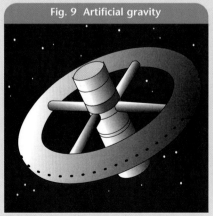

We can relate r and T by combining:

$$T = \frac{2\pi r}{v} \quad \text{and} \quad v = \sqrt{\frac{GM_E}{r}}$$

giving, $\quad r^3 = T^2\,\dfrac{GM_E}{4\pi^2}$

If T is 24 hours ($24 \times 60 \times 60 = 86\,400$ seconds), then r must be 42.2×10^6 m. This is a height of about 36 000 km above the Earth's surface. The geostationary satellite also needs to have the same axis of rotation as the Earth.

The work done by a force is given by force × distance moved in the direction of the force. Because a satellite's velocity is always at right angles to the force no work is done against gravity. Once in orbit, a satellite shouldn't need any energy to keep it there. For a geostationary satellite this is practically true. At a height of 36 000 km there is no atmospheric drag acting against the satellite. Satellites in low Earth orbit have a limited lifetime as their energy transfers to molecules in the outer atmosphere as heat. This causes the satellite to slow down and move to a lower orbit.

10 Explain why a geostationary satellite must be in orbit over the equator.

11 If a satellite was in orbit at a height of 700 km above the surface of the Earth, what would its period be?

6.4 Gravitational field strength

Apollo 13's Service Module photographed just after it was jettisoned.

The explosion of oxygen tank number two of the Apollo 13 spacecraft destroyed an entire panel of the craft's Service Module. The explosion happened fifty-five hours into the Apollo 13 mission, when Commander Jim Lovell heard a bang and discovered that the gauge for number two oxygen tank was reading empty. When he looked out of the window he saw a faint haze issuing from the side of the spacecraft; their oxygen supply was escaping into space. The astronauts climbed into the lunar module. All systems in the main spacecraft were shut down. Its only remaining power supply was the three batteries that would be needed during the re-entry to Earth's atmosphere.

By now Apollo 13 was close to the point where the Moon's gravitational pull takes over from the Earth's. The motors were fired to take the craft back to a free return trajectory. The gravitational field of the Moon would have to turn them round.

Gravitational field strength

Apollo 13 started to accelerate towards the Moon as it entered its **gravitational field**. This is the region of space where a mass is subject to the Moon's gravitational attraction. Every mass produces a gravitational field. The strength of the gravitational field at a point is defined as the force that would be exerted on a unit mass placed at that point:

gravitational field strength = force per unit mass

$$g = \frac{F}{m}$$

In SI units, g is measured in N kg^{-1}, though it can also be thought of as the acceleration due to gravity in m s^{-2}.

We can use Newton's law of gravitation to find an expression for g at the surface of the Earth. Since the force of gravity on a mass m on the surface of the Earth (radius r) is given by:

$$F = -\frac{GM_E m}{r^2}$$

so, $\quad g = \dfrac{F}{m} = -\dfrac{GM_E}{r^2}$

This expression gives the field strength for a radial gravitational field, such as that produced by a spherical mass like the Moon or the Earth. At the Earth's surface, the gravitational field strength is approximately

10 N kg^{-1}. In fact the value varies from place to place. Local variations in g can give important information about the composition of the Earth in that area.

Gravitational field lines

We draw gravitational field lines to show the direction of the force acting on a mass. These are similar to the sketches of magnetic field lines that show the direction of the force on the north pole of a magnet (Fig. 10).

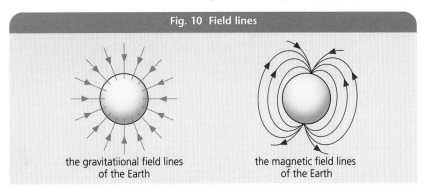

Fig. 10 Field lines

the gravitatiional field lines of the Earth

the magnetic field lines of the Earth

For a sphere like the Earth the field lines are radial. The field is stronger where the lines are closer together.

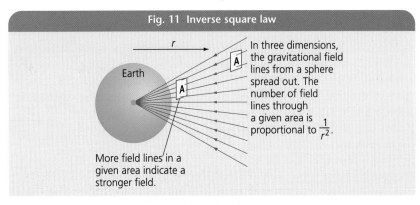

Fig. 11 Inverse square law

Earth

A

A

In three dimensions, the gravitational field lines from a sphere spread out. The number of field lines through a given area is proportional to $\frac{1}{r^2}$.

More field lines in a given area indicate a stronger field.

Einstein had another way of looking at gravitational fields; he saw them as distortions in space itself. Try to picture space as a stretched sheet of rubber; it is simpler to imagine this in two-dimensions. Massive

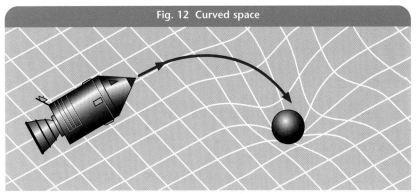

Fig. 12 Curved space

objects, like the Earth and the Moon, distort the sheet (Fig. 12). They produce a gravitational 'well', into which objects such as meteorites, or astronauts, may fall. A more massive object will cause a greater distortion in space and have a deeper gravitational well.

In this picture, gravity is no longer a force; it is a property of space itself. A large mass distorts the space around it, altering the trajectory of a passing object. Einstein said there was no difference between the effects of gravity and the effects of acceleration. An astronaut in a closed space ship could not tell whether she was being pulled towards a mass or just using the ship's engines to accelerate. Both would cause her to experience what we call 'weight'. For most applications it doesn't matter whether you use Einstein's theory or Newton's; they agree in many respects.

The neutral point

Somewhere between the Earth and the Moon there is a point where the gravitational forces from each are equal, but opposite. This is known as a neutral point (Fig. 13). If you could stand exactly at this point, you would experience the same force in each direction and you would be in equilibrium. The equilibrium would be unstable; one slight move in either direction would pull you back to the Earth or on to the Moon.

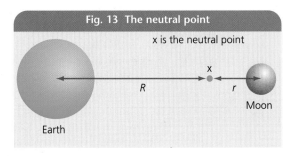

Fig. 13 The neutral point

x is the neutral point

R

r

x

Earth

Moon

If the gravitational field strengths are the same at this point:

$$g_{\text{M}} = g_{\text{E}}$$

$$\frac{GM_{\text{M}}}{r^2} = \frac{GM_{\text{E}}}{R^2}$$

so, $\quad \dfrac{R^2}{r^2} = \dfrac{M_{\text{E}}}{M_{\text{M}}} = 80$

$$R \approx 9r$$

R is the distance from the Earth, r is the distance from the Moon and the Earth is about 80 times more massive than the Moon.

Apollo 13 was approximately 90 per cent of the way to the Moon (350 000 km from Earth) when it passed through the neutral point.

12 The Sun's mass is approximately 1.989×10^{30} kg, the Earth's is 5.978×10^{24} kg. The mean separation of the Earth and the Sun is 1.496×10^{11} m. How far from Earth is the neutral point of the Earth–Sun system?

As the Apollo 13 crew went through the neutral point towards the Moon, they knew that they would eventually move back towards Earth. Even if they didn't fire their engines again, the Moon's gravitational pull would swing them round, and sling them back towards the Earth. The problem was speed. Apollo was travelling too slowly to get the crew back to Earth before their oxygen ran out. Therefore, the rocket motors had to be fired as they came out from behind the Moon. A rocket burn of exactly 4 minutes and 28 seconds accelerated them towards home.

6.5 Gravitational potential

When the astronauts had passed back through the neutral point, the Earth's gravitational field began to accelerate them again. By the time they reached the Earth's atmosphere they would be travelling at enormous speed. We can calculate this speed by looking at the kinetic energy gained by a falling object. If we ignore air resistance, gravitational potential energy is fully transferred to kinetic energy:

$$mg\Delta h = \tfrac{1}{2}mv^2$$
$$v = \sqrt{2g\Delta h}$$

This works well for small values of the change in height, Δh, but for large values we need to take into account the fact that g varies. We use the idea of **gravitational potential** (Fig. 14) to do this:

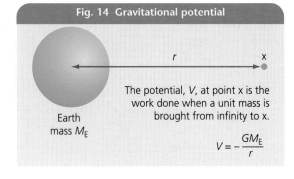

Fig. 14 Gravitational potential

Earth mass M_E

r

x

The potential, V, at point x is the work done when a unit mass is brought from infinity to x.

$$V = -\frac{GM_E}{r}$$

The gravitational potential at a point is defined as the work done in moving a unit mass from infinity to that point.

Earlier, we found that the work done, W, in taking a mass, m, from a distance R to infinity is:

$$W = \frac{GM_E m}{R}$$

The gravitational potential describes the reverse effect, bringing a mass to a point from infinity. Potential is also defined for a unit mass, so the gravitational potential, V, at a distance r from the Earth is given by:

$$V = -\frac{W}{m} = -\frac{GM_E}{r}$$

The gravitational potential is always negative. You would need to do work to take the mass back to infinity. Therefore, the gravitational potential at a point can also be thought of as the potential energy of a unit mass placed there. It is measured in J kg^{-1}. To find the potential energy (E_p) of a real object at a particular point, you need to multiply by its mass:

$$E_p = mV = -\frac{GM_E m}{r}$$

At an infinite distance from the Earth the potential drops to zero. The potential of an

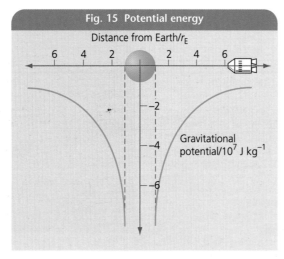

Fig. 15 Potential energy

object becomes increasingly negative as it moves closer to the Earth (Fig. 15).

At the Moon, the potential of the Earth's gravitational field is:

$$V = -\frac{GM_E}{r}$$

$$= -\frac{6.67 \times 10^{-11}\ \text{N m}^2\ \text{kg}^{-2} \times 6 \times 10^{24}\ \text{kg}}{3.844 \times 10^8\ \text{m}}$$

$$= -1.04 \times 10^6\ \text{J kg}^{-1}$$

The potential energy of Apollo 13 (approximate mass = 4.4×10^4 kg) due to the Earth's field was therefore:

$$E_p = mV$$

$$= 4.4 \times 10^4\ \text{kg} \times (-1.04 \times 10^6\ \text{J kg}^{-1})$$

$$= -4.6 \times 10^{10}\ \text{J}$$

This potential energy was transferred to kinetic energy as the spacecraft approached Earth.

The total energy of the spacecraft, E_{total}, is the sum of its kinetic and potential energies:

$$E_{total} = E_k + E_p$$

If the total energy is constant, any decrease in potential energy means a corresponding increase in kinetic energy. As the spacecraft's potential energy becomes more negative, its kinetic energy becomes more positive.

Although the Moon's gravity acted to slow the spacecraft, Apollo's rocket motors helped to overcome this effect. By the time Apollo 13 arrived back at the edge of the Earth's atmosphere, it was travelling at about 11 km s^{-1}.

13

a What is the potential at the edge of the Earth's atmosphere, at a height of about 100 km, due to the Earth's gravity?

b At the Moon's orbit, the potential of the Earth's gravitational field is -1.04×10^6 J kg^{-1}. Use this and your answer to (a) to confirm that Apollo 13 would be travelling at about 11 km s^{-1} when it returned to Earth.

Equipotentials and field lines

The potential at a point in a radial gravitational field, such as that produced by a sphere like the Earth, depends on the distance from the centre of the sphere. If all the points at the same potential are joined up, they form a spherical shell (Fig. 16). A surface like this is known as an equipotential surface. It is like a contour line which connects points of equal height on a map.

Suppose a spacecraft of mass m moves a small distance, Δx, away from the Earth. Its potential will increase by ΔV and its potential energy will change by $m\Delta V$.

In order to pull away from the Earth, the spacecraft had to exert a force equal in magnitude, but opposite in direction, to the gravitational attraction, F. So the work done by the spacecraft is:

work done = force × distance moved

$$= -F \times \Delta x = -mg\Delta x$$

so, $$-mg\Delta x = m\Delta V$$

$$g = -\frac{\Delta V}{\Delta x}$$

The equation can be read as 'field strength equals the negative potential gradient'. The equation implies that the gravitational potential changes quickly where the field is strong.

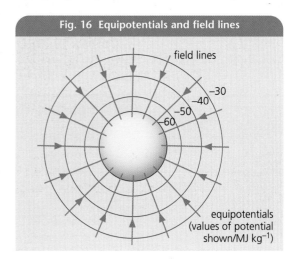

Fig. 16 Equipotentials and field lines

Splash-down

The astronauts were dehydrated, cold and suffering from exhaustion as they made their final preparations to return to Earth. The command module, which had been shut down since the accident, was the only part of the craft which could re-enter the Earth's atmosphere without burning up. Once in the command module, they jettisoned the lunar module which had kept them alive for the last three days and made their final course corrections. The angle of re-entry was critical. Too shallow and Apollo 13 would skim off the atmosphere like a pebble bouncing off the surface of the sea. Too steep and they would burn up in the atmosphere.

Fig. 17 Energy of different orbits

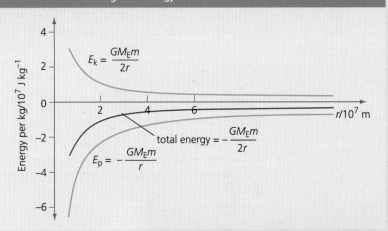

Russia's Mir space station had a chequered 15-year history. A series of technical problems dogged its last years of operation. The 120-tonne station was launched in 1986 into Earth orbit at a height of 400 kilometres (248 miles). Mir was ditched into the ocean in 2001. Much of the station burned up as it re-entered the atmosphere but several large chunks survived to reach the Earth.

Orbital decay

When a satellite enters the atmosphere the drag causes its orbit to decay. The satellite heats up and drops to a lower orbit, where it moves at higher speed. This seems odd as the net effect of drag has been to speed the satellite up. We need to consider the *total* energy of the satellite, the sum of its potential and kinetic energies. If the satellite of mass m is moving at a velocity, v, in a circular orbit of radius r, then:

$$E_{total} = E_k + E_p$$

$$= \frac{1}{2}mv^2 - \frac{GM_E m}{r}$$

But, for a circular orbit:

$$\frac{mv^2}{r} = \frac{GM_E m}{r^2}$$

so, $\quad E_{total} = \frac{1}{2}\frac{GM_E m}{r} - \frac{GM_E m}{r}$

$$= -\frac{1}{2}\frac{GM_E m}{r}$$

As a satellite spirals to Earth, r decreases and so the total energy becomes more negative. The decrease in total energy is only half the decrease in potential energy. This difference is due to the increase in kinetic energy.

As the astronauts entered the denser part of the atmosphere, the effects of heating made radio contact impossible. After three minutes of radio silence, the command module appeared through the clouds. It drifted down, slowed by its three parachutes, and dropped in the Pacific Ocean three miles from the US aircraft carrier Iwo Jima. The astronauts were picked up soon afterwards. They had made it – but only just.

14 Artificial satellites, like Mir, sometimes fall out of orbit towards the Earth. Ignoring the effects of the Earth's atmosphere, state what happens to the satellite's:
a potential energy
b kinetic energy
c speed
d total energy
What difference does the effect of the atmosphere make to your answers?

■ The potential, V, at a point in a gravitational field is the potential energy of a unit mass placed there. The SI units of V are J kg⁻¹.

■ For a radial field, such as that produced by a spherical body of mass M:

$$V = -\frac{GM}{r}$$

■ For any gravitational field:

$$g = -\frac{\Delta V}{\Delta x}$$

1 a State, in words, Newton's law of gravitation. (2)

b Some of the earliest attempts to determine the gravitational constant, G, were regarded as experiments to 'weigh' the Earth. By considering the gravitational force acting on a mass at the surface of the Earth, regarded as a sphere of radius R, show that the mass of the Earth is given by

$M = gR^2/G$,

where g is the value of the gravitational field strength at the Earth's surface. (2)

c In the following calculation use these data.

Radius of the Moon = 1.74×10^6 m
Gravitational field strength at the Moon's surface = 1.62 N kg^{-1}
Mass of the Earth $M = 6.00 \times 10^{24}$ kg
Gravitational constant $G = 6.67 \times 10^{-11}$ N m^2 kg^{-2}

Calculate the mass of the Moon and express its mass as a percentage of the mass of the Earth. (3)

(PH03 March 99 Q6)

2 The gravitational field strength at the surface of a planet, X, is 19 N kg^{-1}.

a (i) Calculate the gravitational potential difference between the surface of X and a point 10 m above the surface, if the gravitational field can be considered to be uniform over such a small distance.
(ii) Calculate the minimum amount of energy required to lift a 9.0 kg rock a vertical distance of 10 m from the surface of X.
(iii) State whether the minimum amount of energy you have found in part (a)(ii) would be different if the 9.0 kg mass were lifted a vertical distance of 10 m from a point near the top of the highest mountain of planet X. Explain your answer. (3)

b Calculate the gravitational field strength at the surface of another planet, Y, that has the same mass as planet X, but twice the diameter of X. (2)

(PH03 June 99 Q2)

3 The path of the Earth around the Sun can be treated as a circle of radius 1.50×10^8 km.

a (i) By considering the distance travelled in one year, show that the average speed of the Earth around the Sun is approximately 3.0×10^4 m s^{-1}.
(ii) Use your answer to part (a)(i) to calculate the centripetal force of the Sun on the Earth. Mass of the Earth = 6.00×10^{24} kg. (4)

b Given that the mass of the Sun is 2.00×10^{30} kg, and that the gravitational constant, G, is 6.67×10^{-11} N m^2 kg^{-2}, use Newton's law to confirm your answer to part (a) (ii) above. (2)

c The orbital radius of Venus is 0.72 times that of the Earth, and its mass is 0.81 times that of the Earth. Decide which planet, Earth or Venus, exerts the larger force on the Sun and explain how you arrive at your answer. (2)

(PH03 March 98 Q1)

4 a Define, in words, the *gravitational potential* at a point in a gravitational field.

b Write down an equation for the value of the gravitational potential at the surface of the Earth, defining the symbols you use.

c Use data from the data booklet to show that the gravitational potential at the surface of the Earth is -6.25×10^7 J kg^{-1}. (4)

(PH03 June 98 Q3)

5 a The graph shows how the gravitational potential varies with distance in the region above the surface of the Earth. R is the radius of the Earth, which is 6400 km. At the surface of the Earth, the gravitational potential is -62.5 MJ kg^{-1}

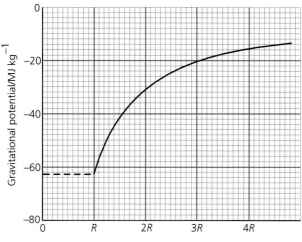

Distance from centre of Earth

Use the graph to calculate

  (i) the gravitational potential at a distance $2R$ from the centre of the Earth,

  (ii) the increase in the potential energy of a 1200 kg satellite when it is raised from the surface of the Earth into a circular orbit of radius $3R$. (4)

b (i) Write down an equation which relates gravitational field strength and gravitational potential.

  (ii) **By use of the graph** in part (a), calculate the gravitational field strength at a distance $2R$ from the centre of the Earth.

  (iii) Show that your result for part (b)(ii) is consistent with the fact that the surface gravitational field strength is about 10 N kg^{-1}.

  (5)

(PH03 June 1997)

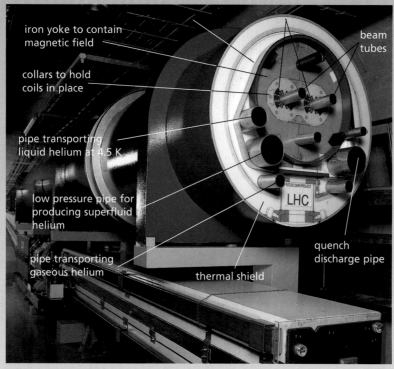

iron yoke to contain magnetic field

collars to hold coils in place

pipe transporting liquid helium at 4.5 K

low pressure pipe for producing superfluid helium

pipe transporting gaseous helium

beam tubes

LHC

quench discharge pipe

thermal shield

The Large Hadron Collider (LHC) at Geneva in Switzerland is being used in the hunt for the Higgs Boson, the mysterious particle which is thought to give mass to all the other particles. The accelerator uses electric and magnetic forces to reach energies of up to 1000 GeV. The particles are accelerated in a ring of 27 km circumference at temperatures approaching absolute zero. In September 2000 scientists made their first tentative claims to have detected the Higgs particle.

The ultimate goal of many theoretical physicists is to produce a theory that will explain the origin of all the fundamental forces and that will predict the existence of all the fundamental particles. These grand unified theories, or GUTs, make predictions that can only be tested at high energies. Such particle energies were common just after the birth of the universe. High-energy particle accelerators like the Large Hadron Collider at CERN in Geneva are used to make particles collide, sometimes with each other, or with target atoms, to produce showers of other particles. These exotic particles often have very short lifetimes. They are detected in drift chambers or bubble chambers where they are deflected by electric and magnetic fields. The size and direction of the deflection enable us to calculate the particles' mass and charge, and so help to verify, or falsify, any new theories.

This cloud chamber photograph shows a 'shower' of electrons and positrons produced by a cosmic ray. The electrons and positrons curve in different directions in the chamber's magnetic field. They are able to produce more gamma rays which interact with the sheets of lead (black) to generate new showers.

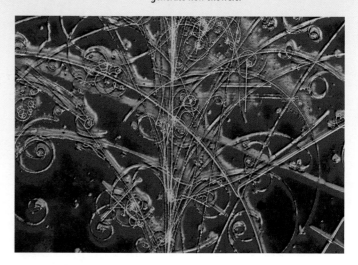

Particles in a bubble chamber pass through liquid hydrogen in the chamber, leaving a fine trail of bubbles as they momentarily superheat the liquid. Electrons and positrons follow spiral paths due to an intense external magnetic field.

7.1 Magnetic fields

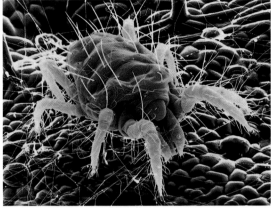

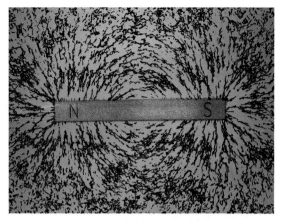

An understanding of how charged particles behave in magnetic fields is used in scanning electron microscopy. This false-colour picture shows a red spider mite climbing over the surface of a leaf.

Magnetic flux density

A magnetic field is a region where other magnets will experience a force. Although a magnetic field does not exert a force on a stationary charged particle, any *moving charges* in this region would experience a force. The size and direction of the force on any given particle depend on the strength and nature of the magnetic field.

Iron filings can be used to visualise the shape and strength of a magnet's field. When they are placed in the field the filings become temporarily magnetised under the influence

Field lines, shown by the pattern of iron filings, indicate the direction of the force on the north-seeking pole of an imaginary tiny magnet within the field.

of the magnetic field and they behave as small magnets. These tiny **induced** magnets form a pattern of lines known as field lines, or lines of **magnetic flux**. The magnetic field is strongest where these flux lines are close together, such as near the ends of a bar magnet (see Fig. 1).

Picture a small area parallel to the end of a bar magnet (see Fig. 1). Wherever a flux line cuts through this area you could imagine a little dot. Near the magnet, where the field is strong, these imaginary dots would be densely packed over the whole area. In a weaker field, they would be less dense. The strength of the magnetic field can be described in terms of the **magnetic flux density**, B. This is measured in **tesla**, T. Magnetic flux density is a vector quantity; it has a magnitude and a direction (see Fig. 2).

If the magnetic flux density is at right angles to an area, A, the total flux, Φ, can be expressed as

Total magnetic flux
= magnetic flux density × area

or in symbols, $\Phi = B \times A$

Magnetic flux is measured in **weber** (Wb), where 1 Wb = 1 T × 1 m^2.

Fig. 1 Density of flux lines

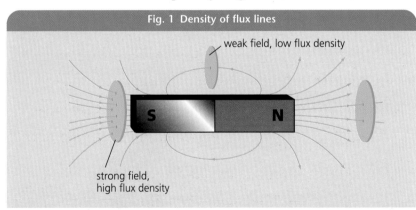

weak field, low flux density

strong field, high flux density

Fig. 2 Flux at different angles

The orientation of the area A in the magnetic field is important. The flux passing through A depends on the angle θ.

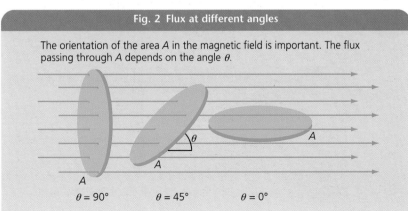

$\theta = 90°$ $\theta = 45°$ $\theta = 0°$

---

1 How much magnetic flux passes through a flat coil of area 2 cm^2 in a field of magnetic flux density 0.05 T if the flux density vector is

a at 90° to the plane of the coil?

b parallel to the plane of the coil?

Fig. 3 Right-hand grip rule

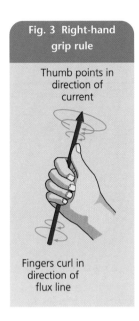

Thumb points in direction of current

Fingers curl in direction of flux line

Defining the tesla: the force on a wire

In 1819, Oersted discovered a link between electricity and magnetism. He noticed that a small compass was deflected by a nearby electric current. Today, we use this effect to define the unit of magnetic flux density. The magnetic field produced by a wire can be thought of as a set of circles in a plane at right angles to the wire. These are closer together near the wire, because the field is stronger there. The direction of the flux lines is linked to the current by the right-hand grip rule (Fig. 3).

If the current-carrying wire is placed in another magnetic field, it will experience a force. This force is largest when the wire is at right angles to the magnetic field. The direction of the force is at right angles to both the flux density and the current. Fleming's left-hand rule is useful for remembering the relative directions of force, flux density and current (see Fig. 4).

Experimentally, we find that the size of the force on the wire depends on:

- the length of wire in the magnetic field, l
- the current, I
- the magnetic flux density, B.

A stronger magnetic field leads to a bigger force. We use this to define the magnetic flux density as the force per metre of wire per unit current:

$$B = \frac{F}{Il}$$

The SI unit of flux density is the tesla, T. A magnetic field of flux density equal to one tesla will cause a force of 1 N to act on every 1 m length of wire carrying a current of 1 amp at right angles to the field. So 1 T = 1 N A^{-1} m^{-1}. The equation can be written as

$$F = BIl \sin \theta$$

where θ is the angle between the direction of the flux and the direction of the current. If the field and the current are at right angles, $\sin \theta = 1$ and we can write

$$F = BIl$$

The strength of the Earth's magnetic field in Britain is about 50 μT inclined downwards at about 70° to the horizontal. The horizontal component of the field is therefore

Horizontal component = $50 \times 10^{-6} \times \cos 70°$
$= 17 \times 10^{-6}$ T

For a 1 m length of horizontal wire carrying a current of 5 A at right angles to the field, the force would be

$$F = 17 \times 10^{-6} \text{ T} \times 5 \text{ A} \times 1 = 85.5 \times 10^{-6} \text{ N}$$

The force would be in a vertical direction, at right angles to the field and to the current.

A 1 T flux is a very strong magnetic field. Strong permanent magnets have magnetic flux densities of around 0.1 T. We need to use electromagnets to achieve higher flux densities.

Fig. 4 Fleming's left-hand rule

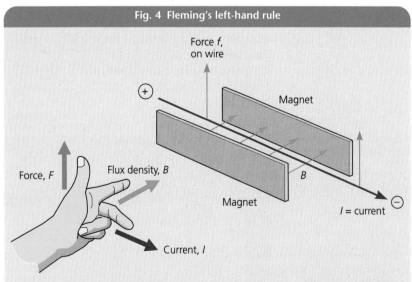

Fleming's left-hand rule is a good way to work out the direction of the force on a wire or a charged particle. The first finger points in the direction of the magnetic flux, from north towards south. The second finger points in the direction of a conventional current, from positive towards negative. The thumb then gives the direction of force.

Fig. 5 The Earth's magnetic field

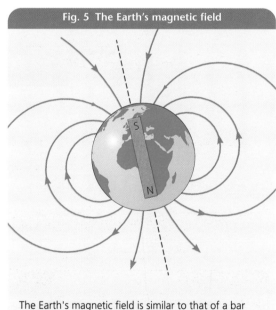

The Earth's magnetic field is similar to that of a bar magnet. The geographic north pole is actually a magnetic south pole. The field lines come in towards the Earth in the northern hemisphere and go out from the Earth in the southern hemisphere.

Most loudspeakers use a circular permanent magnet and a coil of wire which moves in and out as the current through it is altered, vibrating the paper cone.

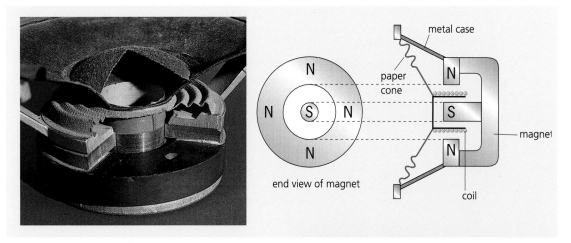

end view of magnet

2 The magnetic flux density in a loudspeaker is about 0.5 T. Calculate the force per metre of wire when a current of 100 mA is flowing. What have you assumed about the shape of the magnetic field?

Fig. 6 Top-pan balance

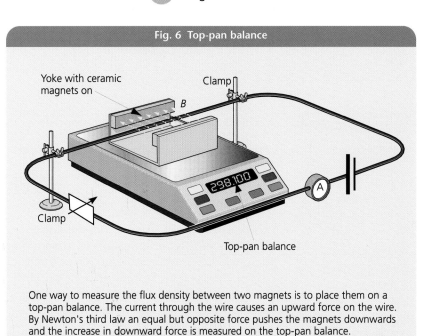

Top-pan balance

One way to measure the flux density between two magnets is to place them on a top-pan balance. The current through the wire causes an upward force on the wire. By Newton's third law an equal but opposite force pushes the magnets downwards and the increase in downward force is measured on the top-pan balance.

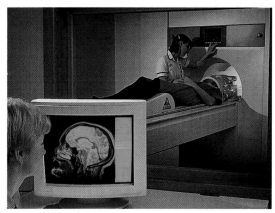

Some of the strongest artificial magnetic fields are used in hospitals. Large superconducting coils are used in MRI scanners to produce magnetic flux densities of several tesla.

3 The apparatus in Fig. 6 can be used to gain an accurate measurement for the magnetic flux density between the magnets. The top-pan balance is calibrated in grams. If it shows an extra deflection of 0.13 g for every amp of current that flows through the wire, calculate the flux density. (Length of magnets = 5 cm.)

Force on a moving charge

A charged particle moving through a magnetic field experiences a force. The size of the force depends on the charge carried by the particle and on its velocity. We can derive an expression for the force by considering the force on a current-carrying wire in more detail (see Fig. 7).

The force on a current-carrying wire is $F = BIl$. This force is due to the moving charges that constitute the current inside the wire. Inside the wire you can picture the current as a flow of charged particles, each

Fig. 7 A charge in a magnetic field

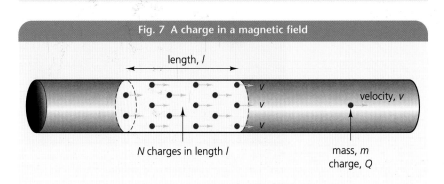

length, l

velocity, v

N charges in length l

mass, m
charge, Q

with a charge Q drifting at an average velocity v. If there are N charges in a length l of the wire

$$\text{current} = \frac{\text{total charge passing a point}}{\text{time to travel length } l}$$

$$I = \frac{NQ}{t}$$

using $t = \dfrac{l}{v}$

$$I = \frac{NQ}{(l/v)}$$

Rearranging this gives

$$Il = NQv$$

If we substitute this into $F = BIl$, we get $F = BNQv$ as the force on N charges. The force on one charge is therefore:

$$\boldsymbol{F = BQv}$$

For example, an electron ($Q = 1.6 \times 10^{-19}$ C) travelling through an accelerator at a velocity of 3×10^6 m s^{-1} in a magnetic field of 0.02 T would experience a force of

$$F = BQv$$
$$= 0.02 \times 1.6 \times 10^{-19} \times 3 \times 10^6$$
$$= 10^{-14} \text{ N}$$

The mass of the electron is only about 10^{-30} kg, so the resulting acceleration of the electron is huge:

$$a = \frac{F}{m}$$
$$\approx 10^{16} \text{ m s}^{-2}$$

The force is at right angles to both the flux density and the velocity. If the particle entered the magnetic field at 90° to the flux lines, the magnetic force will make it travel in a curve (Fig. 8). There is no component of force along the direction of the curve, so the speed will not alter. This means that the particle experiences a constant force, always at right angles to its direction of motion. The curve will therefore be circular.

The acceleration of a body in circular motion at constant speed is $a = v^2/r$. For a particle in the magnetic field, r will be the radius of curvature of its path. This can be measured from photographs of tracks in a cloud chamber. Such measurements gave physicists useful information about particles:

- The force on a particle is: $F = BQv$

- Its acceleration is: $a = \dfrac{F}{m} = \dfrac{BQv}{m}$

- This is the centripetal acceleration: $a = \dfrac{v^2}{r}$

So: $\dfrac{v^2}{r} = \dfrac{BQv}{m}$

Rearranging gives: $r = \dfrac{mv}{BQ} = \left(\dfrac{v}{B}\right) \times \left(\dfrac{m}{Q}\right)$

For each type of particle, the ratio of charge to mass is constant, so the curvature of the track provides information about the sorts of particles present. Protons are almost 2000 times heavier than electrons and **positrons**. Electron tracks therefore have a much smaller radius than proton tracks.

Fig. 8 Circular motion in a magnetic field

particle follows circular track

because force is always at 90° to velocity

flux density is down into page

Fig. 9 Tracks of positive and negative particles

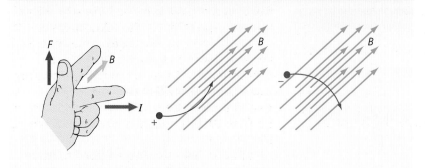

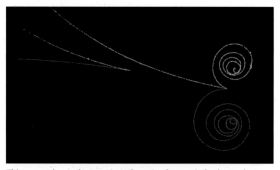

This event shows the creation of a pair of oppositely charged particles that spiral away in different directions in the magnetic field.

When a charged particle transfers energy by ionising air molecules, it slows down. The radius of curvature of its track therefore decreases: it makes a spiral track.

The direction of the force is found using Fleming's left-hand rule. For positive particles, the conventional current is the same as the direction of motion. For negative particles it is the opposite – an electron moving to the left represents a conventional current to the right (Fig. 9).

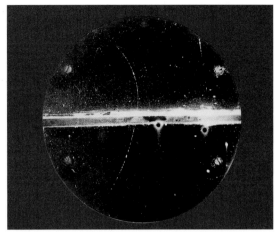

This cloud chamber photograph, taken in 1932, showed for the first time the track of a positron. The particle enters the chamber from below and curves markedly to the left in the magnetic field after passing through a 6 mm thick lead plate.

4 Study the photograph of a positron passing through a lead plate.

a Identify the direction of the magnetic field.

b Where is the positron travelling faster?

7.2 Electrostatic force

Magnetic fields can be used to deflect charged particles, but a uniform magnetic field has no effect on the speed of the particles. Electrostatic force is needed to accelerate particles to high enough kinetic energies to make new isotopes.

All charged particles exert a force on each other (Fig. 10). This force can be investigated experimentally. The results of these experiments show that the size of the force:

• is proportional to the size of each charge;

• follows an inverse square law with distance.

The experimental results can be summarised by the equation

$$F \propto \frac{Q_1 Q_2}{r^2}$$

The constant of proportionality is written in an unusual way:

$$F = \left(\frac{1}{4\pi\varepsilon_0}\right) \times \left(\frac{Q_1 Q_2}{r^2}\right)$$

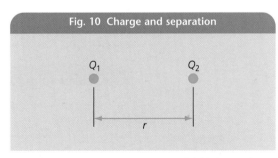

Fig. 10 Charge and separation

The constant ε_0 is called the **permittivity of free space**; it has a value of 8.854×10^{-12} F m^{-1}.

This expression is called Coulomb's law. It applies only to point charges, but a sphere of charge behaves as though all the charge is concentrated at its centre. Electron scattering experiments show that the force between electrons obeys Coulomb's law at distances as small as 10^{-16} m – about a millionth of the size of an atom.

To make new isotopes, we need to make particles collide with nuclei. The forces and

Mass spectrometry

Chemists sometimes need accurate information on the different elements or isotopes present in a sample. From this information, researchers can start to work out the composition of the material. Distinguishing between isotopes of the same element is impossible using normal chemical techniques. A mass spectrometer uses the principle of magnetic deflection to carry out its analysis (Fig. 11).

A small sample of material is ionised, usually by firing electrons at it. The resulting ions are then accelerated by an electric field. Ions of a particular speed are picked out by a **velocity selector**. The ions pass through a uniform magnetic field which deflects them into a semicircular path. The radius of this path depends on the charge-to-mass ratio.

The position of the lines on the photograph reveals the masses of the ions. The darkness of the lines on the photograph indicates the amount of each ion present in the sample. For singly charged ions, the distance across the plate (i.e. the radius of the circular motion) is proportional to the mass of the ion. The instrument can be calibrated by using standard samples. Doubly charged ions will have only half the radius of the path. This can lead to overlap: for example, $^4_2He^{++}$ and $^2_1H^+$ would overlap almost exactly.

By replacing the photographic plate with an electronic detector system which measures the ion current as the ions strike at each point on the screen, a computer can very quickly produce a graph of the isotopes present. The output of this sort of mass spectrometer

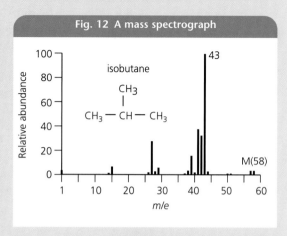

Fig. 12 A mass spectrograph

appears as a series of peaks, each representing ions of a particular isotope (Fig. 12).

5 Explain why this mass spectrometer finds it difficult to distinguish between $^{20}_{10}Ne^{++}$ and $^{10}_5B^+$.

6 A helium ion, $^4_2He^+$, moves in the spectrometer's magnetic field in a circle of radius 5 cm. Another singly charged ion, of a different isotope, moves with a radius of 15 cm. What is the relative mass of the ions?

7 A simple mass spectrometer deflects ions of mass up to 10^{-25} kg in a uniform magnetic field of 0.2 T. The ions are travelling at 1.2×10^5 m s^{-1}. What would be the maximum radius of curvature of the path of ions in the spectrometer? ($e = 1.6 \times 10^{-19}$ C.)

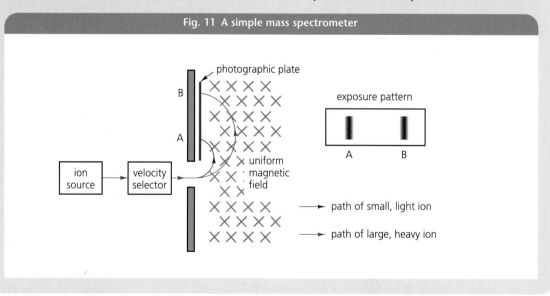

Fig. 11 A simple mass spectrometer

energies involved can be surprisingly large. For example, if we try to make a proton collide with a positively charged carbon nucleus ($Z = 6$), it will experience a repulsive electrostatic force. When they are separated by the diameter of an average nucleus (about 5×10^{-15} m), the force on the proton will be:

$$F = \frac{(1.6 \times 10^{-19}) \times 6 \times (1.6 \times 10^{-19})}{4\pi\varepsilon_0 \times (5 \times 10^{-15})^2}$$

$$= 55 \text{ N}$$

On a particle of mass 10^{-27} kg, this is an astonishing force.

Field strength and potential

One way of accelerating particles is to use an electric field. An electric field is any space where a charged particle experiences a force (Fig. 13).

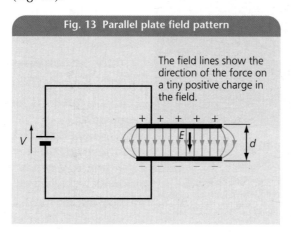

Fig. 13 Parallel plate field pattern

The field lines show the direction of the force on a tiny positive charge in the field.

The **electric field strength**, E, is defined as the force per unit charge on a small charge in an electric field:

$$E = \frac{F}{Q}$$

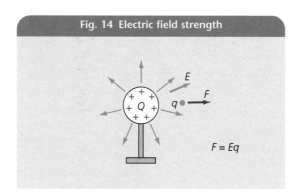

Fig. 14 Electric field strength

$F = Eq$

Electric field strength (Fig. 14) is measured in newtons per coulomb (N C^{-1}), but you may also see it expressed in volts per metre (V m^{-1}). As a charged particle moves through an electric field, it experiences a force. Work is

therefore done when the particle moves. If a positively charged particle moves to a region of high (positive) electric field, the particle gains electric potential energy. Conversely, the electrostatic force becomes very small at large distances. When the particle is at an infinite distance, the electric potential energy is zero. **Electrical potential** (V) is defined as the electrical potential energy per unit charge. This is the work done per unit charge in bringing a small positive charge from infinity to a point in an electric field:

$$V = \frac{W}{Q}$$

Potential difference is the difference in electrical potential between two points in an electric field. If a charged particle moves from a point at potential V_1 to a point at potential V_2, it has moved through a potential difference of $V = V_2 - V_1$. This 'potential difference' is exactly the same as the p.d. (or voltage) in electrical circuits. Although 'infinity' is the theoretical position of zero potential, for all practical purposes we use the surface of planet Earth as our zero. If we say an object is at a potential of 3000 V, it usually means that the p.d. between the object and the Earth is 3000 V.

The definition of potential can be rearranged to give:

$$W = QV$$

For an electron, $Q = e$, so $W = eV$. Work needs to be done to move a charge (e) through a difference of potential of 1 V. This amount of work is called one **electronvolt**; 1 eV = 1.6×10^{-19} J (see *AS Physics*, page 24).

We can derive equations for the electric field strength and potential in simple arrangements. For parallel plates, a distance d apart (Fig. 13):

$$E = \frac{V}{d}$$

Near a point charge Q (or a sphere of charge), the equations are:

$$E = \frac{Q}{4\pi\varepsilon_0 r^2} \quad \text{and} \quad V = \frac{Q}{4\pi\varepsilon_0 r}$$

These equations apply to charges in a vacuum. In any other medium, the molecules can give rise to an opposing field. This decreases the field strength and the potential. Both are decreased by a factor ε_r – the 'relative permittivity' of the medium.

8 A proton ($Q = 1.6 \times 10^{-19}$ C) is given a kinetic energy of 10 MeV by an accelerator. How close could it get to the nucleus of an oxygen atom ($^{16}_{8}$O)?

9 A metal sphere of radius 10 cm is at the centre of a large tank. The sphere is charged to a potential of 20 kV. Calculate the electric field strength at the surface of the sphere if the tank is filled with

a air ($\varepsilon_r \approx 1$)

b ethanol ($\varepsilon_r \approx 26$)

On the atomic scale gravity is insignificantly weak, but it is gravity that holds galaxies together and holds planets and moons in their orbits

Does gravity hold nuclei together?

Using Coulomb's law, a proton on the edge of a large nucleus (e.g. uranium, diameter = 10^{-14} m) experiences a repulsive force of about 80 N. This is big enough to rip the nucleus apart. Another force must be holding the particles together. Despite the high density of the nucleus, the gravitational force on the protons is only about = 2.5×10^{-29} N. Gravity is evidently an insignificant force on the subatomic scale. Something must hold the protons together inside the nucleus. The results from experiments using large particle accelerators have confirmed the existence of the short-range **strong nuclear force** (see *AS Physics*, page 16).

Gravitational and electrostatic force fields

Electrostatic and gravitational forces share some important features:

• the force is inversely proportional to distance squared;

• the force is proportional to the size of the 'property' (i.e. charge or mass) of each body.

Because they have this common ground, some of the mathematical theory developed for gravitational fields can be applied to electric fields. For example, field strengths are defined as:

• force per unit mass for gravitational fields

• force per unit charge for electric fields

Table 1 highlights some of the similarities and differences.

An important difference between electrostatic and gravitational fields is that you can have conductors of electricity. Conductors affect electric field and potential:

• you cannot have an electric field inside a conductor. (An electric field exerts a force on charges: charges would redistribute until the field dropped to zero.)

• all points on the surface of a conductor must be at the same potential. (If points had different potential, there would be an electric field between these points which would make charges move as before.)

The field and potential patterns around conducting spheres give the graphs in Fig. 15.

10 A hydrogen atom can be pictured as an electron ($e = -1.6 \times 10^{-19}$ C) orbiting a positive nucleus of charge $+1.6 \times 10^{-19}$ C. The energy needed to remove the electron completely (to infinity) is 2.2×10^{-18} J. Calculate

a the potential at the position of the normal orbit of the electron;

b the radius of the orbit and so state the diameter of the atom;

c the electric field strength at the position of the electron's orbit.

Table 1	
Electrostatic	**Gravitational**
force $\propto \dfrac{1}{r^2}$	force $\propto \dfrac{1}{r^2}$
force $\propto$ size of charges	force $\propto$ size of masses
potential = work per unit charge	potential = work per unit mass
field strength = force/charge	field strength = force/mass
charges are positive or negative	masses are only positive
force can attract or repel	only attractive forces known
field strength depends on medium	no medium known to affect field strength
field strength, E, measured in N C^{-1}	field strength, g, measured in N kg^{-1}
the field at a distance r from a point charge is	the field at a distance r from a point mass is
$E = \dfrac{Q}{4\pi\varepsilon_0 r^2}$	$g = \dfrac{Gm}{r^2}$

Fig. 15 *E–r* and *V–r* graphs

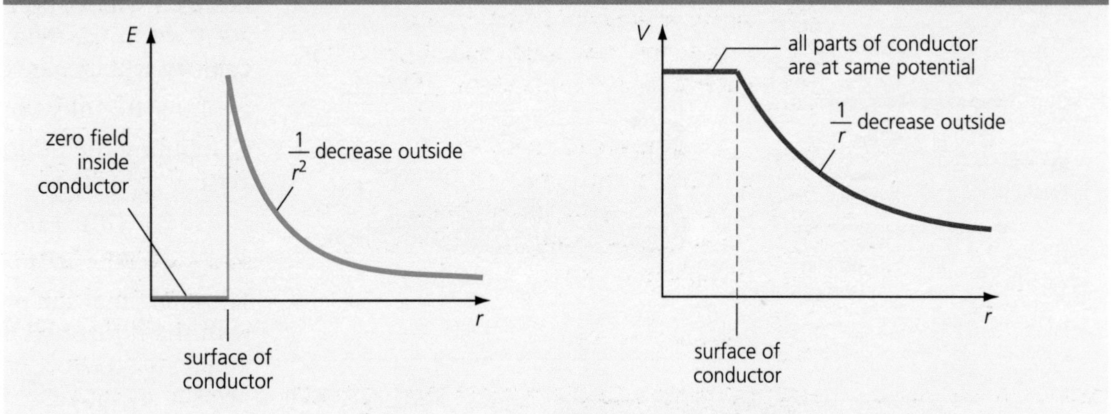

KEY FACTS

■ Coulomb's law shows that charges Q_1 and Q_2 exert a force

$$F = \frac{Q_1 Q_2}{4\pi\varepsilon_0 r^2}$$

in a vacuum. $\varepsilon_0 = 8.85 \times 10^{-12}$ F m^{-1}.

■ Electric field strength is the force per unit charge at a point in the field:

$$E = \frac{F}{Q}$$

It is zero inside conductors.

■ Electric potential is the potential energy per unit charge at any point. The position of zero potential is theoretically at infinity but Earth is at 0 V for practical purposes.

■ Parallel plates at separation *d* have a uniform field

$$E = \frac{V}{d}$$

A point charge in a vacuum has

$$E = \frac{Q}{4\pi\varepsilon_0 r^2} \quad \text{and} \quad V = \frac{Q}{4\pi\varepsilon_0 r}$$

at distance *r* from the point. These equations also apply to the surface of a uniformly distributed conducting sphere of radius *r*.

■ Electric and gravitational fields are similar in their mathematical form (inverse square law, etc.) but differ in that electrical forces may be attractive or repulsive, while gravitational force is always attractive.

7.3 Particle deflection in electric fields

As a charged particle passes through an electric field it experiences a force. This force can be used to deflect the particle. This effect is used in the deflection plates in a cathode ray oscilloscope. (See *AS Physics*, page 174.)

For a charged particle moving in a uniform electric field, the force is always in the same direction: towards the positive plate for a negative charge and towards the negative plate for a positive charge. In a uniform field, the force on the particle is independent of its position. This situation is very much like a mass moving under gravity. Motion that is perpendicular to the field is at uniform velocity, whilst the particle is undergoing constant acceleration in the direction of the field.

Displacement perpendicular to field, *x*,

$$x = v_x t$$

Displacement parallel to field, *y*,

$$y = \frac{1}{2}at^2$$

where *a* is the acceleration.

Since v_x and *a* are constant, *y* is proportional to x^2. This means that the particle will travel in a parabolic path whilst it is in the field.

We can use the equations of motion to calculate the new path of a charged particle moving through the field. Suppose a proton travelling at 500 000 m s^{-1} passes between two horizontal, 1 cm long parallel plates which are 5 cm apart, with a potential difference of 100 V between them (Fig. 16a).

The force on the proton is

charge × field strength $= QE = \dfrac{eV}{d}$

(for a proton in a uniform field)

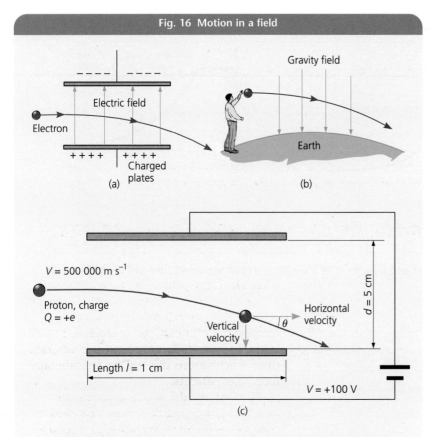

Fig. 16 Motion in a field

(a)

(b)

$V = 500\,000$ m s^{-1}

Proton, charge $Q = +e$

Vertical velocity

Horizontal velocity

θ

$d = 5$ cm

Length $l = 1$ cm

$V = +100$ V

(c)

The motion of a charge in a uniform electric field, such as that between two charged plates (a), is much more like a mass falling in a gravitational field (b) than a charge moving in a magnetic field (c).

N.B. The electric field lines show the direction of the force on a positive particle. The electron is negative and so moves in the opposite direction.

The acceleration of the proton will be

$$a = \frac{F}{m} = \frac{eV}{md} = \frac{1.6 \times 10^{-19}\ \text{C} \times 100\ \text{V}}{1.6 \times 10^{-27}\ \text{C} \times 5 \times 10^{-2}\ \text{m}}$$
$$= 1.9 \times 10^{11}\ \text{m s}^{-2}$$

This is a huge vertical acceleration. As there is no horizontal acceleration, the proton will

maintain its original horizontal velocity. This means it will spend a time $t = 0.01/50\,000 = 2 \times 10^{-7}$ s in the field. In this time its vertical velocity will change by

$v = 1.9 \times 10^{11}$ m s^{-2} × 2×10^{-7} s $= 3.8 \times 10^{4}$ m s^{-1}

Combining the proton's horizontal and vertical velocities:

$v^2 = (3.8 \times 10^4)^2 + (50\,000)^2$

so $v = 6.28 \times 10^4$ m s^{-1}

The angle that the proton's new track makes with the horizontal is

$$\tan \theta = \frac{3.8 \times 10^4}{50\,000} = 0.76$$

So $\theta = 37.2°$

Rutherford scattering

The scattering of alpha particles by gold leaf was the first evidence for the existence of the atomic nucleus (see *AS Physics*, page 13). A closer study of alpha-particle scattering can give us an upper estimate for the size of a nucleus.

A small number of alpha particles are found to 'bounce back' from the gold leaf

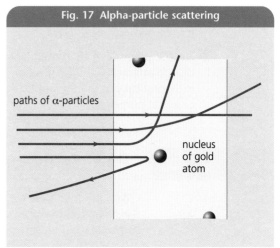

Fig. 17 Alpha-particle scattering

paths of α-particles

nucleus of gold atom

atoms. Nuclei are very small compared with the space between them, so most alpha particles do not pass close enough to a nucleus to be significantly deflected. If an alpha particle does directly approach a gold nucleus, it does not hit the nucleus, but slows down instead. It slows down because of the electrical repulsion between the nucleus and the alpha particle (Fig. 18).

The particle turns back on itself and accelerates away from the nucleus. If we can find out how close these 'direct-hit' particles get to the nucleus, we can take this distance of closest approach as an upper estimate for the size of a gold nucleus.

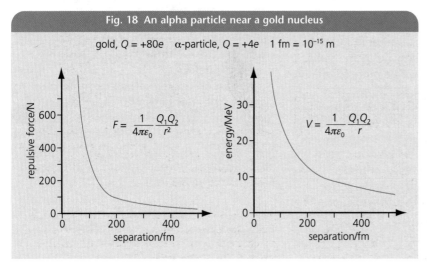

Fig. 18 An alpha particle near a gold nucleus

gold, $Q = +80e$ α-particle, $Q = +4e$ 1 fm $= 10^{-15}$ m

repulsive force/N

$$F = \frac{1}{4\pi\varepsilon_0} \frac{Q_1 Q_2}{r^2}$$

separation/fm

energy/MeV

$$V = \frac{1}{4\pi\varepsilon_0} \frac{Q_1 Q_2}{r}$$

separation/fm

11 An alpha particle with energy 10 MeV approaches a gold nucleus directly.

a What type of energy does the alpha particle have before it nears the nucleus?

b What sort of energy does the alpha particle have at its distance of closest approach?

c Use the potential energy–distance graph in Fig. 18 to estimate the distance of closest approach for an alpha particle with kinetic energy 10 MeV. What does this tell us about the size of the nucleus?

7.4 Circular accelerators: the cyclotron and the synchrotron

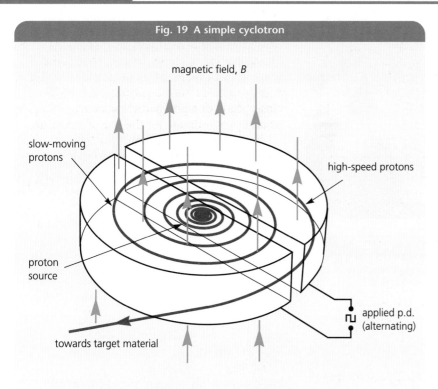

Fig. 19 A simple cyclotron

magnetic field, *B*

slow-moving protons

high-speed protons

proton source

applied p.d. (alternating)

towards target material

Circular accelerators, like CERN's Large Hadron Collider, are used to probe matter at very high energies. Smaller versions are used in hospitals to manufacture radioisotopes for clinical procedures, like PET scans. Some hospitals even use the particles from synchrotrons directly for radiotherapy for cancer patients.

The first circular accelerators, called cyclotrons, used a simple magnetic field to confine the accelerating particles. Like the Van de Graaff generator, cyclotrons use an electric field to accelerate the particles (usually protons). The electric field is created by applying a voltage between the two D-shaped pieces (Fig. 19). At any one moment, one D has a positive potential

The world's first cyclotron, built in 1930 by E. O. Lawrence, could accelerate protons to energies of 8 MeV. More recent cyclotrons are capable of accelerating protons up to 100 MeV. Lawrence often kept his cyclotron running all night to produce radioisotopes for nearby Californian hospitals.

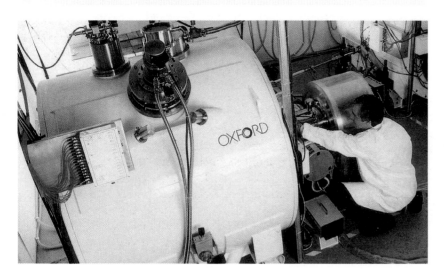

Oxford Instruments make 'desktop' cyclotrons for hospitals and industry. The accelerator uses superconducting magnets to produce strong magnetic fields. The accelerated particles are used to make small quantities of radioactive isotopes.

APPLICATION

Particle accelerators: The Van de Graaff generator

The Van de Graaff generator is useful for teaching about the effects of electrostatics. It was also one of the earliest particle accelerators.

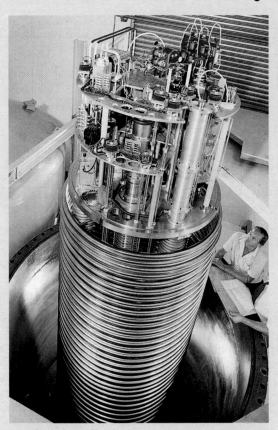

Fig. 20 Van de Graaff accelerator

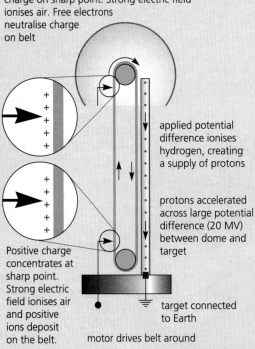

Positive charge arriving on belt induces negative charge on sharp point. Strong electric field ionises air. Free electrons neutralise charge on belt

Positive charge concentrates at sharp point. Strong electric field ionises air and positive ions deposit on the belt.

applied potential difference ionises hydrogen, creating a supply of protons

protons accelerated across large potential difference (20 MV) between dome and target

target connected to Earth

motor drives belt around

Van de Graaff generators are one of the simplest early particle accelerators. They are still used in research and as the *injector* – the first stage – for bigger accelerators. Inside a generator, charge is carried on a moving belt onto a metal dome. Suppose the dome is 1.6 m in diameter and that 180 C of charge accumulates. At the surface of the dome, the electric field strength would be:

$$E = \frac{Q}{4\pi\varepsilon_0 r^2} = 2.5 \text{ MV m}^{-1}$$

This is just below the level at which air conducts. Sparks start flying at ≈ 3 MV m^{-1}. The potential of the sphere will be:

$$V = \frac{Q}{4\pi\varepsilon_0 r} = 2 \text{ MV}$$

The sphere of the Van de Graaff generator is a capacitor (see Chapter 4). Its capacitance is

$$C = \frac{Q}{V} \approx 90 \text{ pF}$$

The work done in charging the Van de Graaff sphere is therefore:

$$W = \tfrac{1}{2}CV^2 \approx \tfrac{1}{2} \times 90 \times 10^{-12} \times \left(2 \times 10^6\right)^2$$

$$= 180 \text{ J}$$

This is surprisingly modest: the energy output of a small domestic light bulb for 3 seconds. Particles of charge e would therefore be accelerated and leave with an energy of 2 MeV. (Van de Graaff generators can produce up to 10 MeV.) Protons with this energy would be travelling quickly.

Using $E_k = \tfrac{1}{2}mv^2$ gives

$$v = \sqrt{\frac{2E_k}{m}} = \sqrt{\frac{2 \times 2 \text{ MeV}}{1.67 \times 10^{-27} \text{ kg}}}$$

$$= \sqrt{\frac{2 \times 2\,000\,000 \times 1.6 \times 10^{-19} \text{ J}}{1.67 \times 10^{-27} \text{ kg}}}$$

$$= 2 \times 10^7 \text{ m s}^{-1}$$

about $^1/_{15}$th of the speed of light.

APPLICATION

Particle accelerators: linear acceleration

At the Stanford Linear Accelerator (SLAC), near San Francisco, USA, electrons 'ride' on electromagnetic waves that effectively create electric fields, accelerating them almost continuously for 3 km. The SLAC can accelerate electrons up to energies of 50 GeV.

Using $E_k = \frac{1}{2}mv^2$ to calculate speed is acceptable at low energies. If you repeat the calculation for protons at 1 GeV, the proton's velocity would be about 1.5 times the speed of light. Einstein's theory of relativity says that nothing with mass can travel at light speed. Instead, we observe an increase in the mass of particles at high energies. In a 1 GeV machine, a proton would have over three times its rest mass. An electron with 1 GeV of kinetic energy would have more than 2000 times its rest mass. Experiments using electron accelerators provided the first direct evidence that Einstein's theory of mass increase was accurate.

Creating huge potential differences is not easy; insulation becomes a real problem, with conduction in gases leading to dangerous spark discharges. Instead of trying to accelerate the particles all at once – by one huge electric field – a more successful technique relies on the repeated use of a smaller electric field. The earliest such design was the linear accelerator (linac, Fig. 21).

The fact that the field strength inside a conductor is zero is exploited in linacs. A high-frequency alternating electric field is used to accelerate particles. The particles travel in 'drift tubes' – conductors where the electric field strength inside is zero – when the a.c. voltage would try to make them go backwards. They emerge from the drift tubes in time to be accelerated by the next 'forwards' voltage half-cycle. Drift tubes need to increase in length along the linac because the particles travel faster at each stage.

For a 50 MeV proton the average speed would be around 50 000 km s^{-1}, so to keep the drift tubes small – say 20 cm average length – would need a very high frequency:

time inside drift tube = distance/speed
= 0.2 m/(5 × 10^7 m s^{-1})
= 4 × 10^{-9} seconds

This is half a cycle of the a.c. so the period is 8 × 10^{-9} seconds, giving a frequency of the order of 100 MHz. Electrons travel faster, so even higher frequencies in the microwave region are used.

The longest linac in the world is at the Stanford Linear Accelerator Center: it is 3 km long and can accelerate electrons to 50 GeV. Working on energy-to-mass ratio, this is equivalent to giving a human being all the solar energy received by the Earth for a month! As theories become more advanced, higher and higher energies are needed to investigate their predictions. The Large Hadron Collider at CERN should be able to accelerate protons to around 7000 GeV: the particle beam would have the energy of several kilograms of high explosive!

Large accelerators often use linacs as the injector stage. Particles are then accelerated in resonant cavities using radio waves or microwaves. The particles are effectively 'surfing' on the electric field vector of the electromagnetic waves. The accelerators are made as giant rings, so that the particles can be accelerated a little more each time they circulate. Magnetic fields are used to make them go around the bending path. The rings need to be very large to keep the centripetal acceleration of the particles low; otherwise, they emit electromagnetic radiation and so slow down. Even with accelerators many kilometres in diameter, the particles emit a lot of radiation – so much so that the intense X-ray emissions from the particle beam are now an important research tool for biochemists and semiconductor technologists.

Fig. 21 A linear accelerator

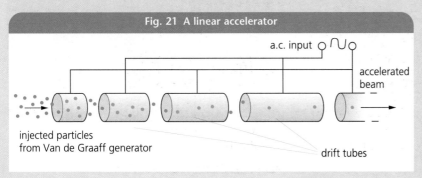

a.c. input

accelerated beam

injected particles from Van de Graaff generator

drift tubes

(which repels the positively charged protons), while the other D has a negative potential (which attracts protons). By alternating the applied voltage to each D, protons are accelerated by being attracted to alternate Ds. In one cycle of the alternating voltage, all the protons in the cyclotron complete one circular 'lap' of the cyclotron.

While the Van de Graaff accelerator depends upon a single, large voltage to accelerate protons, the cyclotron uses a smaller voltage many times over. A proton passes from one D to the other many times as it spirals out from the centre of the cyclotron. Each time a proton moves from one D to the other, it receives another 'kick' forwards from the potential difference between the Ds.

The magnetic field pushes any moving charged particles with a force at right angles to the particle's motion. This provides the centripetal force necessary for the circular motion. If the speed of the protons is v, their mass m, their charge Q, the radius of their path r, and the magnetic field strength B, we can write:

magnetic force = centripetal force

$$BQv = \frac{mv^2}{r}$$

$$r = \frac{mv}{BQ}$$

We would expect the mass (m) and the charge (Q) of the proton to remain constant. If the magnetic field (B) is constant, you can see that the radius of the protons' circular

motion is proportional to the protons' velocity ($r \propto v$). As the protons move from D to D, their speed increases. This means that the protons trace out larger and larger circles in a spiral motion.

As the particles approach the speed of light, their mass does begin to increase significantly. This is an effect described by the special theory of relativity. This tends to increase both the radius of the particles' path and the time to complete a 'lap' of the cyclotron. The protons' circular paths and the alternating voltage lose their synchronisation. Further acceleration is hopeless. This limits the amount of energy that a cyclotron can transfer to protons.

Synchrotrons

A synchrotron, such as the Large Electron--Positron Collider at CERN, is a more sophisticated circular accelerator than the cyclotron. The magnetic field is adjusted in strength in a much more complex way to allow for the synchronisation problems that a cyclotron faces with very fast 'relativistic' particles.

To keep the magnetic field strength down to manageable levels, the radius of the particles' paths is much larger than in a cyclotron. This means that the accelerator is in the form of a large loop (not a disc like the cyclotron) and the radius of the particles' path must be constant at all times (Fig. 22).

For any magnetic field strength B, the radius of the path depends on the velocity of

---

Fig. 22 A synchrotron

particles from a pre-accelerator (linear accelerator or smaller synchrotron)

accelerating cavities, in which an electromagnetic wave creates an electric field that gives energy to the particles

towards target and collision detectors

Particles gain energy every time they pass through a cavity. The particles move around the synchrotron perhaps thousands of times before being ejected and sent to collide.

Synchrotrons are heavily dependent on magnet technology. This large and costly superconducting magnet is being readied for use in CERN's Large Hadron Collider. Much modern superconductivity technology is owed to the effort of synchrotron engineers in the past.

the particles (from $r = mv/BQ$). If v increases, the particles spiral out; if v decreases, the particles spiral in. In both cases the particles leave the accelerating track. This restricts the synchrotron to accelerating bursts of particles that are all at the same speed.

12

a Calculate the energy gained by a proton in a cyclotron when it moves from one D to the other, if the potential difference between the Ds is 8 kV. State your answers in joules and electronvolts.

b Calculate the speed of a proton that has made 1000 such transfers.

c Calculate the radius of the path for the proton in part b, if the magnetic field strength is 0.8 T.

d Approximately how long will it take the proton to complete one semicircular journey through each D?

e What frequency of the alternating voltage would synchronise with the proton's path to accelerate it?

13 Sketch a graph that shows the cycle in applied p.d. against time for the Ds in a cyclotron. Describe the path taken by a proton, explaining what is happening to the proton at each point in the cycle.

14 List the advantages of a fixed-radius particle path in a synchrotron, compared with the spiralling path in a cyclotron.

15 Give two reasons why it is necessary to increase magnetic field strength in a synchrotron as the particles accelerate.

1 The diagram shows an arrangement in a vacuum to deflect protons into a detector using a magnetic field, which can be assumed to be uniform within the square shown and zero outside it. The motion of the protons is in the plane of the paper.

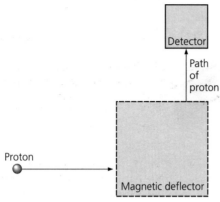

a Sketch the path of a proton through the magnetic deflector. At any point on this path draw an arrow to represent the magnetic force on the proton. Label this arrow F. (2)

b State the direction of the uniform magnetic field causing this motion. (1)

c The speed of a proton as it enters the deflector is 5.0×10^6 m s^{-1}. If the flux density of the magnetic field is 0.50 T, calculate the magnitude of the magnetic force on the proton. (2)

d If the path were that of an electron with the same velocity, what two changes would need to be made to the magnetic field for the electron to enter the detector along the same path? (2)

(PH03 Q1 March 99)

2 The diagram shows an electron entering the space between two charged plates at high speed.

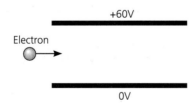

a The electron is deflected by the plates and passes out of the other side. Sketch on the diagram the path of the electron through, and beyond, the plates. For any point on the path between the plates, draw an arrow to show the direction of the force on the electron due to the electric field. (3)

b If the gap between the plates is 100 mm, calculate

(i) the electric field strength between the plates,

(ii) the magnitude of the electrostatic force on the electron. (2)

c This diagram shows the path of an electron as it approaches a point positive charge, P, of 5.0 μC.

(i) Mark on the diagram the direction of the electrostatic force on the electron at X and at Y.

(ii) The distance between the positive charge and X is 40 mm. Calculate the magnitude of the force on the positive charge due to the electron when the electron is at X. (3)

(PH03 Q4 March 98)

3 The diagram shows a current-carrying conductor which is free to move between the poles of a horseshoe magnet. The conductor is a brass rod resting on two conducting parallel rails.

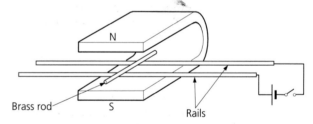

(i) Draw an arrow on the diagram to show the direction of the force on the rod due to the magnetic field when the switch is closed. Label it *F*.

(ii) Using the information below, calculate the magnitude of the force *F*.
The e.m.f. of the cell is 2.0 V.
The flux density of the magnetic field in the region of the rod is 0.080 T.
The total resistance of the circuit is 0.40 Ω.
The rails are 60 mm apart. (3)

(PH03 Q3 March 2000)

4 Both gravitational and electric field strengths can be described by similar equations written in the form
$a = bc/d^2$.

a Complete the following table by writing down the names of the corresponding quantities, together with their SI units, for the two types of field (4)

symbol	gravitational field quantity	SI unit	electrical field quantity	SI unit
a	gravitational field strength			
b			$\dfrac{1}{4\pi\varepsilon_0}$	mF^{-1}
c				
d				

b Two isolated charged objects, A and B, are arranged so that the gravitational force between them is equal and opposite to the electric force between them.

(i) The separation of A and B is doubled without changing their charges or masses. State and explain the effect, if any, that this will have on the resultant force between them.

(ii) At the original separation, the mass of A is doubled, whilst the charge on A and the mass of B remain as they were initially. What would have to happen to the charge on B to keep the resultant force zero? (3)

(PH03 Q2 March 2000)

5 a (i) The force on a current-carrying conductor in a magnetic field is given by $F = BIl$. State the condition for which this equation is valid.

(ii) State **two** necessary conditions for a charged particle to be subject to a magnetic force in a magnetic field. (3)

b An alpha particle is travelling at 8.5×10^6 m s^{-1} and a beta particle is travelling at 3.0×10^7 m s^{-1}. They both enter a magnetic field of flux density 2.5 T, at right angles to the field. Given that the magnitude of the charge of an alpha particle is double that of a beta particle, calculate the ratio

magnetic force on alpha particle/
magnetic force on beta particle. (3)

(NEAB PH03 Q1 June 1997)

6

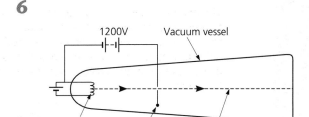

a A side view of a simple electron gun is shown above. Show that the speed with which electrons emerge from the anode of this gun will be about 2×10^7 m s^{-1} when the potential difference between the cathode and the anode is 1200 V. (3)

b Electrons emerging horizontally from the electron gun in part **a** then enter a uniform magnetic field which is directed upwards in the plane of the diagram. Calculate the magnitude of the force on an electron in this magnetic field of flux density 0.080 T. (2)

c Draw the path of an electron passing through the field described in part **b** on each of the two diagrams shown below. No further calculations are expected. (3)

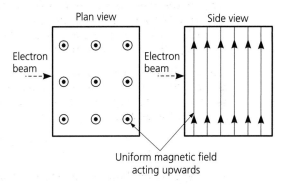

Uniform magnetic field acting upwards

d (i) State whether the speed of an electron changes while it is in the magnetic field. Explain your answer.

(ii) State, with a reason, whether the force on the electron alters while it is in the magnetic field. (2)

(PH03 Q3 June 1999)

8 Electromagnetic induction

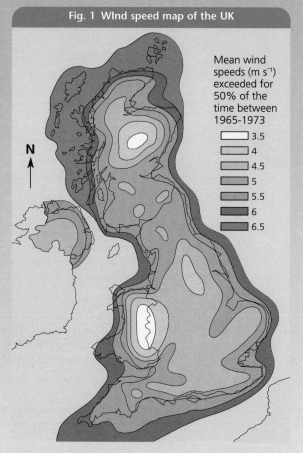

Fig. 1 WInd speed map of the UK

Mean wind speeds (m s⁻¹) exceeded for 50% of the time between 1965-1973

- 3.5
- 4
- 4.5
- 5
- 5.5
- 6
- 6.5

N

Windmills were one of the earliest ways of harnessing energy from the environment. They used the kinetic energy of the wind to drive water pumps and millstones directly. Now, wind farms can be used to generate pollution-free electricity.

Fossil fuels will not last forever. There is a real need to develop alternative, renewable energy sources. One possibility is wind power. Wind power in the UK now has a capacity of 360 MW of electricity, enough to meet the average demands of 200 000 homes. Although this is tiny compared with the 2000 MW generated by a single large coal-powered station, wind power has less impact on the environment – it produces no greenhouse gases, no waste and no acid rain.

Aerogenerators transfer kinetic energy from the moving air into electrical energy. The larger the area swept out by the blades, the more energy is transferred, so the large generators on wind farms have 25 m diameter blades. The energy transferred is crucially dependent on the wind speed. One of the biggest problems facing wind-turbine designers is maximizing power output at low wind speeds; few designs work well at less than 6 m s⁻¹. The structure also needs to be able to withstand high wind speeds without breaking. Hilltops and coastal areas are the best locations (Fig. 1).

As the wind forces the blades of the wind turbine round, the motion is transferred to a dynamo. The dynamo transfers energy by the process of *electromagnetic induction*.

Burning fossil fuels is not an ideal way to generate electricity. It releases carbon dioxide, which contributes to the greenhouse effect.

A generator with small-diameter blades can produce enough power to recharge the batteries on a boat.

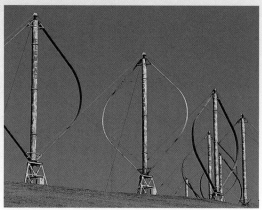

These vertical axis generators do not need to turn to face the wind.

Faraday's law

In 1831, Michael Faraday discovered that electricity is produced in a wire as it moves through a magnetic field. Faraday had already built the first electric motor. This device relied on the magnetic field produced by an electric current. He believed that it should also be possible to make electricity from a magnetic field. Faraday decided to use an electromagnet to provide a magnetic field. Two coils of wire were wound around an iron ring. One coil was connected to a battery. The other coil was

Faraday's original transformer.

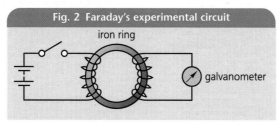

Fig. 2 Faraday's experimental circuit

iron ring

galvanometer

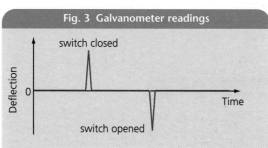

Fig. 3 Galvanometer readings

switch closed

Deflection

0

Time

switch opened

connected to a galvanometer, an uncalibrated electrical current detector (Fig. 2). Faraday expected the current from the battery to set up a strong magnetic field in the iron ring. This would then, he thought, 'induce' a steady flow of electrical current through the galvanometer.

The experiment didn't turn out quite as Faraday expected. Instead, he saw the galvanometer needle move quickly to one side when the switch was turned on and then return to zero. Faraday noticed that when the switch was turned off, the needle jumped again, this time in the opposite direction (Fig. 3).

Faraday was puzzled by the results of his experiment, so he continued his investigation by moving a permanent magnet towards and away from the coil of wire. He saw that the galvanometer registered current flow *only* when the magnet was *moving* (Fig. 4).

Faraday had discovered the essential requirement for electromagnetic induction: a **change of flux**. This could be achieved either by changing the flux itself or by physically moving a conductor through flux lines. The faster and larger the change of flux, the bigger the **induced e.m.f.** The e.m.f. is proportional to the rate of cutting through flux lines. This law of electromagnetic induction is represented by Faraday's law:

The induced e.m.f. in a circuit is equal to the rate at which the circuit cuts flux.

In SI units, a flux change of $\Delta\Phi$ Webers in time Δt seconds gives an e.m.f. of

$$\varepsilon = \frac{\Delta\Phi}{\Delta t}$$

You can work out the direction of the induced e.m.f. using the principle of conservation of energy. The induced e.m.f. can make a current flow. If this current

Fig. 4 Electromagnetic induction

When the magnet approaches, a 'like' pole is induced – this tries to push the magnet back.

Stationary magnet. No induced current.

When the magnet is pulled away, an opposite pole is induced – this tries to pull the magnet back.

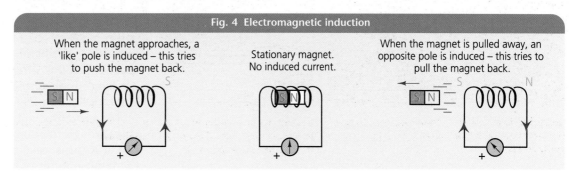

'helped' the change of flux, you would be able to make a machine which caused a steadily increasing current without any energy input: a machine in perpetual motion. This is impossible under the law of conservation of energy, so the e.m.f. must try to oppose whatever flux change is causing it. This rule is called Lenz's law.

1 The blade of a wind turbine has a radius of 12 m and turns through a full circle every 6 s. The turbine's axis is aligned North–South, so the blade cuts through the horizontal component of the Earth's magnetic field. This has a horizontal component of flux density of 20 μT. Explain why an e.m.f. is induced across the blade and calculate its magnitude.

KEY FACTS

- Faraday's law of electromagnetic induction: an e.m.f. is induced when flux changes. The e.m.f. is equal to the rate of change of flux.
- Lenz's law states that the direction of the induced e.m.f. is such that it opposes the change of flux.

8.2 Dynamos

Any equipment which contains a conductor cutting through flux lines will work as a **dynamo**. A dynamo is a device for converting mechanical energy into electrical energy. Commercial dynamos consist of a coil spinning inside a magnetic field. We can investigate which factors determine the size of the induced e.m.f. in the coil by analysing a single straight wire of length l moving with speed v through a uniform field of flux density B (Fig. 5).

In Δt seconds, the wire moves a distance $v\Delta t$ metres, and cuts through an area $A = lv\Delta t$. Therefore, the wire cuts through flux:

$$\Delta\Phi = BA = Blv\Delta t$$

$$\text{so,} \quad \varepsilon = \frac{\Delta\Phi}{\Delta t} = \frac{Blv\Delta t}{\Delta t}$$

$$\varepsilon = Blv$$

Fig. 5 Induced e.m.f.

Fig. 6 Fleming's right-hand rule applied to a moving wire

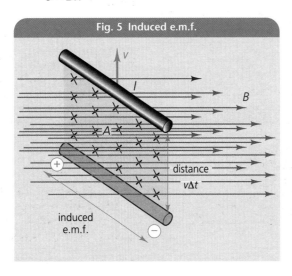

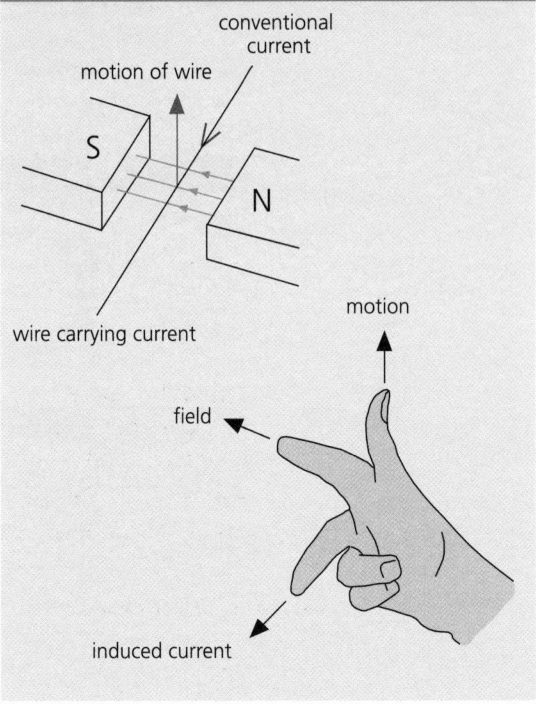

To work out the direction of the current you could use Lenz's law. Alternatively, Fleming's right-hand dynamo rule can be used. This follows the same principles as the left-hand (motor) rule to give the correct current direction (Fig. 6).

For a rotating coil, each turn of the coil cuts through the magnetic flux lines. For a coil of N turns, each turn would contribute the same amount of e.m.f. All the turns are in

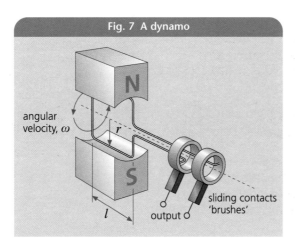

Fig. 7 A dynamo

An aircraft cuts through the vertical component of the Earth's magnetic field. This induces an e.m.f. across the wing tips.

series, so the total e.m.f. adds up to:

$$\varepsilon = N\frac{\Delta\Phi}{\Delta t}$$

Only the wires on the edge of the coil are cutting through the magnetic flux. We can produce an expression for the maximum magnitude of the e.m.f. The coil has radius r and side length l. It rotates at angular velocity ω. The speed of the edge of the coil is:

$$v = r\omega$$
$$so \quad \varepsilon = Blv$$
$$= Bl\omega r$$

The coil has width $2r$, so $2rl$ = area A of the coil. For N turns, we have $2N$ coil edges, so the total e.m.f. will be:

$$\varepsilon = 2N \times Blr\omega$$
$$= NB \times 2rl \times \omega$$
$$= NBA\omega$$

Induced e.m.f.s

Any conductor that sweeps through a magnetic field will induce an e.m.f. As an aircraft flies, its wings cut through the vertical

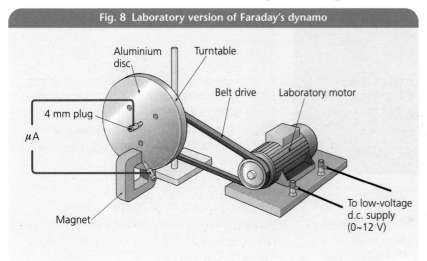

Fig. 8 Laboratory version of Faraday's dynamo

component of the Earth's magnetic field, so an e.m.f. will be induced across them. We can use Faraday's law to estimate the size of that e.m.f.:

$$\varepsilon = \frac{\Delta\Phi}{\Delta t}$$

But $\Phi = BA$

so $\frac{\Delta\Phi}{\Delta t} = B\left(\frac{\Delta A}{\Delta t}\right)$

The flux density, B, is constant and equal to about 4.0×10^{-5} T. We need to calculate the rate of change in area, i.e. the area swept out by the wings in one second.

Assuming the aircraft flies at 600 km h^{-1} and has a wingspan of 50 m, the area swept out in one second is

$$\frac{\Delta A}{\Delta t} = 50 \text{ m} \times \left(\frac{600\,000}{60 \times 60}\right) \text{ m}^2\text{ s}^{-1}$$

$$= 8333 \text{ m}^2\text{ s}^{-1}$$

The rate of change of flux is therefore given by:

$$\frac{\Delta\Phi}{\Delta t} = 4.0 \times 10^{-5} \text{ T} \times 8333 \text{ m}^2\text{ s}^{-1}$$

so the induced e.m.f. is 0.333 V.

If the aircraft is flying in the Northern Hemisphere, the flux density is down towards the Earth. You can use Fleming's right-hand rule to show that the left-hand wing tip will be positive.

Faraday's disc

Faraday generated an e.m.f. in a metal disc by spinning it in a magnetic field (see Fig. 8). If the disc has a radius r and spins at n times per second, the area swept out in one second is

$$A = n\pi r^2$$

So the total flux change in one second, and hence the induced e.m.f., will be

$$\varepsilon = \frac{\Delta\Phi}{\Delta t} = B\left(\frac{\Delta A}{\Delta t}\right) = Bn\pi r^2$$

2 A horizontal metal disc of radius 30 cm is spun clockwise in a vertical magnetic field of flux density 0.1 T. A potential difference of 3 mV is measured between the centre of the disc and the rim. What is the rotational speed of the disc? Which terminal is positive, the centre or the rim?

3 A designer plans to use the e.m.f. generated across an aircraft's wing tips to measure the aircraft's speed. He argues that the faster the aircraft travels, the greater the area swept out by the wings and the larger the e.m.f. between the wing tips. Why is his plan doomed to failure?

8.3 Generating alternating current

Wind generators need to generate alternating current at a useful voltage and at an acceptable frequency.

Suppose a large wind turbine rotates once every ten seconds ($\omega = 2\pi/10 = 0.63$ rad s^{-1}). Using strong permanent magnets, we can achieve a magnetic flux density of around 0.1 T. It would be possible to mount a coil of perhaps 0.5 m^2 with 500 turns at the centre of a wind turbine. This would give an e.m.f. of:

$$\varepsilon = NBA\omega$$
$$= 500 \times 0.1 \text{ T} \times 0.5 \text{ m}^2 \times 0.63 \text{ s}^{-1}$$
$$= 16 \text{ V}$$

To increase the e.m.f. to a useful size, we need to have an arrangement of gears which makes the dynamo spin quickly while the wind-turbine blades sweep slowly around. The faster rotation will help to make the frequency of the output more acceptable to consumers.

4
a List the factors which affect the e.m.f. produced by a rotating coil.
b A dynamo coil of 5000 turns has length 50 cm and radius 10 cm. It rotates at 3000 rpm in a uniform field of flux density 15 mT. Calculate the magnitude of the maximum e.m.f. output.

Alternating output
We can see why the dynamo produces an alternating output by looking at one side of the coil. Half of the time it is moving left through the field, the other half to the right.

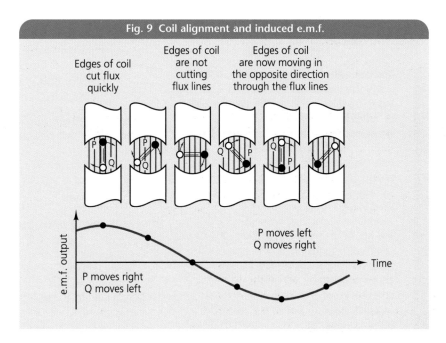

Fig. 9 Coil alignment and induced e.m.f.

This change of direction causes a change of polarity in the induced current. When the coil edges are moving parallel to the field, they are not cutting through flux lines. The e.m.f. will then be zero (Fig. 9).

The faster the coil rotates, the more often it completes a full cycle of the alternating current. For a simple, single-coil dynamo the frequency of the dynamo output is equal to the number of revolutions per second. To match the 50 Hz national grid, this generator would need 50 revolutions per second. The speed of rotation also affects the e.m.f. and power output of the generator. For example, doubling the speed of rotation:

• doubles the frequency because twice as many revolutions are completed per second;

• doubles the maximum e.m.f. because the rate of cutting flux has doubled;

• quadruples the power for a particular load, because both current and p.d. are doubled ($P = IV$).

Wind speeds can change enormously, yet few electrical appliances can work over a wide voltage range. Designers of aerogenerators have had to develop control mechanisms, either to regulate allowed speeds or to vary the flux density.

Transmitting electricity

High-voltage transmission needs tall pylons and large insulators to carry the wires at such high potential.

The best sites for aerogenerators in the UK are in the exposed, unpopulated areas of North Scotland, and on the Western sides of Wales and Cornwall. The electricity generated at these locations needs to be transported to people further afield. If wind farms are to be financially viable, this energy must be transported efficiently.

A group of landowners in the North West Highlands is proposing to build a wind farm capable of generating 100 kW. It will be 30 km from Fort William, the nearest centre of population, so the cost of the cables linking the wind farm to the consumers will be significant. Domestic consumers use a p.d. of 240 V (Fig. 10). Allowing for a 10% energy loss in the supply cables, how thick would these cables need to be?

If the consumers receive 90 kW at 240 V, the current will be:

$$I = \frac{P}{V} = \frac{90\,000\text{ W}}{240\text{ V}} = 375\text{ A}$$

The cables dissipate 10 kW. Using $P = I^2R$ for the cables:

$$R = \frac{P}{I^2} = \frac{10\,000\text{ W}}{375^2\text{ A}^2} = 0.0711\,\Omega$$

The cables need to be 60 km long (30 km each way) and are made of copper ($\rho = 1.7 \times 10^{-8}\,\Omega$ m). Using

$$A = \frac{\rho l}{R} = \frac{1.7 \times 10^{-8}\,\Omega\text{ m} \times 60\,000\text{ m}}{0.0711\,\Omega}$$

$$= 0.0144\text{ m}^2$$

Assuming circular cross-section, the area is πr^2, so $r = 0.068$ m. The wires would need to have a diameter of more than 13 cm! The mass of these cables would be about 7000 tonnes. The cost of generating and transporting electricity in this way would be prohibitive.

The solution is to use **transformers** to transport the electricity at very high voltage. The same amount of power can then be transmitted at a low current. For example, the 100 kW from the wind farm could be transmitted as 10 A at 10 000 V, or 2 A at 50 000 V, or even 1 A at 100 000 V.

Heating of the transmission wires causes power loss. The heating effect depends on the square of the current in the wires. For example, reducing the current by a factor of 10 would reduce power loss by a factor of 100. Using a higher voltage decreases the current, so reducing the power loss in the wires. Suppose we transmitted the 100 kW from the wind farm at 11 000 V. We can repeat the calculation of cable diameter (Fig. 11).

If the consumer's transformer receives 90 kW at 11 000 V, the current will be 8.18 A. The cables dissipate 10 kW, so using

$$P = I^2R, \qquad R = 149\,\Omega$$

Again, using $R = \frac{\rho l}{A}$ and $A = \pi r^2$,

$$r = 1.9 \times 10^{-3}\text{ m}$$

The diameter of the wire would then be less than 4 mm, making the transmission of electricity significantly less expensive. Domestic consumers cannot use electricity at very high voltage, so a transformer is used to reduce the voltage for use in the home.

Fig. 10 Transmission of electricity

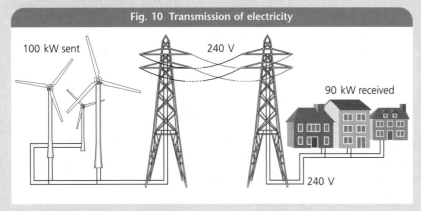

100 kW sent — 240 V — 90 kW received — 240 V

Fig. 11 High-voltage transmission

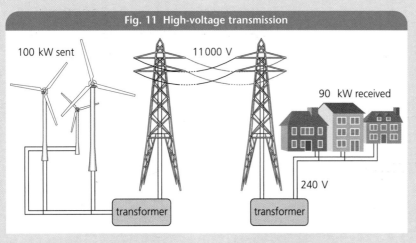

100 kW sent — 11 000 V — 90 kW received — 240 V — transformer — transformer

5 A series of wind farms along the Western coast of Scotland could generate 1000 MW. If the resistance of the transmission lines is 10 Ω, calculate the percentage power loss in the cables for transmissions at

a 200 kV

b 400 kV

1 A student investigates the behaviour of a magnetic pendulum. A magnet swings above a coil attached to a counter. A count is made every time the voltage across the terminals changes polarity.

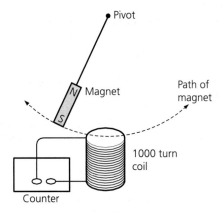

a Explain why a voltage is induced in the coil. (2)

b Label with an X on the diagram every position of the magnet where the induced voltage changes polarity. (2)

c The counter is replaced with one that counts each time the induced voltage exceeds 2.0 mV. Calculate the rate of change of flux needed to induce this voltage in the coil, which has 1000 turns. (2)

d Write down three changes that could be made to increase the maximum voltage induced in the coil. (3)

(PH03 Q2 June 1998)

2 a State Lenz's law of electromagnetic induction. (2)

b The diagram below shows a magnet being dropped through the centre of a narrow coil. The e.m.f. across the coil is monitored on an oscilloscope.

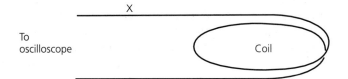

(i) What is the induced polarity on the top side of the coil as the magnet falls towards the coil? Give your answer by placing a letter N (induced north pole) or S (induced south pole) near the top of the coil in the diagram.

(ii) Draw an arrow at position X to indicate the direction of current flow as the magnet falls towards the coil. (2)

c The diagram below shows the variation of e.m.f. with time as the magnet falls.

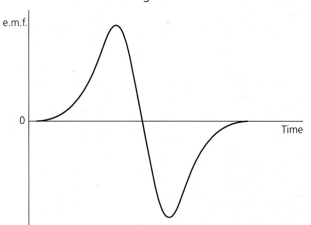

State **two** ways in which this graph would change if the magnet were dropped from a greater height. (2)

(PH03 Q6 March 1998)

3 a Explain why you would expect an electromotive force to be developed between the wing tips of an aircraft flying above the Earth. (1)

b An aircraft, whose wing tips are 20 m apart, flies horizontally at a speed of 600 km h^{-1} in a region where the vertical component of the Earth's magnetic flux density is 4.0 x 10^{-5} T. Calculate

(i) the area swept out by the aircraft's wings in 1 s,

(ii) the e.m.f. between the wing tips. (4)

(PH03 Q3 Feb 1997)

9 Nuclear power: fission and fusion

Nuclear fusion

On Thursday 23 March 1989, the scientific world was shaken when two chemists seemed to have solved global energy problems at a stroke. Martin Fleischmann and Stanley Pons announced at a televised press conference that they had achieved nuclear fusion.

Since World War II, it has been fission, the splitting of the uranium atom, that has offered the nuclear industry's best prospect of cheap electricity. The UK's first reactor was opened in 1956 and fission reactors currently generate about 20% of UK electricity. Unfortunately, they produce highly radioactive waste and have proved costly to maintain, so the prospect of fusion, with its almost limitless supply of 'clean' energy, is more appealing than ever.

Millions of pounds have been invested in giant plasma machines and immensely powerful lasers in an attempt get two hydrogen nuclei to undergo fusion. When the two men announced that they had managed it using £100 worth of heavy water and laboratory glassware, scientists all over the world dropped their own work to investigate. Japan threw millions of dollars into 'cold fusion' research and the USA opened a 'National Cold Fusion Institute'. Fleischmann and Pons became media stars overnight. To understand why the announcement caused so much excitement we need to look closely at the physics behind nuclear power.

Scientists claim energy breakthrough

Two scientists from Britain and America last night claimed to have carried out controlled nuclear fusion in a test tube. If confirmed, their discovery could become the greatest breakthrough of the century.

Professor Martin Fleischmann, of Southampton University, and Professor Stan Pons, of the University of Utah, released the results of research which could open the door to a limitless source of 'clean' energy.

Source: *The Times, 24th March 1989*

9.1 Splitting the atom

Fermi called his reactor a nuclear pile; over 400 tonnes of graphite blocks and uranium rods were stacked together in a squash court.

The first public demonstration of the colossal power of the nucleus was the explosion of a uranium bomb over Hiroshima in August 1945. Three years earlier, Enrico Fermi and his team had achieved a controlled release of nuclear power when they built the world's first nuclear reactor at the University of Chicago. Inside this reactor, uranium nuclei were allowed to break up into smaller nuclei in a process called nuclear **fission**.

Fission occurs in large, unstable nuclei which decay by splitting themselves completely in two. Isotopes which decay in this way are said to be fissile. One such isotope is uranium-235, which is used as the fuel in most nuclear reactors.

Uranium-235 (or $^{235}_{92}$U) atoms can undergo **spontaneous** fission, but this is a relatively rare event. It would take over 700 million years for half of the atoms of a $^{235}_{92}$U sample to decay. A nuclear reactor increases the fission-rate by bombarding the uranium with neutrons (Fig. 1).

When an atom of $^{235}_{92}$U absorbs a neutron it changes to $^{236}_{92}$U. This is a very unstable isotope that splits almost instantly into two fission products and a number of neutrons. It is a matter of chance which isotopes are created, though some are more likely than others.

The fission products and neutrons fly apart at high speed and their kinetic energy is eventually converted to electricity in a nuclear power station (Fig. 2). But where does the kinetic energy of the fission products and neutrons come from in the first place?

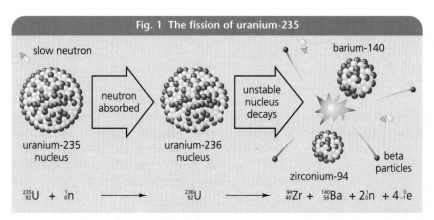

Fig. 1 The fission of uranium-235

slow neutron

uranium-235 nucleus

neutron absorbed

uranium-236 nucleus

unstable nucleus decays

barium-140

zirconium-94

beta particles

$^{235}_{92}U + ^{1}_{0}n \longrightarrow ^{236}_{92}U \longrightarrow ^{94}_{40}Zr + ^{140}_{56}Ba + 2^{1}_{0}n + 4^{0}_{-1}e$

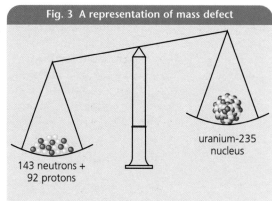

Fig. 3 A representation of mass defect

143 neutrons + 92 protons

uranium-235 nucleus

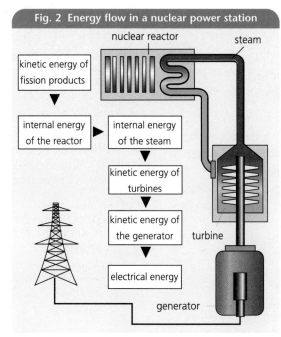

Fig. 2 Energy flow in a nuclear power station

nuclear reactor

steam

kinetic energy of fission products

internal energy of the reactor

internal energy of the steam

kinetic energy of turbines

kinetic energy of the generator

electrical energy

turbine

generator

1 Fission of a uranium-235 nucleus (atomic number, $Z = 92$) can lead to the formation of xenon ($Z = 54$) and strontium ($Z = 38$). Write down an equation which describes this reaction.

Mass defect

A peculiar kind of arithmetic applies to nuclear physics. If you add up the masses of several neutrons and protons, and then put them together to make a nucleus, you end up with less mass than you started with. A nucleus weighs less than the nuclear particles it is made from (Fig. 3).

The missing mass, or **mass defect**, is a very small quantity. Instead of using kilograms, or even grams, the mass defect is measured using the **atomic (or unified) mass unit**, u. One atomic mass unit is defined as being one-twelfth of the mass of a carbon-12 atom:

$1u = 1.66043 \times 10^{-27}$ kg

A proton has a mass of $1.0073\ u$ and a neutron has a mass of $1.0087\ u$ (to 5 s.f.). Uranium-235 consists of 92 protons and 143 neutrons, so you might expect its total mass to be:

$92 \times 1.0073\ u + 143 \times 1.0087\ u = 236.92\ u$

However, accurate measurements give the mass of a uranium-235 nucleus as $235.04\ u$. Mass appears to have been 'lost'. We say that uranium has a mass defect of

$236.92\ u - 235.04\ u = 1.88\ u.$

This principle applies to all nuclei. Iron-56 has a mass defect of $0.516\ u$; a gold nucleus has a mass defect of $1.637\ u$.

2 $^{239}_{94}Pu$ is an isotope of plutonium that is produced in nuclear reactors. It has a mass of $239.052\ u$. Find its mass defect.

Binding energy

A clue to the missing mass, and to the secret of nuclear power, came in Einstein's work on **special relativity**. In a paper published in 1905 he made the remarkable claim that mass and energy are equivalent. His new mechanics suggested that a particle of mass m moving at a velocity v had an energy E given by the equation:

Albert Einstein.

$$E = \frac{mc^2}{\sqrt{1 - v^2/c^2}}$$

where c is the velocity of light.

But Newtonian mechanics gives the energy of a moving mass as:

$$E = \frac{1}{2}mv^2$$

113

The Newtonian expression works very well in most situations. It is only for objects moving close to the speed of light that Einstein's expression for kinetic energy has to be used. At low velocities the two equations should be equivalent.

When the velocity, v, is much less than the speed of light, c, Einstein's equation gives:

$$E = \frac{mc^2}{\sqrt{1 - v^2/c^2}}$$

$$= mc^2(1 - v^2/c^2)^{-1/2}$$

If $v \ll c$ we can use the binomial expansion, $(1 + x)^n \approx 1 + nx + \ldots$, to give:

$$E \approx mc^2(1 + \tfrac{1}{2}v^2/c^2)$$

$$= mc^2 + \tfrac{1}{2}mv^2$$

Compare this with the Newtonian expression:

$$E = \tfrac{1}{2}mv^2$$

Einstein's equation has an extra term, mc^2. This represents a 'rest' energy that depends upon the mass of the object.

When the object is stationary (relative to the observer), $v = 0$, and Einstein's equation becomes:

$$E = mc^2(1 - v^2/c^2)^{-1/2} = mc^2$$

So: $E = mc^2$

This expression, probably the best known of all physics equations, describes the equivalence of mass and energy. Einstein rocked the foundations of the physics world with his suggestion that these two apparently different properties are interconvertible. In his 1905 paper on relativity, Einstein said:

If a body gives off energy, E, in the form of radiation, its mass diminishes by E/c^2.

This explains where the 'missing' mass has gone. When 143 neutrons and 92 protons are put together to make a uranium nucleus, some of the mass is 'radiated away' as energy. For a nucleus of uranium-235, the mass defect is 1.88 u, or 3.12×10^{-27} kg, so the amount of energy radiated away is:

$$E = mc^2 = 3.12 \times 10^{-27} \text{ kg} \times (3 \times 10^8 \text{ m s}^{-1})^2$$

$$= 2.8 \times 10^{-10} \text{ J}$$

To convert a uranium nucleus back to 92 protons and 143 neutrons we would have to put back the 2.8×10^{-10} J that was radiated away when it was formed. This energy is known as the **binding energy**:

binding energy = mass defect $\times c^2$

Because the amounts of energy are comparatively small, binding energy is usually given in electronvolts, rather than joules. Since one electronvolt = 1.6×10^{-19} J, the binding energy of ^{235}U is 1.749×10^9 eV.

When a uranium nucleus *splits* into two smaller nuclei, the total mass of the fission products is *less* than the original uranium nucleus. The mass difference has been converted to energy. This is the source of the energy released by nuclear fission.

In the fission reaction

$$^{235}_{92}\text{U} + ^{1}_{0}\text{n} \rightarrow ^{236}_{92}\text{U} \rightarrow ^{94}_{40}\text{Zr} + ^{140}_{56}\text{Ba} + 2^{1}_{0}\text{n} + 4^{0}_{-1}\text{e}$$

the total mass was originally

235.044 u (^{235}U) + 1.009 u ($^{1}_{0}$n) = 236.053 u

After the fission the mass is:

93.906 u (Zr) + 139.91 u (Ba)
$\qquad$ + 2 $\times$ 1.009 u ($^{1}_{0}$n) + 4 $\times$ 0.00055 u ($^{0}_{-1}$e)
= 235.836 u

The mass defect is 0.217 u, an energy release of 200 MeV per fission. This is a huge energy output compared with even the most energetic chemical reactions.

3 What is the binding energy of a plutonium-239 nucleus? (Give your answer in eV.)

4 Calculate the energy released by the fission of ^{239}Pu in the reaction:
$$^{239}_{94}\text{Pu} + ^{1}_{0}\text{n} \rightarrow ^{240}_{94}\text{Pu} \rightarrow$$
$$^{87}_{35}\text{Br} + ^{150}_{60}\text{Nd} + 3^{1}_{0}\text{n} + ^{0}_{-1}\text{e}$$

Nuclear masses: ^{239}Pu = 239.052 u, ^{87}Br = 86.922 u , ^{150}Nd = 149.920 u

Nuclear stability

We can not only release energy by splitting a heavy nucleus; it is also possible to release energy by fusing two lighter nuclei. The idea of binding energy can be used to explain this.

The binding energy of a nucleus tells us how much energy is required to pull it to pieces. The more energy that is needed, the more stable the nucleus is likely to be. The average energy needed to pull out each proton and neutron is known as the binding energy per **nucleon**. For uranium, the binding energy per nucleon is:

$$\frac{1800 \text{ MeV}}{235} = 7.6 \text{ MeV}$$

The value of the binding energy per nucleon varies with atomic number and has a maximum value at iron-56 (Fig. 4).

EXTENSION   Einstein and Newton compared

Einstein's theory applies to all energy changes. If we measure an object's mass when it is moving relative to us, it will have a greater mass than when it is at rest compared to us. This effect is negligible for everyday velocities but for masses that are moving at a significant fraction of the speed of light, the effect becomes very noticeable. If we are to calculate the speed of the fast-moving protons in a synchrotron (see Chapter 7), or even the electrons in a TV tube, we need to take into account the change in mass.

Suppose an electron is accelerated in an electric field. We could calculate its velocity, v, after it has passed through a potential difference, V, using the Newtonian expression where the change in energy, eV, equals the increase in kinetic energy, $\frac{1}{2}mv^2$:

$$eV = \tfrac{1}{2}mv^2$$

As the potential difference is increased, the velocity of the electron keeps increasing (Table 1).

Unfortunately this approach does not work at higher energies. By the time the potential difference has reached 500 kV we are predicting velocities greater than the speed of light, which cannot be true. Einstein would argue that the constant force still increases the momentum of the electron, just as in Newton's second law, but the apparent mass of the electron increases with its relative velocity to the electric field. This makes it harder to accelerate. We should be using $eV = \Delta mc^2$, where the change in mass is

$$\Delta m = m_0\left(1 - \frac{1}{\sqrt{\left(1 - v^2/c^2\right)}}\right)$$

Now as the voltage increases, the kinetic energy increases as before, but the velocity increase is less, because the mass of the electron increases (Table 2).

Table 1		

The velocity of an electron as it passes through an increasing potential difference. This has been calculated using Newtonian mechanics, which doesn't work well at high velocities.

Potential difference/V	Kinetic energy/joules	Velocity/m s⁻¹
$1.00 \times 10^{+01}$	1.60×10^{-18}	$1.88 \times 10^{+06}$
$1.00 \times 10^{+02}$	1.60×10^{-17}	$5.93 \times 10^{+06}$
$1.00 \times 10^{+03}$	1.60×10^{-16}	$1.88 \times 10^{+07}$
$1.00 \times 10^{+04}$	1.60×10^{-15}	$5.93 \times 10^{+07}$
$1.00 \times 10^{+05}$	1.60×10^{-14}	$1.88 \times 10^{+08}$
$5.00 \times 10^{+05}$	8.00×10^{-14}	$4.19 \times 10^{+08}$

Table 2			

The velocity of an electron as it passes through an increasing potential difference. This is done using relativistic mechanics, which allows for the change in mass as the energy increases.

Potential difference/volts	Energy /joules	Change in mass/kg	Velocity /m s⁻¹
$1.00 \times 10^{+01}$	1.60×10^{-18}	1.78×10^{-35}	$1.33 \times 10^{+06}$
$1.00 \times 10^{+02}$	1.60×10^{-17}	1.78×10^{-34}	$4.19 \times 10^{+06}$
$1.00 \times 10^{+03}$	1.60×10^{-16}	1.78×10^{-33}	$1.32 \times 10^{+07}$
$1.00 \times 10^{+04}$	1.60×10^{-15}	1.78×10^{-32}	$4.15 \times 10^{+07}$
$1.00 \times 10^{+05}$	1.60×10^{-14}	1.78×10^{-31}	$1.21 \times 10^{+08}$
$5.00 \times 10^{+05}$	8.00×10^{-14}	8.89×10^{-31}	$2.11 \times 10^{+08}$

5   Einstein's special theory of relativity works both ways. If you put energy *into* an object it will increase its mass. Why don't you notice the gain in mass of a kettle when you are making a cup of tea? (It takes about 400 kJ to boil a kettle of water.)

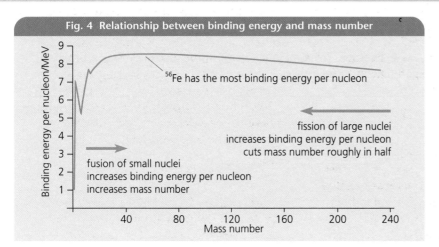

Fig. 4 Relationship between binding energy and mass number

⁵⁶Fe has the most binding energy per nucleon

fission of large nuclei increases binding energy per nucleon cuts mass number roughly in half

fusion of small nuclei increases binding energy per nucleon increases mass number

Binding energy per nucleon/MeV — Mass number

Iron-56 has the most stable nucleus. A nucleus will increase its stability, and release energy, if a reaction brings it closer to iron-56. There are two ways that this can happen:

- Nuclei which are heavier than iron can increase their stability by breaking up into lighter isotopes. This is exactly what happens in nuclear fission.

- Nuclei which are lighter than iron can increase their stability by amalgamating with others to form a heavier isotope. This is what happens in nuclear fusion.

Fig. 5 The liquid drop model of nuclear fission

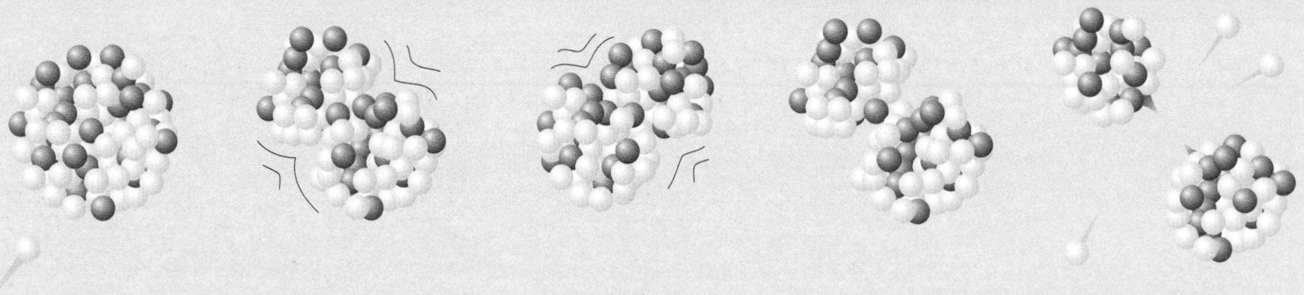

Absorption of a neutron by a nucleus of uranium-235

...creates an unstable nucleus of uranium-236 that wobbles until...

... the repulsion due to the electric charge is greater than the forces of attraction that hold the nucleus together...

...and the two halves fly apart, together with some free neutrons.

$$^{235}_{92}U + ^{1}_{0}n \rightarrow ^{236}_{92}U$$

$$^{236}_{92}U \rightarrow ^{92}_{36}Kr + ^{141}_{56}Ba + 3^{1}_{0}n$$

6 Why can't we get energy by splitting a carbon nucleus into smaller pieces?

Energy from fusion

Before World War II, scientists had realised that it would be possible to release energy by fusing hydrogen nuclei together to make helium. The energy released by this fusion reaction can be calculated by finding the mass defect.

Helium can be formed by the fusion of two hydrogen isotopes, deuterium $^{2}_{1}H$, and tritium $^{3}_{1}H$:

$$^{2}_{1}H + ^{3}_{1}H \rightarrow ^{4}_{2}He + ^{1}_{0}n$$

The original mass was:

$2.0141\ u\ (^{2}_{1}H) + 3.0160\ u\ (^{3}_{1}H) = 5.0301\ u$

After the reaction the mass is:

$4.0026\ u\ (^{4}_{2}He) + 1.0087\ u\ (n) = 5.0113\ u$

This is a mass defect of

$5.0301\ u - 5.0113\ u$

$\quad = 0.0188\ u$

$\quad = 0.0188 \times 1.6604 \times 10^{-27}\ kg$

$\quad = 3.1216 \times 10^{-29}\ kg$

The energy released is given by

$E = mc^2$

$\quad = 3.1216 \times 10^{-29} \times (2.9979 \times 10^8)^2$

$\quad = 2.81 \times 10^{-12}\ J\ (about\ 18\ MeV)$

Fusion is capable of much greater energy output per kilogram of fuel than fission. One kilogram of deuterium and tritium fuel could produce about 1.2×10^{26} fusion reactions. This would release about 3.4×10^{14} J, enough energy to satisfy the UK's electricity requirements for several hours!

KEY FACTS

■ All nuclei weigh less than the combined mass of their protons and neutrons. The difference between the mass of a nucleus and the mass of its constituents is the mass defect.

■ The binding energy is the energy needed to split the nucleus back into its constituents. Binding energy, E, and mass defect, m, are related by the equation $E = mc^2$.

■ Energy is released when heavy nuclei decay by fission or when light nuclei fuse.

Nuclear fission reactors

Nuclear power and radioactivity

By 1989, when cold fusion hit the headlines, nuclear fission reactors were becoming more and more unpopular. The storage of nuclear waste was proving to be a major problem and the costs of nuclear technology were continuing to rise. The promise of cheap electricity had not been fulfilled. In addition, the tragedy at Chernobyl in 1986 convinced a sceptical public that nuclear power was dangerous as well as expensive.

Russian helicopter pilots flew 1800 missions over the reactor, dropping sand, boron and lead in an attempt to contain the fire and radioactive materials.

During a test, the power output of the Russian reactor surged to a point where the cooling system could not cope and the water boiled out of control. Rather like a huge pan of boiling water, the reactor blew off its lid. The 2500 tonne concrete shield tilted, lifted and fell back into the reactor. This caused a second explosion and fires which destroyed the core of the reactor. The reactor burnt for 10 days, scattering radioactive isotopes into the atmosphere.

The nuclear reactors in Great Britain are of a completely different design to Chernobyl, and although there have been some minor incidents, there has never been a major accident.

Advanced Gas-cooled Reactors (AGRs) supply most of Britain's nuclear electricity. They can generate about 600 MW of electrical power at an efficiency of approximately 35%. To achieve this, the reactor has to produce energy at a rate of around 1700 MW. Since each fission releases about 200 MeV, 5×10^{13} fissions are required each second. For a constant and safe power output this reaction rate has to be carefully controlled. Every fission needs a collision with a 'slow' neutron, so if we can control the number and speed of

The Advanced Gas-cooled Reactor, Hinkley Point 'B'.

the neutrons in the reactor, we can control the power output.

The chain reaction

Every time that a uranium nucleus decays by fission it releases a number of free neutrons. If these go on to cause further fissions a chain reaction will be established (Fig. 6).

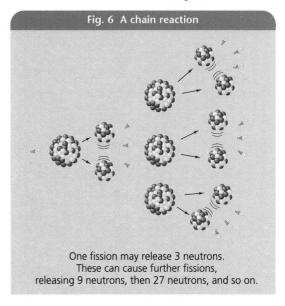

Fig. 6 A chain reaction

One fission may release 3 neutrons. These can cause further fissions, releasing 9 neutrons, then 27 neutrons, and so on.

In an AGR it takes around 1 ms for a neutron released by one fission reaction to cause another. If each fission released three neutrons, there would be 81 neutrons 4 ms later. If this process went on unchecked there would be a huge release of energy in a very short time.

7 If the chain reaction described above carried on for just $1/20^{th}$ of a second how much energy would be released?

The control rods

Not all the neutrons released by a reaction go on to cause another fission. To do that they have to be absorbed by another ^{235}U nucleus. There are a number of other things which can happen to the neutron (Fig. 7).

If the amount of uranium is too small, most of the neutrons will escape from its surface before they have caused any more fissions. There is a minimum mass, called the **critical mass**, which is needed before a chain reaction can take place. This mass depends upon the shape and purity of the uranium. In a reactor, the uranium fuel rods are all *below* the critical mass, but they are arranged so that neutrons from one rod may cause fission in an adjacent one (Fig. 8).

It can be quite difficult to sustain the chain reaction. Natural uranium is 1% fissile ^{235}U and 99% non-fissile ^{238}U, so fuel rods are made from enriched uranium which has a higher proportion of ^{235}U atoms. Even so, many neutrons will be absorbed by uranium-238 or by the fission products from previous reactions. These are called 'reactor poisons', as they soak up neutrons and kill off the chain reaction. On average, only one neutron from each fission should cause a further fission. Control rods are used to prevent the number of neutrons from becoming too large, enabling the reactor to run at constant power.

Control rods are usually made from a boron-steel alloy that absorbs neutrons. The rods can be raised or lowered into the reactor. A second set of control rods is held out of the reactor by electromagnets. If a power failure threatens the reactor's cooling system, the rods automatically drop in and shut the reactor down.

Moderation

The neutrons released from fission travel at around 1×10^7 m s^{-1}. They must be slowed to 2×10^3 m s^{-1} to have a good chance of causing another fission. The neutron has to lose 99.99975% of its kinetic energy before it can be absorbed by other nuclei. This is done in the **moderator**, where the neutron collides with the moderator atoms.

A good moderator reduces the kinetic energy of the neutron in as few collisions as possible. Ideally, the mass of the moderator's atoms should be similar to that of a neutron. In practice, most reactors use graphite or water as a moderator. On average, a neutron will travel 0.191 m through graphite before it can cause a new fission. This 'slowing-down' length is crucial in reactor design. In a nuclear-powered submarine, where space is at a premium, water is used as a moderator. Its slowing-down length is only 0.053 m.

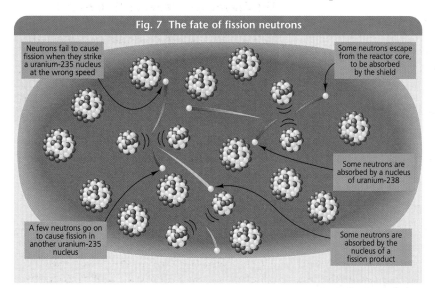

Fig. 7 The fate of fission neutrons

Neutrons fail to cause fission when they strike a uranium-235 nucleus at the wrong speed

Some neutrons escape from the reactor core, to be absorbed by the shield

Some neutrons are absorbed by a nucleus of uranium-238

A few neutrons go on to cause fission in another uranium-235 nucleus

Some neutrons are absorbed by the nucleus of a fission product

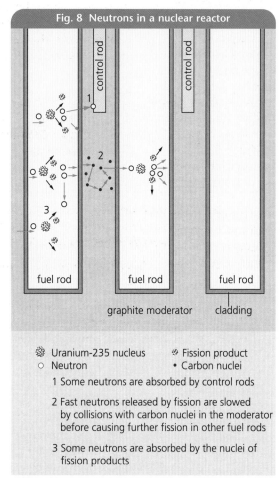

Fig. 8 Neutrons in a nuclear reactor

control rod
control rod
1
2
3
fuel rod
fuel rod
fuel rod
graphite moderator   cladding

🦠 Uranium-235 nucleus   ✿ Fission product
○ Neutron   • Carbon nuclei

1 Some neutrons are absorbed by control rods

2 Fast neutrons released by fission are slowed by collisions with carbon nuclei in the moderator before causing further fission in other fuel rods

3 Some neutrons are absorbed by the nuclei of fission products

8 When unused uranium fuel is stored, great care is taken to ensure that

a Only small amounts are stored in any one place.

b No water can enter the storage areas. Explain why these safety rules help to prevent fission.

9 The uranium fuel rods have to be removed from the reactor after several years, even though only a small fraction of the ^{235}U has been used. Why?

Negative feedback

Control rods are not the only defence against the chain reaction getting out of hand. If the rate of fission increases, then so does the temperature of the fuel and of the moderator. An increase in temperature reduces the number of neutrons that can be absorbed by uranium-235 and cause fission. For example, in a water-cooled reactor, the hotter the water the more it mops up neutrons. Also the hotter the moderator the less it slows down the

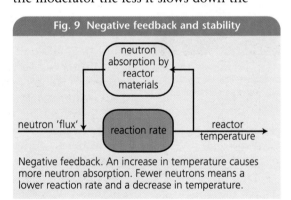

Fig. 9 Negative feedback and stability

Negative feedback. An increase in temperature causes more neutron absorption. Fewer neutrons means a lower reaction rate and a decrease in temperature.

neutrons, and so more neutrons are absorbed by uranium-238 instead of uranium-235. A chain reaction in a well-designed reactor is inherently stable – the behaviour of the materials provides some negative feedback (Fig. 9).

Out of control?

The Chernobyl disaster of 1986 spread nuclear waste isotopes – fission products – over a huge area. In countries far from the exploded reactor, such as France and the UK, thousands of people may yet die of cancer as a result of food and drink contaminated by Chernobyl's dust. This was one of the world's worst industrial accidents.

Chernobyl was not a nuclear explosion. Because of the design of the reactor and unauthorised experiments by the operating staff, the chain reaction did speed up and cause the reactor temperature to rise very quickly. It was boiling water that burst the reactor open. The hydrogen released from the water then exploded. It was an ordinary physical and chemical reaction, but the resulting fire sent a great deal of radioactive material up into the atmosphere. If the power plant had been designed with proper containment, the misery that followed would never have happened.

10
a What are thermal neutrons?
b What is the difference in behaviour of uranium-235 nuclei towards thermal and fast neutrons?

9.3 Reactor materials and design

Practising in a model of the reactor at the Three Mile Island nuclear installation. An accident in 1979 flooded the real building with hazardous radioactive material. Secondary containment ensured that the incident was not a full-scale environmental disaster.

The danger of releasing radioactive material into the environment means that containment for a nuclear power station is a primary concern. The Chernobyl nuclear power station was built to a design known as RBMK, a design unique to the old Soviet Union. The RBMK reactor only had what is called 'primary' containment – the reactor building itself – which had to contain all possible releases of radioactivity. All other designs of power station ever built have 'secondary' containment, an extra layer of containment built around the power station. Effective secondary containment costs, but it is a cost that has to be paid.

Choosing a coolant

In a coal or gas fired system, the pipes that carry the steam to the turbine come into close contact with the burning fuel. But in a nuclear power station there are two systems of pipes. The primary system transfers energy from the hot heart of the reactor where the nuclear processes are taking place. Then in a heat exchanger or steam generator the pipes of the primary system run close to pipes of a secondary system which carries the steam for turning the turbines (Fig. 10).

The reason for this double system is that coolant material near the fuel rods absorbs neutrons, so some of its nuclei become neutron-rich and radioactive. Such material must not be allowed to escape and is kept sealed within the primary cooling system. The steam that turns the turbines cannot be kept from contact with the atmosphere so easily. It flows in the secondary cooling system that has no direct contact with the reactor.

The coolant must, of course, be fluid: gas or liquid. A high specific heat capacity is desirable. Materials with high specific heat capacities can carry energy away very effectively without need for very high temperatures. A material with a low specific heat capacity can still be used provided that it flows quickly around the system, transferring energy quickly enough to match the rate of energy release by the chain reaction in the reactor.

The first French nuclear power stations were gas-cooled, using carbon dioxide (Fig. 10). Carbon dioxide is chemically inert and does not react with pipework. As a gas it can be pressurised and it can flow quickly around the pipes from reactor to steam generator. Another advantage is that neither carbon nor oxygen nuclei are strong absorbers of neutrons and therefore the gas does not become highly radioactive. It can be allowed

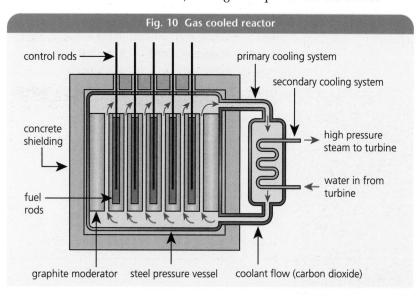

Fig. 10 Gas cooled reactor

control rods →

primary cooling system

secondary cooling system

concrete shielding →

high pressure steam to turbine

water in from turbine

fuel rods —

graphite moderator   steel pressure vessel   coolant flow (carbon dioxide)

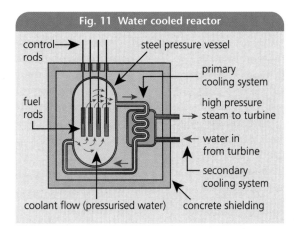

Fig. 11 Water cooled reactor

control rods

steel pressure vessel

fuel rods

primary cooling system

high pressure steam to turbine

water in from turbine

secondary cooling system

coolant flow (pressurised water)

concrete shielding

to pass out of the reactor's concrete shielding to the steam generator.

The Americans, however, developed smaller, water-cooled, systems for use in military submarines (Fig. 11). Water has a particularly high specific heat capacity. These reactors do not require a large block of graphite as a moderator because the coolant water itself has a moderating effect. They can therefore be quite small, and cheaper to build.

One disadvantage is that the hydrogen nuclei in the water are comparatively good neutron absorbers and become radioactive, so the water must always be kept inside the concrete shielding. Also, natural uranium is not suitable as a fuel for pressurised water reactors. The neutrons are not slowed enough by the water to maintain a chain reaction when the proportion of uranium-235 in the fuel is too small. The uranium must be enriched. French nuclear power stations built since the 1970s have been American-style pressurised-water reactors, or PWRs.

 Explain why the steam generator in a PWR must be inside the reactor shielding, whereas in a gas-cooled reactor it can be on the outside.

Nuclear submarines use much more compact water-cooled reactors.

 Describe one advantage and one disadvantage of water over carbon dioxide as reactor coolant.

Choosing moderator materials

The free neutrons produced by fission in the fuel rods are very energetic and not easily absorbed by nuclei of uranium-235. The moderator is there to slow the neutrons down so that they return into the fuel rods at thermal speeds and induce more fission to maintain a stable chain reaction.

A moderator should not have a high tendency to absorb neutrons. Once neutrons are absorbed, they cannot induce further fission and cannot contribute to the chain reaction. Also, the moderator would then become more radioactive. For example, 'heavy water', in which the hydrogen is a heavy isotope (hydrogen-2, also known as deuterium), is a better moderator than ordinary water. The heavier isotope of hydrogen is already neutron-rich and so has a low tendency to absorb more neutrons.

Water, heavy or not, contains nuclei which are quite small. When two objects collide the energy is more evenly shared if the particles have similar size. Neutrons colliding with large nuclei would lose only a small proportion of their energy on each collision – they would be inclined to bounce off with little change in their speed.

Gas cooled reactors use graphite (carbon) as the moderator. This, like heavy water, has the necessary low tendency to absorb neutrons, together with quite small particle size.

Choosing control rod material

Control rods that can be inserted and removed from a reactor make it possible for power station staff to control the fission rate. Control rods are made of materials that are good at absorbing neutrons (Table 3).

Table 3 Neutron absorption	
Nuclide	**Thermal neutron absorbing cross-section (barns)**
$^{1}_{1}H$	3.32×10^{-1}
$^{2}_{1}H$	5.30×10^{-4}
$^{12}_{6}C$	3.40×10^{-3}
$^{16}_{8}O$	2.70×10^{-4}
$^{238}_{92}U$	7.59
$^{10}_{5}B$	7.59×10^{2}
$^{114}_{48}Cd$	2.45×10^{3} 1 barn = 10^{-28} m^2

13 PWRs use water as their moderator as well as their coolant.

a If ordinary water is installed in a new reactor what will happen to the hydrogen nuclei under the influence of a constant stream of neutrons?

b Use data from Table 3 to consider whether absorption of neutrons by oxygen nuclei in the water is a problem.

c The water becomes radioactive. What sort of radiation does it then predominantly emit?

14

a Assuming that both momentum and kinetic energy are conserved, calculate the speed of a neutron initially travelling at 10^5 m s^{-1} that makes a direct hit on a stationary carbon nucleus in a reactor moderator block.

b If the temperature of a moderator is 800 K, use the kinetic theory equation,

$$\tfrac{1}{2}m\overline{c^2} = \tfrac{3}{2}kT$$

to calculate the speed of a thermal neutron within the moderator.

15

a Compare the required neutron-absorbing properties of coolant, moderator and control rod materials.

b Use the table to select two possible control rod materials.

16

a Calculate the minimum rate at which fuel rods must decrease in mass in a power unit with a 900 MW power output.

b Why will actual rate of mass loss be bigger than this?

9.4 Radiation safety

Workers must wear protective clothing in radioactive environments.

The high-energy neutrons that are emitted by a nuclear reactor are very dangerous. Neutron irradiation causes the casing and building around the reactor itself to become radioactive. The gas coolant and the graphite moderator absorb neutrons to become radioisotopes. The radiation from these, as well as directly from fission, means that there is a high gamma-ray output from the reactor.

The reactor shielding is designed to protect people from this radiation. Several metres of reinforced concrete are used as a radiation barrier, and as a pressure vessel to contain the gas coolant. Because concrete loses strength as it heats up, there is a carbon-steel lining which is cooled using water.

Occasionally it is necessary for people to work in radioactive areas. It is vital that they observe safety rules:

- Work quickly: this will reduce the total radiation dose.
- Work cleanly: disposable protective clothing is often worn.
- Keep your distance: alpha and beta rays have a limited range; they get absorbed or scattered by air molecules. If you stay a few metres away from these sources, you are unlikely to receive a significant dose. Gamma radiation, however, is not absorbed or scattered much by air so it has an almost infinite range. The **intensity** decreases with distance according to the **inverse square law** (see Chapter 10). In practice, if you move twice as far away from a gamma source, your radiation dose will drop to one quarter.

Nuclear waste

Nuclear fission produces radioactive waste. The quantities are quite small; each power station produces about 100 m³ per year, of which 95% is low-level waste. The fuel rods are reprocessed and much of the uranium is recovered, but the remaining cladding and fission products are very radioactive.

Daughter nuclei accumulate steadily as fission proceeds in a reactor. These nuclei have nearly the same ratio of neutrons to protons as their parent nucleus. That makes them neutron-rich compared with stable nuclides of their size (Fig. 12). This means the daughter nuclei are highly radioactive, usually have short half-lives and emit beta radiation.

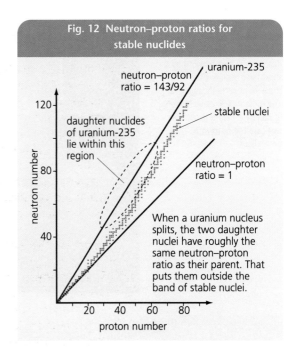

Fig. 12 Neutron–proton ratios for stable nuclides

This highly radioactive material is classed as 'high level' waste (Table 4) and is kept cool to compensate for the continuous energy release from radioactive decay. Because many of the daughter nuclides have short half-lives, the activity of the waste eventually falls and heating is no longer a problem. But some of the nuclides do have long half-lives, and, even after it is cool enough to handle, the material must be isolated so that it cannot irradiate the environment.

Table 4 Grades of radioactive waste	
Type	**Definition/radioactivity**
High level	separated fission products from irradiated fuels
Intermediate level	> 12 GBq per tonne (β and γ) > 4 GBq per tonne (α)
Low level	> 400 KBq per tonne

Nuclear fission also creates waste in another way. Fission produces neutrons set free from the splitting nucleus. Though some neutrons remain in the reactor and play an active part in keeping it going, a continuous flow of neutrons emerges from the reactor in all directions. The reactor materials and surroundings absorb these neutrons. The neutrons change the mass numbers of the nuclei which they join, producing isotopes which are usually radioactive. Thus all materials in and around a reactor become radioactive. Eventually they present another disposal problem. The 'decommissioning' of a

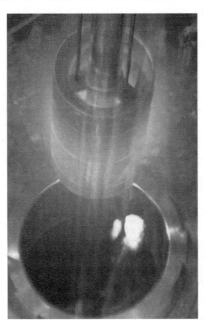

This used fuel element contains unused uranium and highly radioactive fission products. It is submerged in water to allow it to cool down. The blue glow is caused by energetic particles travelling through the water at speeds greater than that of light in water.

This gamma camera is scanning the head of a person suffering from bone cancer. The camera detects radiation emitted by a short-lived radionuclide that the patient recently ingested. The radionuclide concentrates in rapidly growing tissue – in this case the cancerous bone tissue.

power station at the end of its life must be done to the highest possible standard, which makes it a very expensive process.

There is one major benefit from the neutron flux. Radionuclides, especially gamma emitters, are useful as medical and industrial tracers. Patients can take in radioactive material by mouth or by injection, and gamma radiation detectors can then follow the material as it spreads around the body. Selected materials placed close to a reactor absorb neutrons and provide a supply of tracer nuclides.

EXTENSION

Making radioisotopes

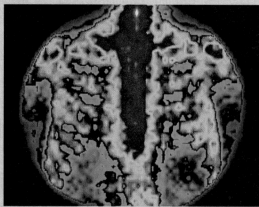

Radioisotopes are used in medicine as tracers and to produce images.

Fig. 13 Producing technetium-99

- lead shielding
- evacuated vial for Tc–99
- tap
- lead shielding
- alumina column
- sterile saline

The radioisotopes used in medicine and industry often have short half-lives. That means that they decay quickly and a regular supply of new material is needed.

There are four ways of producing radioisotopes:

Nuclear fission
Some heavy nuclei, like uranium or plutonium, decay by splitting into two. This process is called fission and the products may be useful radioisotopes. For example, caesium-137, which is used in radiotherapy, is produced by fission of uranium in nuclear fuel rods:

$$^{235}_{92}U + {}^{1}_{0}n \rightarrow {}^{236}_{92}U \rightarrow {}^{137}_{55}Cs + {}^{95}_{37}Rb + 4\,{}^{1}_{0}n$$

Neutron capture
A stable isotope can be placed in a nuclear reactor where there are high numbers of free neutrons. The nucleus can capture a neutron and become radioactive. Sodium-24 is made in this way:

$$^{23}_{11}Na + {}^{1}_{0}n \rightarrow {}^{24}_{11}Na + \gamma$$

Charged particle bombardment
Gallium-67 is a particularly useful radioisotope. Abnormal cells in tumours absorb the gallium-67 and show up on radiation scans. It can be produced in a charged-particle accelerator by bombarding zinc-68 with protons:

$$^{68}_{30}Zn + {}^{1}_{1}p \rightarrow {}^{67}_{31}Ga + 2\,{}^{1}_{0}n$$

A radionuclide generator
Molybdenum-99 is produced in a nuclear reactor. It decays into technetium-99, which has a half-life of 6 hours and only emits gamma rays of a single energy. This makes it ideal for medical imaging (Fig. 13).

This slab of glass contains all the high-level waste from a nuclear reaction that would supply a person with electricity for life.

Waste disposal

The nuclear industry has not yet solved the problem of long-term storage of nuclear waste. One plan is to embed this waste in glass, so that it cannot leak out, and bury it deep underground. In the meantime, the French nuclear industry separates high-level nuclear waste from the fuel rods during fuel 'reprocessing' and stores it at a base on the Channel coast.

Storing high-level nuclear waste so that it will remain securely confined is a real challenge. Some of it will be radioactive for thousands of years. In addition to plutonium, radionuclides like strontium and caesium have had to be stored. Strontium-90 is a very dangerous fission product, especially if swallowed. It has a half-life of 28 years and it emits beta particles with a maximum energy of 0.54 MeV.

To find the amount of energy produced by 1 kg of strontium-90 as it decays, we must first calculate the activity. 1 mole of strontium-90 has a mass of about 90 g.

90 g contains 6.022×10^{23} atoms, so 1 kg contains:

$6.022 \times 10^{23} \times 1000/90 = 6.69 \times 10^{24}$ atoms

The activity, A, of a source depends on the number of atoms, N (see Chapter 10).

$A = \lambda N$

where the decay constant is

$$\lambda = \frac{\ln 2}{T_{1/2}}$$

For strontium-90,
$\lambda = 7.85 \times 10^{-10} \text{ s}^{-1}$

So the activity is

$A = 7.85 \times 10^{-10} \times 6.69 \times 10^{24}$
$= 5.25 \times 10^{15}$ Bq

This is the *specific* activity, the activity per kilogram. Since each emitted beta particle carries 0.54 MeV, the energy released per second, i.e. the power, P, by each kilogram of strontium-90 is:

$P = 0.54 \times 10^6 \times 1.6 \times 10^{-19} \times 5.25 \times 10^{15}$
$= 450$ W

Since the beta particles will be stopped in a very short range, *all* this energy goes into heating the waste. Unless the heat is removed, the waste products become very hot indeed.

Supporters of nuclear power maintain that radioactivity decays with time, whereas mercury or cadmium dumped by other industries stay toxic for ever. Unlike fossil fuels, nuclear power does not contribute to the air pollution that causes acid rain or the greenhouse effect.

An energy source that would not pollute the air *or* create waste would solve many problems, particularly if its fuel was as abundant as sea-water. Such are the hopes for fusion.

Radioisotope heating can be a useful source of energy; NASA's space probe Galileo, launched in 1989, was powered in this way.

17 Plutonium-239 has a half-life of 24 000 years.

a How long before its activity has dropped to 1% of its original value?

b Why is this an underestimate of the total radioactivity due to plutonium waste?

18 When fuel rods are first removed from a nuclear reactor they are dropped into storage ponds where they are stored for up to a year, before being transported to Sellafield for reprocessing. Give two reasons why the rods need to be kept under water.

19
a Uranium-235 is radioactive. What radiation does it emit?

b Explain fully how and why the radiation emitted from used nuclear fuel, removed from the reactor, is not the same as the radiation emitted by new fuel.

20 The concrete shielding around a reactor prevents significant escape of neutrons by absorbing them.

a Concrete contains oxygen-16 chemically combined with other elements. Complete this nuclear reaction for an oxygen nucleus that absorbs a total of three neutrons:
$$^{16}_{8}O + 3\,^{1}_{0}n \rightarrow$$

b Show the nuclear reaction for the decay of the resulting oxygen nucleus. Use the Data section.

c What might be the effect of such decays on the strength of the concrete?

KEY FACTS

- Radioactive waste is classified as high, intermediate or low level.

- High-level waste arises in fuel rods after use because the fission products are highly radioactive.

- High-level waste is cooled under water and then securely stored indefinitely.

- Artificial radioisotopes are isolated from fission products or manufactured by allowing stable isotopes to absorb neutrons. These radioisotopes are used in medicine and as tracers.

9.4 Fusion

In the heart of the Sun, a chain of reactions is gradually turning hydrogen into helium and releasing energy (Fig. 14). The sequence of reactions begins when two protons ($^{1}_{1}H$) collide head-on and fuse to form deuterium:

$$^{1}_{1}H + ^{1}_{1}H \rightarrow ^{2}_{1}H + ^{0}_{+1}e \text{ (a positron)}$$

This reaction is so unlikely to occur that each proton in the Sun travels around for an average of 14 billion years before it reacts with another in this way.

One obstacle is that protons are positively charged. Electrostatic repulsion pushes them apart. Just like trying to compress a spring, the closer you push the protons together the stronger the force that keeps them apart. At a separation of 10^{-15} m the force of repulsion is about 200 N. This force is enough to push the protons apart with an acceleration of 10^{28} g. To overcome this enormous repulsion the protons have to approach each other at great speed, which demands very high temperatures. If the protons can get to within

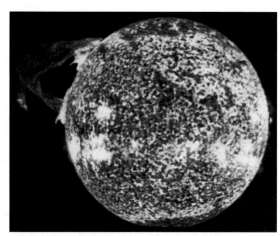

It is hardly surprising that power from fusion has eluded us for so long. After all, we are trying to harness the power which drives the stars.

10^{-15} m of each other, a force of attraction, called the **strong nuclear force**, takes over and pulls the protons together.

In the core of the Sun, the temperature is 15×10^6 K and the density is 12 times that

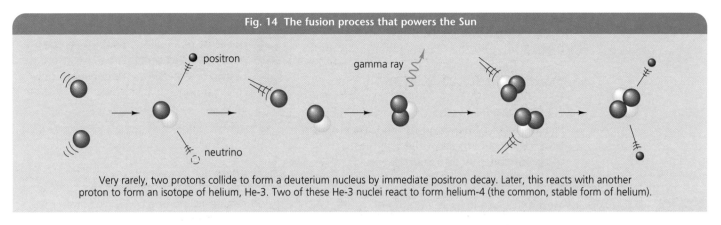

Fig. 14 The fusion process that powers the Sun

positron

gamma ray

neutrino

Very rarely, two protons collide to form a deuterium nucleus by immediate positron decay. Later, this reacts with another proton to form an isotope of helium, He-3. Two of these He-3 nuclei react to form helium-4 (the common, stable form of helium).

of solid lead. Even here, the reaction proceeds so slowly that it only generates about 20 W m^{-3}. The reaction is not suitable for a fusion reactor.

Fortunately there are more promising fusion reactions which we might be able to use here on Earth. Deuterium and tritium can react to make helium:

$$^2_1H + {}^3_1H \rightarrow {}^4_2He + {}^1_0n$$

This reaction releases about 18 MeV of energy and is relatively easy to achieve using a particle accelerator. It has been used in

Fig. 15 The JET fusion reactor

support limbs

outer polloidal field coil

toroidal field coil

inner polloidal field coil

vacuum vessel

hospitals to provide a beam of neutrons for radiotherapy. Unfortunately, more energy has to be put in than is released by the fusion reaction. For electricity generation you must get more energy out than you have put in, and so far that has not been achieved.

Hot fusion

One way to force deuterium and tritium together is to heat them to a temperature of around 100×10^6 K. At these temperatures – far higher than those in the Sun – deuterium and tritium are completely ionised. The mixture of ions and free electrons is a conducting gas called a plasma.

The Joint European Torus (JET) project at Culham has achieved temperatures of over 300 million degrees Celsius (Fig. 15). For fusion to occur, the plasma must be held together at a density of one thousandth of a gram per cubic metre. Strong magnetic fields are used to confine the plasma long enough for the reaction to become self-sustaining (Fig. 16).

Unfortunately, the hot plasma can become unstable and leak out of the magnetic trap. If it touches the walls of its vacuum

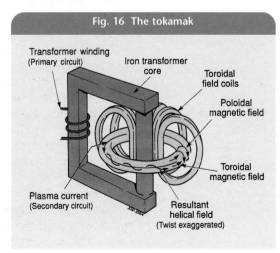

Fig. 16 The tokamak

Transformer winding (Primary circuit)

Iron transformer core

Toroidal field coils

Poloidal magnetic field

Toroidal magnetic field

Plasma current (Secondary circuit)

Resultant helical field (Twist exaggerated)

containment vessel then it becomes contaminated and cools. It has proved difficult to hold the plasma together long enough for much power to be generated, though fusion reactions have been achieved. In December 1993, an American team achieved a power output of 10 MW which lasted for 0.4 of a second, though they had to provide 33 MW to drive the reaction. The quest for controlled fusion continues.

21 Tritium has a half-life of 12 years and does not exist naturally on Earth. It can be made by allowing lithium-7 to absorb a neutron. Write down an equation for this reaction.

KEY FACTS

■ Nuclear fusion is difficult to achieve because of the electrostatic repulsion between nuclei.

■ Nuclear fusion releases more energy per kilogram of fuel than nuclear fission and produces no radioactive waste.

EXTENSION

Cold fusion

The cost of hot fusion research is high and there is little prospect of an early return on the investment. So when Fleischmann and Pons announced that they had achieved fusion in a test-tube full of cold water the whole world took notice.

Cold fusion is based on electrochemistry (Fig. 17). When water is electrolysed, the positively charged hydrogen ions travel to the cathode. Fleischmann used palladium as the cathode, since it absorbs hydrogen. Hydrogen ions migrate into the palladium and move freely around in the crystal lattice. The concentration of hydrogen within the metal can be very high. If 'heavy' water, deuterium oxide, is used as the electrolyte, then collisions and hence fusion between two deuterium nuclei might occur in the palladium.

Fleischmann and Pons measured the temperature rise in their electrochemical cells and found it to be higher than that due to the electrical current going in. They also claimed to have found other evidence in the form of neutron and gamma radiation. They were convinced that fusion was taking place.

Unfortunately, Pons and Fleischmann announced their results to the press before submitting them to the scrutiny of fellow scientists. Accusations were made that critical data had been mysteriously altered and, despite strenuous efforts, laboratories around the world failed to reproduce the results.

Theoretical physicists were openly sceptical. Pons and Fleischmann were claiming thousands of fusions per second, but that would require a mass of cold deuterium bigger than the Sun. Furthermore, the neutron radiation from that many reactions would have killed them!

Within a year of the 'discovery' most nuclear scientists returned to conventional avenues of fusion research. Today there are only a few enthusiasts still working on cold fusion. What seemed like a major scientific breakthrough now looks like the biggest wild goose chase of the twentieth century.

Fig. 17 A cold fusion electrolysis cell

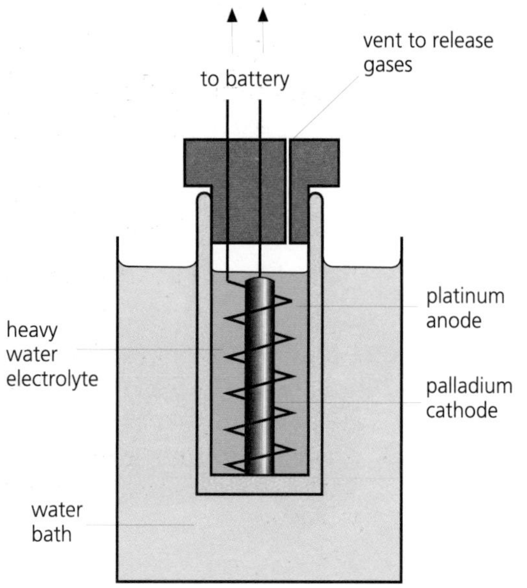

EXAMINATION QUESTIONS

1 a Nuclear fission can occur when a neutron is absorbed by a nucleus of uranium-235. An incomplete equation for a typical fission reaction is given below.

$$^{235}_{92}U + ^{1}_{0}n \rightarrow ^{141}_{56}Ba + X + 3 \, ^{1}_{0}n$$

(i) State the nuclear composition of X.

(ii) Name the element of which X is an isotope. (3)

b In a small nuclear power plant one fifth of the fission energy is converted into useful output power of 10 MW. If the energy released per fission is 3.2×10^{-11} J, calculate the number of uranium-235 nuclei which will undergo fission per day. (3)

(PH02 June 1999 Q2(part))

2 a Explain what is meant by the *binding energy* of a nucleus. (2)

Using data from the Data section, calculate the binding energy, in MeV, of a nucleus of ^{5}Li. (3)

(PH02 March 2000 Q2(part))

3 a (i) The iron isotope $^{56}_{26}Fe$ has a very high binding energy per nucleon. Calculate its value in MeV.

(ii) If the isotope $^{56}_{26}Fe$ were assembled from its constituent particles, what would be the mass change, in kg, during its formation? (6)

(PH06 June 2000 Q6)

4 a The diagram shows α-particle tracks from a radioactive source in a cloud chamber.

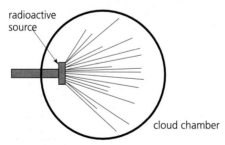

radioactive source

cloud chamber

(i) Explain how a track is produced by an α particle from the source.

(ii) What feature of the diagram shows that α particles are emitted with **two** distinct values of kinetic energy? (4)

b The isotope $^{212}_{84}Po$ is formed when $^{212}_{83}Bi$ decays. Complete the equation below representing this decay.

$$^{212}_{83}Bi \rightarrow ^{212}_{84}Po +$$ (1)

b (i) The $^{212}_{84}Po$ nucleus emits an α particle when it decays. Complete the equation below representing this decay.

$$^{212}_{84}Po \rightarrow ^{4}_{2}\alpha +$$

(ii) Show that the Q value for this change is 9.0 MeV.

(iii) A source containing $^{212}_{83}Bi$ and its daughter $^{212}_{84}Po$ emits α particles of kinetic energies 8.9 MeV and 9.7 MeV. Suggest an explanation for the emission of the α particle of kinetic energy 9.7 MeV. (4)

(AQA PH06 June 1998 Q4)

5 The results of electron-scattering experiments using different target elements show that the radius, R, of the nuclei varies with the nucleon number, A, of the target nuclei according to the equation

$$R = r_0 A^{1/3} \quad \text{where } r_0 = 1.3 \times 10^{-15} \text{ m.}$$

a Use this equation to show that the density of nuclear matter is independent of its mass. (3)

b The binding energy per nucleon of a large nucleus is about 8 MeV.

(i) Calculate the work done, in J, to remove a nucleon from a large nucleus.

(ii) State an approximate value for the range of the strong nuclear force.

(iii) Estimate the magnitude of the strong nuclear force between two neighbouring nucleons in the nucleus. (3)

(AQA PH06 June 1998 Q5)

6 a Explain why graphite is a suitable moderator in a thermal nuclear reactor. (3)

b Describe and explain **one** method of producing artificial nuclides. (2)

(AQA PH06 June 1998 Q6)

7 a The unstable uranium nucleus $^{236}_{92}U$ is produced in a nuclear reactor.

(i) Complete the equation which shows the formation of $^{236}_{92}U$.

$$+ \quad \rightarrow \quad ^{236}_{92}U$$

(ii) $^{236}_{92}U$ can decay by nuclear fission in many different ways. Complete the equation which shows one possible decay channel.

$$^{236}_{92}U \rightarrow ^{145}_{56}Ba + \quad + 4 \, ^{1}_{0}n$$ (2)

b Calculate the energy released, in MeV, in the fission reaction. (Atomic mass of $^{145}_{56}Ba = 144.92694 \, u.$)

10 Radioactivity

'To see a World in a Grain of Sand
And a Heaven in a Wild Flower,
Hold Infinity in the palm of your hand
And Eternity in an hour'

from *Auguries of Innocence*, William Blake

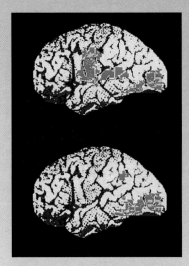

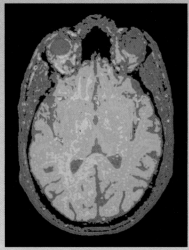

PET scans show a human brain performing a series of tasks related to words. The positron emission tomographic technique highlights areas of high blood flow, showing that different parts of the brain are used for each task.

Computerised X-rays scans are effective at showing the anatomy of the brain.

As you read a piece of poetry, a complex mixture of thought and emotion flows through your mind. Your brain is alive with activity. Some areas are busy with routine functions, like controlling your eye movements, while others are dealing with language and memory.

Until recently it has proved difficult to link particular areas of the brain with specific mental functions. The brain is awkward to examine. The skull is opaque to most parts of the electromagnetic spectrum and ultrasound is strongly reflected by bone. In the 1970s a new technique, known as X-ray computed tomography, or CT scanning, was developed. CT scanning uses beams of X-rays to produce detailed images of the brain, but it still cannot show the brain working.

Now scientists have found a way of watching the brain in action. Positron emission tomography, or PET, was developed during the early 1980s. A radioactive isotope is injected into the body and the radiation emitted from the brain is measured. The data is processed by computer to produce an image, rather like CT scanning, but there is one important difference. PET scans show activity rather than structure. By choosing a suitable radioisotope, it is possible to measure blood flow, oxygen consumption or glucose metabolism. A PET scan can actually 'see' you thinking.

PET scans are being used to investigate conditions such as depression and Alzheimer's disease. PET scans are also being used to investigate deeper questions. One day, PET scans may even help us to understand the nature of consciousness itself.

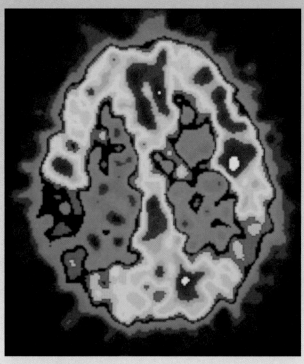

This scan shows the lesions in the brain that are typical of an Alzheimer's patient.

Ronald Reagan began suffering from Alzheimer's disease whilst he was still President of the United States of America. Alzheimer's is so common that 1 in 10 of us will suffer from it by the time we are 65. Symptoms include memory loss. There is currently no cure.

Rays from the nucleus

Nuclear structure

Radioactive chemicals were first used in medicine over 60 years ago to investigate thyroid disease. At that time the structure of the atomic nucleus was only just becoming clear (see *AS Physics*, Chapter 1). It is the nucleus that is entirely responsible for radioactivity.

The nucleus is made up of two different particles of roughly equal mass: protons and neutrons. Protons are positively charged and neutrons are uncharged.

The number of protons and neutrons in the nucleus varies from element to element. The most common form of carbon has six protons and six neutrons in its nucleus. Some forms of carbon have one or two extra neutrons. These different forms of carbon are called isotopes (Fig. 1).

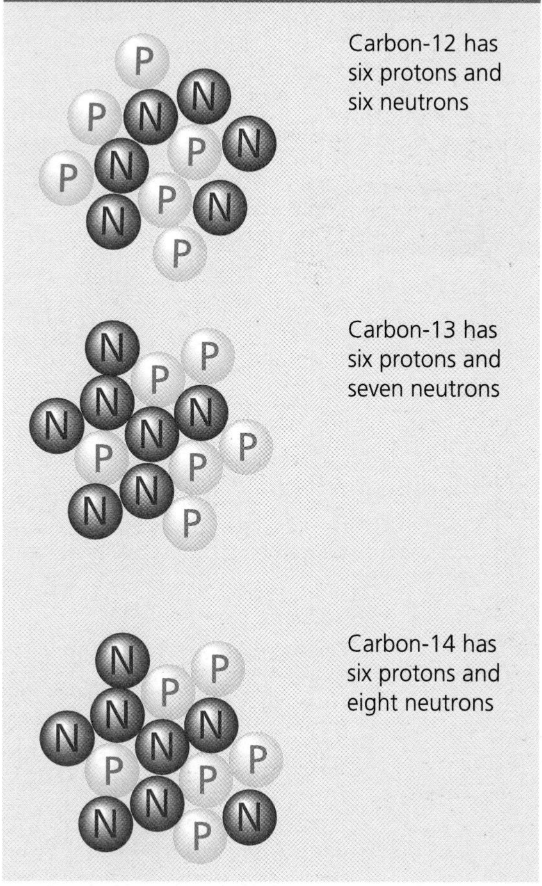

The nuclear composition of an isotope can be described using symbols. The most common isotope of carbon has six protons and six neutrons in its nucleus. It can be written as:

$$^{12}_{6}C$$

The upper figure is the nucleon number - the total number of protons and neutrons. The lower figure is the atomic number – the total number of protons. The nucleon number, sometimes called the mass number, is given the symbol A. In a neutral atom (one that has not been ionised) the atomic number, Z, is equal to the number of electrons in the atom.

Different isotopes of carbon all have the same atomic number. They all have six protons, but they may have more or less than six neutrons. For example, carbon-14 has eight neutrons and is written $^{14}_{6}C$. Although it is chemically identical to carbon-12, a major difference is that carbon-14 is radioactive. It is a **radioisotope**.

Radioisotopes are very useful to doctors. In the body they react just like the stable isotope, but we can trace their movement by the radiation they emit. All we need to do is choose the right radioisotope for each diagnostic test.

Fig. 1 C12, C13 and C14 isotopes

Carbon-12 has six protons and six neutrons

Carbon-13 has six protons and seven neutrons

Carbon-14 has six protons and eight neutrons

1 Iodine-131 was the first radioisotope to be used in medicine. It can be written $^{131}_{53}I$. How many protons, neutrons and electrons does an atom of this isotope have?

2 There are three naturally occurring isotopes of the simplest atom, hydrogen. The most common has just one proton in its nucleus. Deuterium has a neutron as well, and tritium has two extra neutrons. Write down nuclear symbols for the three isotopes of hydrogen.

KEY FACTS

■ Atomic nuclei consist of positively charged protons and uncharged neutrons.

■ A nucleus of element X can be described in symbols as: $^{A}_{Z}X$.

■ A, the nucleon number, gives the total number of protons and neutrons.

■ Z, the atomic number, gives the number of protons in the nucleus.

■ Isotopes of the same element are chemically identical to each other. They have the same number of protons and electrons, but the number of neutrons in their nuclei is different.

The discovery of radioactivity

The discovery of radioactivity owed something to chance. In 1896 Henri Becquerel was researching the action of light on fluorescent materials. He was investigating the possibility that light might cause these fluorescent materials to emit X-rays and so darken photographic plates. Becquerel's technique was to wrap the unexposed film in black paper and place a thin copper cross between the film and the fluorescent material he was investigating. He would then expose the fluorescent material, one of which was uranium salts, to sunlight. For some weeks his experiments had produced only negative results, and when the skies turned overcast he put all the apparatus, uranium salts, screen and film, into a dark cupboard to await sunnier weather. After four days of continuous cloud cover, Becquerel grew tired of waiting and decided to develop the film anyway. To his astonishment the photographic plate had darkened strongly, with the image of the copper cross standing out white against a dark background.

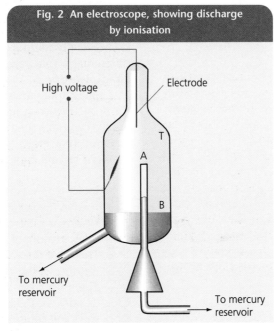

Fig. 2 An electroscope, showing discharge by ionisation

High voltage

Electrode

T

A

B

To mercury reservoir

To mercury reservoir

Becquerel reported that he had discovered a natural radiation that could penetrate paper that was opaque to light. He also found that these rays could ionise gases and so could discharge an electroscope (Fig. 2). Marie Curie and her husband Pierre took Becquerel's work further. They discovered other materials, thorium and radium, which also gave off ionising rays. In 1903 the Nobel Prize for Physics was awarded jointly to Becquerel and the Curies for the discovery of radioactivity.

The Curies gave Becquerel a small glass tube containing a few tenths of a gram of radium. He put it into his shirt pocket and forgot about it. As a result he suffered severe skin burns from the radiation that was emitted. Both Pierre and Marie Curie suffered from radiation sickness.

Activity

Some radioisotopes emit more radiation in a given time than others do. The *activity*, *A*, of a radioisotope is defined as the number of nuclei that decay in one second; this is equal to the number of emissions per second. Activity is measured in units of becquerels. If a source has an activity of 1 becquerel, 1 Bq, then on average, one of its nuclei decays every second. This is an extremely small unit and activities of kilobecquerel, kBq, or megabecquerel, MBq, are much more likely. Although the becquerel is the SI unit of activity, an older unit which is still commonly used is the curie, Ci. One curie is the number of disintegrations per second in one gram of radium; this is equivalent to 3.7×10^{10} Bq.

Alpha, beta and gamma rays

It quickly became clear that the rays that emanated from these radioactive elements were not all the same. Ernest Rutherford realised that there were at least two different sorts of rays. One type, which Rutherford called **alpha** (α) radiation, was easily absorbed. The other type, which was more penetrating, he named **beta** (β) radiation. A third type of very penetrating radiation became known as **gamma** (γ) rays.

Alpha radiation

Rutherford passed alpha radiation through strong electric and magnetic fields and showed that they carried a positive charge equal in magnitude to 2*e*, where *e* is the charge on the electron. The alpha particles were found to have a short range in air, only a few centimetres. Thin sheets of paper could also stop alpha particles. It took an ingenious experiment, completed in 1908, to show what an alpha particle actually was.

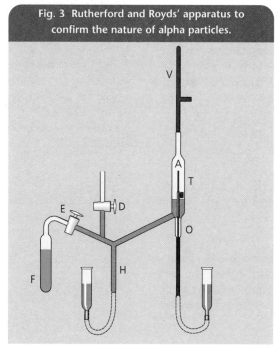

Fig. 3 Rutherford and Royds' apparatus to confirm the nature of alpha particles.

Rutherford and Royds sealed some radon gas into a thin-walled glass tube (labelled A in Fig. 3). The glass was thin enough to allow alpha particles to pass through it, but strong enough to withstand atmospheric pressure. The outer tube, T, was evacuated. After a few days the level of mercury, B, was raised to compress any gas that might have collected in the tube. A spark was passed between the two electrodes and the spectrum was observed. After six days all the spectral lines of helium were observed. Rutherford and Royds concluded that alpha particles were doubly charged helium atoms.

We now know that alpha particles are helium nuclei, a tightly bound group of two protons and two neutrons, with a charge of +2e and a mass of about 8000 times that of the electron. This combination of relatively large mass and strong electric field makes them highly ionising. As alpha particles pass through a material they have frequent collisions with atoms. The alpha's large kinetic energy means that it can easily knock an atomic electron out of its orbit. The alpha's large momentum means that it is hardly deflected by the collision. An alpha particle will undergo thousands of collisions in a short distance until it comes to a halt. After some time it will collect two electrons to become a neutral helium atom.

Alpha decay tends to occur in large nuclei. Inside the nucleus a stable group of two neutrons and two protons is formed. This is expelled from the nucleus at high speed. The emitting, or **parent**, nucleus is transformed into a new isotope, known as the **daughter**.

The total number of nucleons (protons and neutrons) is not changed by radioactive decay. The total charge is also left unchanged, so the sum of the atomic numbers must be the same before and after any emission.

In alpha decay, the daughter nucleus has a nucleon number, A, reduced by 4 and an atomic number, Z, reduced by 2 compared to the parent. We can represent this in a nuclear decay equation, using X as the symbol for the parent radioisotope and Y for the daughter. The alpha decay can be written

$$^{A}_{Z}X \rightarrow {}^{A-4}_{Z-2}Y + {}^{4}_{2}He$$

An example of an alpha emitter is radium-226. Radium-226 decays into radon, Rn, gas. This decay can be written

$$^{226}_{88}Ra \rightarrow {}^{222}_{86}Rn + {}^{4}_{2}He$$

Fig. 4 Alpha emission from uranium-238

$$^{238}_{92}U \longrightarrow {}^{234}_{90}Th + {}^{4}_{2}He(\alpha)$$

A uranium-238 nucleus is made up of 92 protons and 146 neutrons. It decays to thorium-234 (90 protons and 144 neutrons) by emitting an alpha particle (2 protons and 2 neutrons)

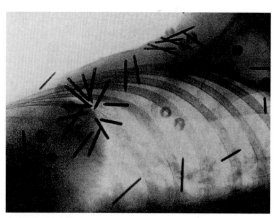

Alpha emitters, like these radium needles, are used to treat some cancers.

3 When alpha rays were first discovered, it was thought that they were not charged, since they did not appear to deviate when they travelled through electric and magnetic fields. Explain what the problem might have been with these early experiments.

4 An alpha particle is emitted with an energy of around 5 MeV. Suppose it takes 10 eV on average to ionise an atom. On average, how many ion pairs will an alpha particle create before it comes to a stop?

5 Radioisotopes that just emit alpha particles are not considered hazardous, provided that they are kept a few centimetres from the body. However they are extremely dangerous if they come into contact with the body, for example if they are swallowed or breathed in.
Explain why this is.

6 The radioisotope americium-241 ($^{241}_{95}$Am) is used in smoke detectors. It decays by alpha emission to neptunium (Np). Write an equation describing this nuclear decay.

Beta particles

Beta particles are much more penetrating than alpha particles. They have a range in air of several metres and can pass through thin sheets of an absorber like plastic or paper. Beta particles are deflected by a magnetic field much more easily than alpha particles and in the opposite direction. Beta particles are also deflected by an electric field in a way that shows them to be negatively charged.

Experiments using magnetic fields showed that beta particles have exactly the same charge-to-mass ratio as electrons. In fact we now know that beta particles *are* electrons, even though they are emitted from the nucleus. Beta decay occurs when one of the neutrons in an unstable nucleus decays into a proton and an electron. The proton remains in the nucleus but the electron is emitted at very high speed, often over 90% of the speed of light. Beta decay leaves the nucleon number of the radioisotope unchanged, since a neutron has simply been exchanged for a proton. This extra proton makes the atomic number increase by one. Beta decay can be written as:

$$^{A}_{Z}X \rightarrow {}_{Z+1}^{A}Y + {}_{-1}^{0}e$$

Beta particles cause ionisation by colliding with atomic electrons. Because the beta particle and the electron have the same mass, the beta particle may be widely deflected by a collision. Not all collisions will cause ionisation; some may simply excite the atomic electron to a higher energy level. Other collisions may just deflect the beta particle with little change in its kinetic energy. The beta particle has a much less densely ionising track than an alpha particle and its path will be more tortuous, especially as it begins to slow down.

7 The isotope carbon-14 is a beta emitter that decays into nitrogen, N. Write an equation to represent the decay

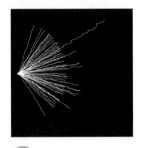

8 The cloud chamber pictures (above) show the tracks left by ionising radiation. Explain which tracks were made by alpha particles and which by betas.

9 An alpha particle and a beta particle are emitted with the same initial energy, say 1 MeV. Which would have the greater range in air? Explain your answer.

Fig. 5 The effect of electric and magnetic fields on alpha, beta and gamma rays

(a)

beta

gamma

alpha

++++ +++

In an electric field, α particles are deflected towards the negatively charged plate; β particles are deflected towards the positively charged plate; gamma radiation is undeflected.

(b)

N

S

alpha particles deflected

gamma radiation undeviated

beta particles deflected

Charged α and β particles are deflected at right angles to the magnetic field; gamma radiation is undeflected.

KEY FACTS

■ Unstable isotopes decay into other isotopes, emitting radiation in the process.

■ Unstable nuclei emit alpha, beta or gamma rays.

■ An alpha particle is a helium nucleus. An alpha decay can be written:

$$^A_Z X \rightarrow \, ^{A-4}_{Z-2} Y + \, ^4_2 He$$

■ A beta particle is a high-energy electron emitted from the nucleus. A beta decay can be written: $^A_Z X \rightarrow \, ^A_{Z+1} Y + \, ^0_{-1} e$

Gamma radiation

Soon after the discovery of radioactivity it was realised that at least part of the radiation was very penetrating indeed. In 1900 Paul Villard discovered that some rays could pass through thick sheets of metal and still have the ability to blacken photographic plates. He also discovered that the radiation could not be deflected by electric or magnetic fields (see Fig. 5). Villard had discovered gamma radiation.

Gamma rays are high-energy photons of electromagnetic radiation. They have no charge and no **rest mass**. Gamma rays can cause ionisation. However, the probability of interaction with an electron is lower than that for alpha or beta particles and so gamma

A cloud chamber photograph showing the ionisation caused by a gamma ray. Most of the tracks are made by secondary electrons, knocked out of their atoms by the gamma ray.

radiation is much less densely ionising.

Gamma emission changes the energy of the parent nucleus, but does not change its nuclear structure. To explain this we can think of energy levels within a nucleus, similar to those in the atom (See *AS Physics*, page 74). A nucleus may exist in an **excited** state, with more energy than usual. Sooner or later the nucleus will lose this excess energy by emitting a gamma ray.

A nucleus can be left in an excited state following an alpha decay. Alpha particles tend to be emitted with well defined energies (see Fig. 6); indeed some radioisotopes emit alpha particles which all have exactly the same energy. However, most alpha emitters emit particles that have an energy equal to one of a few specific values.

The parent isotope can decay by alpha emission to either an excited state of the daughter nucleus, or to its ground state. If the daughter nucleus is in an excited state, it will later emit a gamma ray.

Some isotopes have relatively long-lived excited states. One of these is technetium-99. Technetium is produced from the decay of molybdenum and has a half-life of 6 hours. Technetium decays by emitting gamma rays of a single energy. This makes it ideal for use in medical imaging.

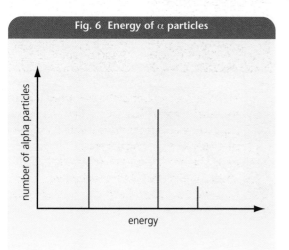

Fig. 6 Energy of α particles

number of alpha particles

energy

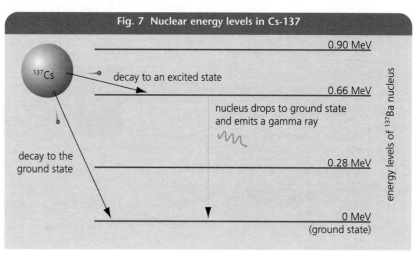

Fig. 7 Nuclear energy levels in Cs-137

^{137}Cs

decay to an excited state

0.90 MeV

0.66 MeV

nucleus drops to ground state and emits a gamma ray

decay to the ground state

0.28 MeV

energy levels of ^{137}Ba nucleus

0 MeV
(ground state)

10 Calculate a value for the wavelength of a gamma ray emitted with an energy of 1 MeV. (Remember that the energy of a photon (in joules) is given by $E = hf$. You will also need to convert electronvolts to joules, 1 eV = 1.6×10^{-19} J.)

11 Calculate the possible gamma ray photon frequencies emitted from a sample of caesium-137 (see Fig. 7).

Gamma rays and the inverse-square law

All radiation that emanates from a point source spreads out, or dissipates, according to the inverse-square law. This could be the light from a small bulb or the infrared radiation from a star. The inverse-square law predicts that the intensity, I, of radiation at a distance, x, from a source of intensity I_0, will be given by:

$$I = \frac{kI_0}{x^2} \quad \text{where } k \text{ is a constant.}$$

The inverse-square law is only exactly true in a vacuum where there are no atoms or molecules in the way to absorb any of the energy. Because gamma rays are very penetrating, and are absorbed only slightly by air at atmospheric pressure, the inverse-square law is a good approximation for describing the intensity of gamma rays in air. This can be shown experimentally in the laboratory using the apparatus shown in Fig. 8.

The source used in a school laboratory is usually a small piece of cobalt-60 in a sealed holder. A Geiger–Muller (GM) tube is used to detect the ionisation caused by the gamma source. The digicounter displays the count-rate, R, which is the number of ionisations detected per second. This will not be the same as the number of gamma photons that pass through the detector because gamma rays are not heavily ionising and the Geiger–Muller counter is not very efficient (less than 1%) at detecting them. On average this will affect all readings by the same factor and should not affect the verification of the inverse-square law.

Background radiation from the surroundings will be detected. This will have a proportionally larger effect on low count-rates and so we must make some allowance for background radiation. This can be done by taking several readings of the count-rate, whilst the radioisotope is kept in its lead-lined box at some distance from the apparatus. This background reading is then subtracted from all the other readings to give the **corrected count-rate**, C.

The corrected count-rate needs to be observed at a number of different separations, x, between the source and the detector. Because radioactive decay is a random event the readings at any given distance will vary. Each reading should be repeated several times and an average count calculated.

A small uncertainty in the distance measurement is introduced partly because it is difficult to tell exactly where the source is inside its sealed container, and partly because the sensitive area of the GM tube is somewhere inside the tube. If these add a total distance, d, to the results we should get:

Corrected count-rate,

$$C \propto \frac{1}{(x + d)^2} \quad \text{or} \quad x + d = \frac{k}{\sqrt{C}} \quad \text{so} \quad x = kC^{-\frac{1}{2}} - d$$

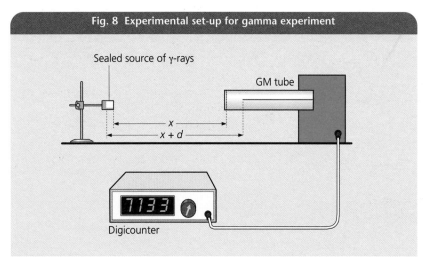

Fig. 8 Experimental set-up for gamma experiment

Sealed source of γ-rays

GM tube

x

$x + d$

Digicounter

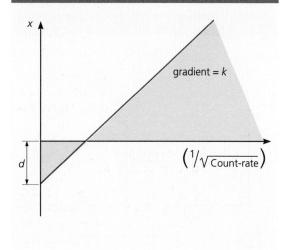

Fig. 9 Graph to verify the inverse-square law for gamma radiation.

x

gradient = k

d

$\left(\frac{1}{\sqrt{\text{Count-rate}}}\right)$

Table 1 Summary of the properties of alpha, beta and gamma radiation

	Alpha	Beta	Gamma
structure	2 protons and 2 neutrons	an electron	very short wavelength electromagnetic wave
symbol	^4_2He (a)	$^{\ 0}_{-1}\text{e}$ (β)	(γ)
range in air	a few cm	a few metres	infinite
ionising ability	very strong	strong	weak
penetration (stopped by)	paper, skin	aluminium, a few cm of flesh/bone	reduced significantly by several metres of lead/concrete
charge	+2e	-1e	0
mass (kg)	6.644×10^{-27}	9.109×10^{-31}	zero rest mass

If we compare this to the equation for a straight line, $y = mx + c$, we can see that a graph of distance (y-axis) against $C^{-\frac{1}{2}}$ (x-axis) should give a straight line with a gradient of k and an intercept of $-d$.

14 The following data were collected from an experiment to measure the gamma ray count-rate at different distances from a sample of cobalt-60. The background count was measured five times.

Background count (per minute)
= 12 14 10 15 12

Count on GM tube (per minute)	413	161	92	60	43	40	35	26	23
Distance between source and GM tube (cm)	1.0	2.0	3.0	4.0	5.0	6.0	7.0	8.0	10.0

12 Why doesn't the inverse-square law generally apply to alpha and beta radiation? Under what circumstances would the law apply to an alpha or beta source?

13 Why should the cobalt-60 used in the experiment above always be handled with tongs? (Give two reasons.)

a Plot a suitable graph to verify the inverse square law.

b Use your graph to estimate the extra distance, d, between the source and the detector (see Table 1).

c Which readings are the most unreliable?

d Suggest improvements to the way that readings are taken in this experiment.

KEY FACTS

■ During gamma decay the nucleus loses energy but does not change to a different isotope.

■ Nuclei can exist in an excited state, following alpha decay for example. An excited nucleus returns to its ground state via gamma emission.

■ Gamma radiation obeys the inverse-square law:

$$I = \frac{kI_0}{x^2}$$

APPLICATION   A dose of radiation

The remains of the nuclear reactor at Chernobyl.

800 000 volunteers were used as 'liquidators' to put out the fires that raged for 10 days in the reactor. They worked for 10 minutes at a time, shovelling debris over the reactor, burying waste and finally sealing the reactor in concrete.

Early in the morning of April 26th 1986 the nuclear reactor at Chernobyl in northern Ukraine went out of control. The power in the core reached 100 times the safe level and the resulting explosions blew the 2000 tonne metal and concrete lid off the reactor. Deep inside the reactor the core itself was burning. The rising smoke and hot gases carried radioactive isotopes high into the atmosphere where the wind scattered them over the entire Northern Hemisphere.

Chernobyl was the worst accident involving radiation that the world has yet seen. In the first few days after the Chernobyl accident many brave fire fighters exposed themselves to large doses of radiation. Within a few weeks thirty of them were dead from acute radiation sickness. Later, children caught in the fall-out began to suffer different effects, such as leukaemia and cancers of the thyroid.

Some of the effects of radiation may take thirty years to appear and these long-term effects are hard to quantify. We cannot be sure whether people who suffer from a genetic disease, or an illness such as cancer, were actually affected by radiation or whether their disease was due to some other cause. Estimates of the deaths from cancer and other diseases due to the Chernobyl disaster vary widely, from 5000 to 500 000.

The effect of radiation on cells

The effect of radiation on the human body depends strongly on the dose of radiation that is received. Absorbed radiation dose is the amount of energy deposited in a kilogram of material. This is measured in joules per kilogram, or gray (Gy). A radiation dose of more than 10 Gy is likely to be fatal.

The type of radiation is also important; alpha particles can cause ten times the damage of beta or gamma rays. To understand why we must consider the effect of radiation on living cells. Radiation can kill or damage cells in a number of ways. It is the nucleus of the cell that is particularly sensitive to radiation. In each nucleus there are 46 chromosomes which each contain strands of DNA, the chemical that carries the genetic code for life. Ionising radiation can damage the DNA directly, by removing electrons from atoms and thereby causing chemical changes. Radiation can also have an indirect effect by causing chemical changes in the cell, which eventually damage the DNA.

Radiation-induced damage to DNA does not always cause the death of a cell. Human cells have a repair mechanism that allows the DNA to be restored. This is not surprising since the DNA in a normal human cell is constantly being broken and restored about 10 000 times every hour. The ability of a cell to repair itself depends on the type of damage to the DNA helix. A break in a single strand may be quite easy to repair, since the second strand of the helix acts as a template, but a double break may be irreparable. Radiation that is densely ionising, such as an alpha particle, is more likely to cause double or compound breaks in DNA. The **radiation dose equivalent**, measured in sieverts (sv), takes this into account.

Table 2 Whole-body radiation syndromes		
Absorbed dose	Typical lifespan after irradiation	Symptoms
> 100 Gy	Minutes to 48 hrs	Central nervous system damage. Epileptic fits, coma and respiratory failure.
10–100 Gy	Between 5 and 14 days	Gastro-intestinal damage. Vomiting, diarrhoea, dehydration and starvation.
2-10 Gy	10–30 days	Bone marrow damage. Acute anaemia, internal bleeding and low resistance to infection

Fig. 10 Possible effects of radiation on DNA

(a) DNA - Double-helix molecule

(b) Single breaks in the DNA are easy to repair

(c) densely ionising radiation can cause a break in both strands of the DNA molecule

(d) compound breaks may be impossible to repair

Densely ionising radiation is more likely to cause a double break in the DNA. The accumulated damage may be impossible to repair.

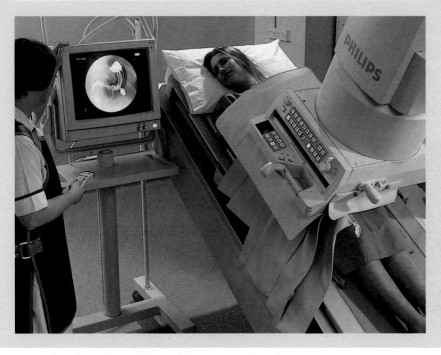

Permanent damage to the DNA does not always result in cell death. A cell that has been irradiated may form an abortive or slow-growing colony, or it may divide abnormally and eventually result in a cancer. Non-fatal changes in the DNA may be passed on from irradiated parents to their children. Any increase in the number of these mutations is likely to increase the risk of spontaneous abortions and genetic diseases in the next generation.

15 An internal exposure to alpha radiation may cause far more damage to cells than a larger dose of gamma rays. Explain why this is the case.

16 Strontium-90 is a beta emitting radioisotope that occurs as a by-product of nuclear fission. It is chemically similar to calcium which the body uses to make bone. Explain why ingesting strontium-90 is particularly dangerous.

Radiation has a general life-shortening effect. A study of radiologists in the USA in the 1960s found that the mean lifespan of men exposed to radiation throughout their working lives was only 60.5 years. This compared to a mean age of death at that time of 65.7 years for the general population. A similar study in the UK found no such evidence, but radiation precautions were implemented earlier in the UK and were more rigorous than those in America.

KEY FACTS

- Radiation can kill or damage cells by directly changing DNA in the nucleus or by indirect chemical action.

- Alpha particles cause more damage than beta particles or gamma rays.

- Large doses of radiation lead to acute effects that can be fatal.

- Lower doses of radiation lead to delayed effects, principally cancers and leukaemia.

10.2 Background radiation

Scientists make the assumption that there is no 'safe' level of radioactivity; even low doses carry some risk. One way of assessing when this risk has reached an acceptable level is to compare the radiation dose with that due to background radiation.

We live in a radioactive world. We are continually exposed to radiation from the sky above us and from the ground we walk on. We get an internal dose from the air we breathe and the food we eat. The total dose that we receive due to this background radiation varies from place to place, but the average dose in Britain is 2.5 mSv per year. Most of this, about 2.2 mSv, comes from natural sources. Artificial sources contribute another 0.3 mSv, although this will vary widely from person to person.

Sources of background radiation

1 Cosmic radiation:

The Earth is constantly bombarded by a shower of high-energy particles and gamma rays from the Sun and from other sources outside our solar system. The atmosphere acts as a shield and reduces the dose at sea level to about 0.3 mSv (Fig. 12). On average just over one hundred cosmic rays will pass through you each second, though the actual number varies from place to place. There is a larger dose at the poles than there is at the equator because the Earth's magnetic field diverts some of the radiation.

2 Radiation from rocks:

Most of the radioactivity in rocks arises from the decay products of uranium-238 and thorium-232, two radioisotopes with a very long half-life which have been present on

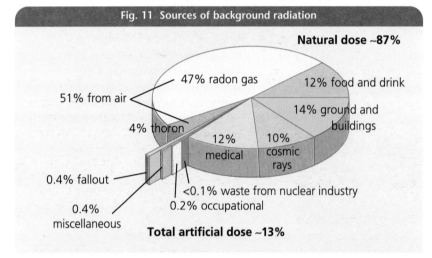

Fig. 11 Sources of background radiation

Natural dose ~87%

47% radon gas
51% from air
4% thoron
12% food and drink
14% ground and buildings
12% medical
10% cosmic rays
0.4% fallout
<0.1% waste from nuclear industry
0.2% occupational
0.4% miscellaneous

Total artificial dose ~13%

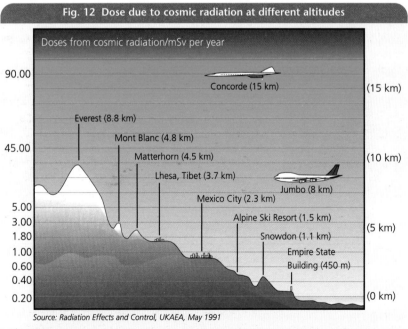

Fig. 12 Dose due to cosmic radiation at different altitudes

Doses from cosmic radiation/mSv per year

Concorde (15 km)   (15 km)
Everest (8.8 km)
Mont Blanc (4.8 km)   (10 km)
Matterhorn (4.5 km)
Lhesa, Tibet (3.7 km)
Jumbo (8 km)
Mexico City (2.3 km)
Alpine Ski Resort (1.5 km)
Snowdon (1.1 km)   (5 km)
Empire State Building (450 m)
(0 km)

Source: Radiation Effects and Control, UKAEA, May 1991

Concorde flies at an altitude of about 15 km. A transatlantic trip in Concorde will add about 20 microsievert to your annual dose. This is 20% less than travelling by Jumbo jet. Although the jumbo flies lower, the journey takes much longer.

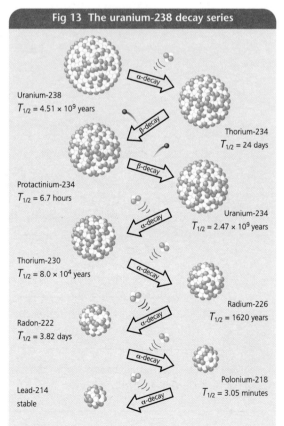

Fig 13 The uranium-238 decay series

Uranium-238
$T_{1/2} = 4.51 \times 10^9$ years

α-decay

β-decay

Thorium-234
$T_{1/2} = 24$ days

β-decay

Protactinium-234
$T_{1/2} = 6.7$ hours

Uranium-234
$T_{1/2} = 2.47 \times 10^9$ years

α-decay

Thorium-230
$T_{1/2} = 8.0 \times 10^4$ years

α-decay

Radium-226
$T_{1/2} = 1620$ years

α-decay

Radon-222
$T_{1/2} = 3.82$ days

α-decay

Polonium-218
$T_{1/2} = 3.05$ minutes

Lead-214 stable

α-decay

Earth since it was formed (see Fig. 13). For most people this radiation adds about 0.5 mSv to their annual dose, but some places are much more radioactive.

Radioactive isotopes still exist on Earth because of long decay series like that due to uranium-238. Each stage in the decay has its own half-life and some of these are thousands of years.

A week's holiday in Cornwall will add about 0.13 mSv to your radiation dose, slightly more than the dose from two chest X-rays. The dose is partly due to gamma radiation from the ground and buildings but mainly from radon in the air.

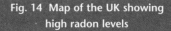
Fig. 14 Map of the UK showing high radon levels

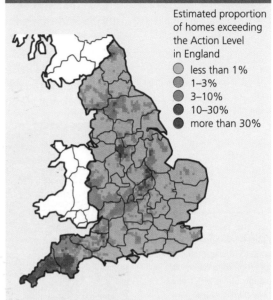

Estimated proportion of homes exceeding the Action Level in England
- less than 1%
- 1–3%
- 3–10%
- 10–30%
- more than 30%

The average radon level in homes in the UK is about 20 Bq m^{-3}. 100 000 homes are thought to have radon levels above 200 Bq m^{-3}, the Action Level set by the government. At this level, the lifetime risk of lung cancer is estimated to be 10 cases per 1000 people. Smoking 15 cigarettes per day gives a lifetime risk of 100 cases of lung cancer per 1000 people.

3 Radiation from the air:

Radon gas in the air that we breathe is by far the most significant source of background radiation (Fig. 14). Radon gas is formed as part of the decay series of uranium-238 and it seeps upwards through fissures in the rock. We get our main exposure to radon gas inside buildings where it can accumulate (Fig. 15). Improvements in home insulation, like double-glazing and draught-proofing, have reduced the ventilation in houses so that very high levels of radon can build-up. When we breathe in radon gas our lungs are irradiated by radon and its daughter products, polonium-214 and polonium-218, which are all alpha emitters. Long-term exposure to radon may increase the incidence of lung cancer.

Radon dissolved in water also contributes to our radiation dose. Boiling the water releases most of the radon so the main intake is from drinking cold water. A greater risk is in the bathroom where concentrations are often 40 times higher than in living rooms. Radon is released into the air during a shower and it takes several hours for the room to return to normal radon levels.

Fig. 15 Radon gas in buildings

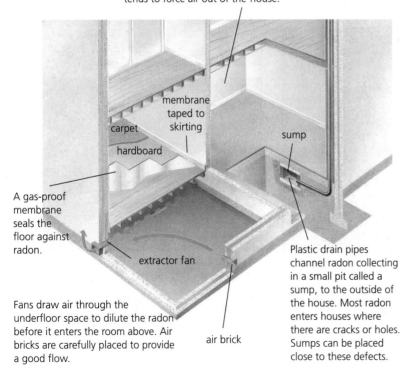

Fans fitted in the loft create slightly higher pressure, which tends to force air out of the house.

membrane taped to skirting

carpet

hardboard

sump

A gas-proof membrane seals the floor against radon.

extractor fan

Plastic drain pipes channel radon collecting in a small pit called a sump, to the outside of the house. Most radon enters houses where there are cracks or holes. Sumps can be placed close to these defects.

air brick

Fans draw air through the underfloor space to dilute the radon before it enters the room above. Air bricks are carefully placed to provide a good flow.

4 Radiation from food and drink:

Radioactive materials become dissolved in water and are taken up by plants and animals. All food and drink is radioactive to some extent, though some foods, like tea, coffee, brazil nuts and even bread are slightly more radioactive than others. Because we ingest radioactive materials, we are all radioactive at a level of about 50 Bq kg^{-1}.

Most of the radioactivity in our bodies is due to potassium-40 which tends to concentrate in muscle. Living with a body builder will increase your radiation dose!

5 Radiation from artificial sources:

We get around 12% of our annual radiation dose from artificial sources of radiation, mainly from medical procedures. Diagnostic X-rays are the most common source of medical radiation. A chest X-ray gives a dose of around 0.05 mSv whilst an X-ray of the lower abdomen could easily give a dose of ten times this amount. Much larger doses are given to some cancer patients during their radiotherapy treatment. Patients typically

In 1954 the USA exploded its first full scale hydrogen bomb near Bikini Atoll. Four hours later fall-out settled on the nearby Marshall Islands. The islanders suffered acute radiation sickness, skin burns and hair loss. They received a dose that was 25 times greater than the maximum lifetime dose. Two days later the US government evacuated the islanders.

receive a dose of a few thousand mSv, though the dose is likely to be spread over several sessions.

Nuclear medicine involves the injection of a radioisotope into the body to diagnose certain diseases. The use of these techniques is now growing and we now get an average dose of 0.02 mSv per person each year.

Atmospheric testing of nuclear weapons has spread radioisotopes across most of the world; these contribute a small but measurable amount to our annual radiation dose.

6 Miscellaneous sources of radiation cover a wide range of consumer products. Radium was widely used to paint luminous watch faces until it was replaced by tritium in the 1960s. Tritium is safer than radium, being a beta emitter, and it is now used in fluorescent exit signs. Thorium is used in the mantles of gas lamps used for camping. Industrial and research establishments contribute about 0.3% to the average annual dose.

Nuclear power contributes a small average dose to the population as a whole, only about 0.001 mSv per year.

Smoke detectors contain americium-241, an alpha emitter with a half-life of 432 years.

Sitting too near to the TV is bad for your health. There is a small X-ray dose from the screen. Men in the USA receive an average annual dose to their gonads of 0.01 mSv from watching TV.

10.3 Radioactive decay

Radioactivity has an unusual property; there is no observable cause that triggers a decay. It is not possible to predict when a given nucleus will decay, nor is it possible to stimulate a nucleus to emit radiation. We say that radioactivity is **random** and **spontaneous**.

The random nature of radioactivity means that there is no way of knowing exactly when a particular nucleus will decay. The most we can say is that the nucleus of a given radioisotope has a certain probability of decay in a given time. Radioactive decay is like playing dice. Although you never know exactly when you will get a six, you know that in every 6000 throws of the dice, roughly 1000 will show a six. In a radioisotope there are millions of nuclei, and though we don't know when individual nuclei will decay, we can still make an accurate prediction of the number of nuclei that will decay in each second.

Radioactivity is not influenced by external factors. It is not possible to change the rate at which a nucleus will decay by subjecting a radioisotope to high pressure or temperature, or by using strong electric fields. Neither is it affected by chemical change. We can be sure that the count-rate from a radioisotope will not be affected by its surroundings.

The **activity** of a sample of a given radioisotope is affected by just one thing, the number of nuclei that are present. The activity of the sample can be increased by adding more radioisotope, just as the number of sixes thrown can be increased by rolling more dice.

The activity, A, is proportional to the number of nuclei, N:

$$A \propto N \quad \text{or} \quad A = \lambda N$$

The constant of proportionality, λ, is different for each radioisotope. It is known as the **decay constant**. The decay constant is a measure of how likely a radioactive decay is (Table 3). To see this more clearly we can think of the activity as the rate of decrease of the radioactive nuclei:

$$A = -\frac{\Delta N}{\Delta t}$$

(The number of radioactive nuclei always gets less, so ΔN is negative.)
Eliminating A from the equation gives:

$$\frac{\Delta N}{\Delta t} = -\lambda N$$

We can rearrange this to get a better idea of what the decay constant means:

$$\lambda = -\frac{\Delta N}{N \Delta t}$$

The decay constant is the fraction of nuclei that decay every second. For any particular nucleus, λ is the probability that it will decay in one second.

Table 3 Radioisotope data				
Radioisotope	**Emission**	**Half-life**	**Decay constant (s⁻¹)**	**Comments**
^{5}helium	neutron	6×10^{-20} s	1.15×10^{19}	This stuff doesn't hang around!
^{99}technetium	gamma	6 hours	3.2×10^{-5}	Used in over 90% of nuclear medicine tests
^{131}iodine	beta, gamma	8.05 days	9.9×10^{-7}	Used in the diagnosis and treatment of thyroid disease
^{239}plutonium	alpha	24 000 years	9.2×10^{-13}	Nuclear waste product from fission reactors
^{238}uranium	alpha	4.5×10^9 years	4.4×10^{18}	The most common naturally occurring uranium isotope

KEY FACTS

- Radioactive decay is spontaneous and random. The activity is proportional to the number of nuclei, N.

- $A = -\dfrac{\Delta N}{\Delta t} = \lambda N$,

  where λ is the decay constant.

Testing for thyroid disease

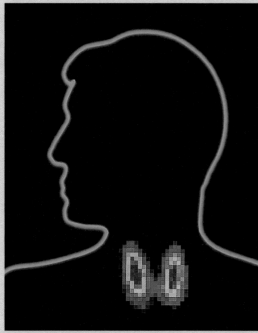

Use of gamma source in a thyroid examination

Radioactive iodine is used to diagnose thyroid disease. The thyroid gland uses iodine to manufacture thyroxin, a hormone that controls metabolism. A patient with a hyperactive thyroid gland will be overactive and will lose weight. A normal gland contains about 25% of the body's iodine, but a hyperactive gland may take up almost all of the available iodine. We can monitor the performance of the thyroid by measuring how quickly it takes up iodine. If a patient drinks a solution of sodium iodide,

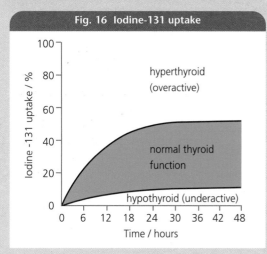

Fig. 16 Iodine-131 uptake

containing a small amount of radioactive iodine-131, a detector can be used to count the rate of gamma-ray emission from the thyroid over the next few hours. This count-rate can be plotted against time and compared with a curve for a normal thyroid (Fig. 16).

If the patient needs a dose of iodine-131 with an activity of 2 MBq, we need to be able to calculate the right mass of radioisotope to administer.

We must first calculate the number of atoms that are needed. The activity $A = 2$ MBq and the decay constant for iodine-131 is $\lambda = 9.9 \times 10^{-7}$ s^{-1}, so from:

$$A = \lambda N$$

we have

$$N = \frac{A}{\lambda} = \frac{2 \times 10^6 \text{ Bq}}{9.9 \times 10^{-7} \text{ s}^{-1}} = 2 \times 10^{12} \text{ atoms}$$

To calculate the mass of 2×10^{12} atoms of iodine-131 we need to use the concept of the **mole**.

The mole is the SI unit for number of particles, such as atoms or molecules. It is defined in terms of the stable isotope carbon-12.

A **mole** is the amount of a substance that contains the same number of particles as there are atoms in 12 g of the isotope carbon-12.

There are 6.022×10^{23} atoms in 12 g of carbon-12. This number is called the Avogadro constant, N_A. The nucleon number of any isotope tells you approximately what the mass of 1 mole will be in grams.

This means that 1 mole (6.022×10^{23} atoms) of iodine-131 will have a mass of approximately 131 g. Therefore, we need

$$\text{Mass} = 2 \times 10^{12} \times \frac{131 \text{g}}{6.02 \times 10^{23}}$$

$$= 4 \times 10^{-10} \text{g}$$

17 A 5×10^{-10} g dose of technetium-99 is given to a patient undergoing thyroid tests. Estimate the initial activity of this mass, using data from Table 3.

10.4 Half-life

The use of iodine-131 in diagnosis has declined in the last few years, although it is still used to *treat* hyperactive thyroid glands. It has been largely replaced by a gamma emitter, technetium-99. One of technetium-99's major advantages is its decay rate. It decays slowly enough to allow sufficient time to carry out the investigation, but quickly enough so that the patient is not radioactive for the rest of the week.

A convenient measure of how quickly a radioisotope decays is its **half-life**. This is the time taken for half of its nuclei to decay. The half-life is also the time taken for the activity to drop to half of its initial value. For a given radioisotope sample, the half-life is the same, regardless of the initial activity of the sample.

The type of constant reduction shown in the graph is an **exponential decrease**. An equation can be used to link the activity, A, at time t, to the initial activity, A_0:

$$A = A_0 e^{-\lambda t}$$

where λ is the decay constant.

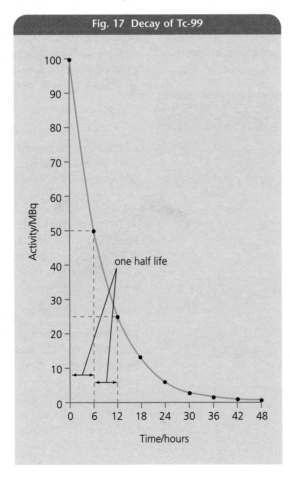

Fig. 17 Decay of Tc-99

one half life

Activity/MBq

Time/hours

Because the activity is proportional to the number of nuclei remaining, $A \propto N$, the same relationship exists between the initial number of nuclei, N_0, and the number, N, remaining after time t:

$$N = N_0 e^{-\lambda t}$$

We can use logarithms to find out how the half-life of an isotope depends on its decay constant. From

$$A = A_0 e^{-\lambda t}$$

we have

$$\frac{A}{A_0} = e^{-\lambda t}$$

Taking natural logs of each side leads to:

$$\ln\left(\frac{A}{A_0}\right) = \ln(e^{-\lambda t})$$

As $\ln(e^x) = x$

$$\ln\left(\frac{A}{A_0}\right) = -\lambda t$$

so,

$$t = -\frac{1}{\lambda}\ln\left(\frac{A}{A_0}\right)$$

When the activity drops to half its original value then $A = 0.5\,A_0$, and $t = T_{\frac{1}{2}}$, the half-life.

$$T_{\frac{1}{2}} = -\frac{1}{\lambda}\ln 0.5$$

or,

$$T_{\frac{1}{2}} = \frac{\ln 2}{\lambda}$$

which relates the half-life to the decay constant.

Radioactive isotopes suitable for use in nuclear medicine usually have half-lives of a matter of hours. Iodine-131 has a decay constant of 9.9×10^{-7} s^{-1}. Its half-life is therefore:

$$T_{\frac{1}{2}} = \frac{0.693}{9.9 \times 10^{-7}\,\text{s}^{-1}} = 7 \times 10^5 \text{ s} = \text{about 8 days}$$

In fact, its effective half-life in the body is only about 6 days since we excrete some of the isotope. Even so, this is much longer than technetium's half-life of 6 hours.

18 Plutonium-239 has a half-life of 24 000 years.
a If a sample of the isotope has an initial activity of 20 MBq, what will its activity be after 48 000 yrs?
b What is the decay constant of plutonium 239?
c Use the decay constant, and the equation $A = A_0 e^{-\lambda t}$, to calculate the activity after 100 000 years. (Hint. Watch out for the units of time, if you are working in years, then λ must be in yr^{-1}.)

10.5 Nuclear instability

Why is it that some nuclei are stable, while others are not? A clue to understanding this problem is to examine a graph showing the stable nuclei. If the neutron number, N, is plotted against the proton (atomic) number, Z, the stable nuclei lie along a well defined curve.

For nuclei with low mass numbers, up to about 40, there are roughly equal numbers of protons and neutrons in the nuclei. Above a mass number of 40 there are more neutrons than protons. This is necessary to keep the

nucleus stable since the attraction of the strong nuclear interaction is very short range, whilst the repulsion due to the electrostatic force between protons has a greater range. More neutrons are needed to 'glue' the nucleus together.

Nuclei that lie to either side of this curve are unstable and radioactive. Nuclei that lie above the curve have too many neutrons and can reach stability by emitting a beta particle. In beta decay a neutron is transformed into a proton. For example the isotope aluminium-29 decays by beta decay to silicon:

$$^{29}_{13}\text{Al} \rightarrow ^{29}_{14}\text{Si} + ^{0}_{-1}\text{e} + \bar{\nu}_e$$

On the other hand, the isotope aluminium-25 would be plotted below the line. This isotope has too many protons to be stable and it decays by emitting a positron.

$$^{25}_{13}\text{Al} \rightarrow ^{25}_{12}\text{Mg} + ^{0}_{+1}\text{e} + \nu_e$$

Some of the isotopes below the curve, like aluminium-26, reach stability by another form of decay, **electron capture**. One of the atom's electrons is absorbed by the nucleus, transforming a proton into a neutron:

$$^{26}_{13}\text{Al} + ^{0}_{-1}\text{e} \rightarrow ^{26}_{12}\text{Mg} + \bar{\nu}_e$$

Electron capture does not give rise to a daughter that is ionised since the parent has lost an electron and a proton and gained a neutron.

Alpha decay tends to happen in heavier nuclei. If alpha decay is to take place the mass of the parent nuclide must be greater than the mass of the daughter and the emitted alpha particle. For example, the radioisotope

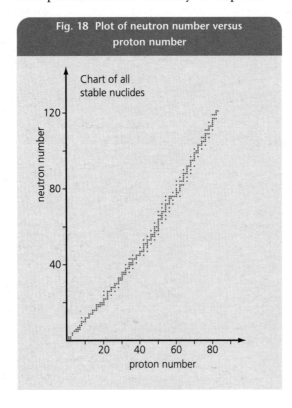

Fig. 18 Plot of neutron number versus proton number

Chart of all stable nuclides

neutron number

120 –

80 –

40 –

20   40   60   80
proton number

Radiocarbon dating

The Turin shroud bears an impression of a man who appears to have been crucified. The shroud was first shown in France in the 1350s and has been held in Turin since 1578. In 1988 samples of the shroud were sent to laboratories in Oxford, Zurich and Arizona so that radiocarbon analysis could be used to fix a date for the shroud.

Radiocarbon dating relies on measuring the activity due to the radioisotope carbon-14 in a piece of organic matter, like the linen of the shroud, and comparing it to the activity in living matter today.

Carbon-14 is a radioactive isotope of carbon that emits beta radiation. It is a small proportion of the total carbon in the world; it account for only 0.000 000 000 10 %. There is one carbon-14 atom for every 0.8×10^{12} carbon-12 atoms in living material. This unstable isotope is formed in the upper atmosphere through the effect of cosmic ray neutrons upon nitrogen-14. The reaction is:

$$^{14}_{7}N + ^{1}_{0}n \rightarrow ^{14}_{6}C + ^{1}_{1}p$$

The carbon-14 is quickly assimilated into carbon dioxide and becomes incorporated into plants through photosynthesis. During a plant's lifetime the proportion of carbon-14 stays more or less constant, but when the plant dies and no more photosynthesis takes place, the amount of carbon-14 drops as radioactive decay takes place.

The half-life of carbon-14 is 5730 ± 40 years, so by measuring the level of carbon-14 activity in a sample of old organic material, we can estimate its age.

Suppose that radiocarbon dating is to be used to estimate the age of some old timber. A sample of carbon from the wood is chemically prepared. If the activity due to carbon-14 in the sample is 0.33 Bq, we can calculate how many C-14 atoms are present.

First we calculate the decay constant, λ, from

$$\lambda = \frac{\ln 2}{T_{\frac{1}{2}}}.$$

$$\lambda = \frac{0.6931}{5730} = 1.210 \times 10^{-4} \ \text{yr}^{-1}$$
$$= 3.833 \times 10^{-12} \ \text{s}^{-1}$$

Now, using $A = \lambda N$, the number of C-14 atoms is given by

$$N = \frac{A}{\lambda} = \frac{0.33 \ \text{Bq}}{3.833 \times 10^{-12} \text{s}^{-1}}$$

$$= 8.609 \times 10^{10} \ \text{atoms}$$

A mole of carbon has a mass of 12 g, so that 4 g of carbon is $\frac{4}{12} = \frac{1}{3}$ of a mole. Therefore the total number of atoms in a 4 g sample of carbon is approximately

$$\frac{1}{3} \times N_A = \frac{1}{3} \times 6.02 \times 10^{23}$$
$$= 2.007 \times 10^{23} \ \text{atoms.}$$

The ratio of carbon-14 to carbon-12 atoms is therefore

$$\frac{8.609 \times 10^{10}}{2.007 \times 10^{23}} = 4.29 \times 10^{-13}$$

This compares to a ratio in living wood of

$$\frac{1.25}{1 \times 10^{12}} = 1.25 \times 10^{-12}$$

The ratio of C-14 in the old timber, to that of living wood is therefore

$$\frac{N}{N_0} = \frac{4.29 \times 10^{-13}}{1.25 \times 10^{-12}} = 0.3432$$

Using $N = N_0 e^{-\lambda t}$ or $\ln\left(\frac{N}{N_0}\right) = -\lambda t$

$$\ln(0.3432) = -3.833 \times 10^{-12} \ \text{s}^{-1} \times t$$

so $t = \dfrac{\ln(0.3432)}{-3.833 \times 10^{-12} \text{s}^{-1}}$

$$= 2.79 \times 10^{11} \ \text{s or 8800 years.}$$

The remarkable imprint on the Turin shroud was thought be the face of Jesus Christ. Radiocarbon dating has shown the shroud to be medieval.

Modern methods of radiocarbon dating use accelerator mass spectrometry to count the number of carbon-14 atoms directly, rather than counting the beta particles that are emitted.

19 Radiocarbon dating cannot be used reliably to date items more than about 50–60 000 years old. Why do you think this is?

20 Calculate the mass of a carbon sample that is needed to give a count-rate of 100 Bq. (Remember that carbon-14 atoms only account for one atom in 8×10^{11} of natural carbon.)

21 Accelerator mass spectrometry (see photo above) is useful because it requires samples of carbon that are 100 times smaller than are needed for conventional radiocarbon dating. Use your answer to the last question to explain why this is important.

Fig. 19 Calibration curve for radioisotope dating

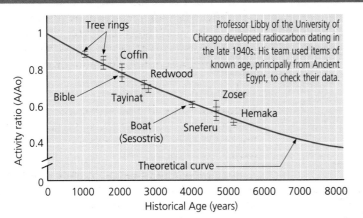

Professor Libby of the University of Chicago developed radiocarbon dating in the late 1940s. His team used items of known age, principally from Ancient Egypt, to check their data.

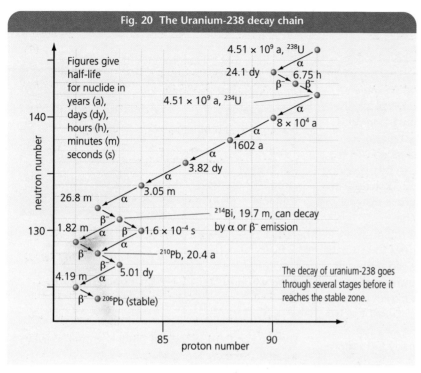

Fig. 20 The Uranium-238 decay chain

Figures give
half-life
for nuclide in
years (a),
days (dy),
hours (h),
minutes (m)
seconds (s)

^{214}Bi, 19.7 m, can decay
by α or β$^-$ emission

^{210}Pb, 20.4 a

The decay of uranium-238 goes
through several stages before it
reaches the stable zone.

neutron number

proton number

(where u denotes atomic mass units; see
Chapter 9)

Atomic mass of the daughter nuclide
neptunium-237 = 237.0480 u

Atomic mass of helium (alpha particle)
= 4.0030 u

The combined mass of Np-237 and the
alpha particle is 241.051 u, which is less than
that of the parent. This means that the decay
can take place.

Rarely a nucleon, a proton or a neutron, is
emitted directly from the nucleus. For
example the highly unstable isotope
helium-5, which has a half-life of only
6×10^{-20} s, decays by emitting a neutron:

$$^{5}_{2}\text{He} \rightarrow \,^{1}_{0}\text{n} + \,^{4}_{2}\text{He}$$

22 Show that the neutron decay of helium-5
is energetically possible. (Atomic mass of
$^{5}_{2}$He is 5.0123 u, mass of a neutron =
1.008 665 u, mass of $^{4}_{2}$He = 4.002604 u.)

23 The isotope lithium-5, $^{5}_{3}$Li, decays by
emitting a proton. Write down the
equation that describes the decay.

americium-241 is an alpha emitter that is
commonly used in schools and is the source
of the radioactivity in a smoke detector.
Atomic mass of americium-241 = 241.0566 u

EXAMINATION QUESTIONS

1 a Explain what is meant by the decay constant, λ, of
a radioactive nuclide. (2)

b A given sample of a certain isotope decays so that
after 20 s there are 8.0×10^{20} parent nuclei
remaining.
After 50 s there are 4.0×10^{19} parent remaining.
Calculate for the isotope:

(i) the decay constant, λ,

(ii) the half-life, $T_{1/2}$. (5)

NEAB PH02 February 1997 Q4

2 Use a data source for this question.

a Give an equation for each of the following decay
processes. State in each case the number of
neutrons and the number of protons in the
daughter nucleus.

(i) $^{15}_{6}$C emits a β$^-$ particle.

(ii) $^{230}_{90}$Th emits an α particle. (4)

b Calculate the energy, in MeV, which is released in
the decay process in part a(ii). (3)

NEAB PH02 March 1998 Q2

3 a (i) What is meant by the *random nature* of
radioactive decay?

(ii) Explain what is meant by each of the
following:
isotopes
radioactive half-life
radioactive decay constant (6)

b The radioactive isotope of iodine ^{131}I has a half-life
of 8.04 days. Calculate:

(i) the decay constant of ^{131}I,

(ii) the number of atoms of ^{131}I necessary to produce a sample with an activity of 5.0×10^4 disintegrations s^{-1} (Bq),

(iii) the time taken, in hours, for the activity of the same sample of ^{131}I to fall from 5.4×10^4 disintegrations s^{-1} to 5.0×10^4 disintegrations s^{-1}. (6)

NEAB PH02 March 1999 Q2

4 Nuclei of $^{218}_{84}$Po decay by the emission of an α particle to form a stable isotope of an element X. You may assume that no γ emission accompanies the decay.

a (i) State the proton number and the nucleon number of X.

(ii) Identify the element X. (2)

b Each decaying nucleus of Po releases 8.6×10^{-13} J of energy.

(i) State the form in which this energy initially appears.

(ii) Using **only** the information provided in the question, calculate the difference in mass between the original $^{218}_{84}$Po atom and the combined mass of an atom of X and an α particle. Speed of light in vacuum $= 3.0 \times 10^8$ m s^{-1} (3)

NEAB PH03 March 1999 Q1

5 Refer to data sources for decay sequences.

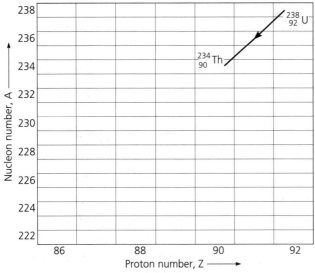

A sequence of nuclear transformation takes place starting from $^{238}_{92}$U.

$$^{238}_{92}\text{U} \xrightarrow{\alpha} \text{Th} \xrightarrow{\beta^-} \text{Pa} \xrightarrow{\beta^-} \text{U} \xrightarrow{\alpha} \text{Th} \xrightarrow{\alpha} \text{Ra} \xrightarrow{\alpha} \text{Rn}$$

Write the symbol for each successive product in the appropriate box in the table and link them by arrows

showing the decay sequence. The first one has been done for you. (4)

Calculate the maximum possible kinetic energy released by the first decay. (3)

NEAB PH02 June 1998 Q1

6 The activity (disintegration rate) of a sample of a radioactive isotope of iodine is 3.7×10^4 Bq. 48 hours later, the activity is found to be 3.1×10^4 Bq.

(i) Show that the decay constant is about 1.0×10^{-6} s^{-1}.

(ii) Calculate the half-life of the iodine isotope. (4)

NEAB PH02 June 1998 Q2

7 You are to investigate the way in which β radiation is absorbed by aluminium sheets of different thickness.

a Draw a labelled diagram showing an arrangement to carry out the investigation. (4)

b Describe how you would carry out the investigation. (3)

11 Probing matter

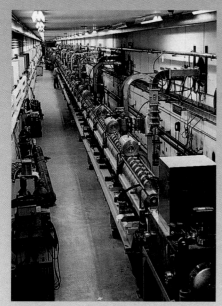

Linear accelerator at the ISIS neutron scattering facility

Trains that magnetically levitate above the track have reached speeds of over 340 mph. The trains rely on new high-temperature superconducting materials.

Neutron scattering is particularly useful for investigating the magnetic properties of materials. New lightweight magnets have been developed and the manufacture of high-temperature superconducting materials has been made possible by neutron scattering.

Neutrons are only 1/1000th the size of the smallest atom and they are particularly useful for probing deep into matter. They can easily travel through centimetres of solid steel. Because they are uncharged they do not interact with atomic electrons, they only interact with the nuclei themselves. Neutrons are the only accurate way to measure the position of hydrogen atoms - the most common atom found in all living things. Because of this, neutron scattering is an essential tool for solving many important scientific problems.

Neutron scattering has been the key to obtaining basic knowledge about microstructures in oils and creams (including ice-cream).

Mention high-energy particle accelerators and most people will think of 'blue sky' research. Trying to understand the structure deep within matter may be interesting for physicists, but it is expensive and seems unlikely to produce any practical benefits. Nothing could be further from the truth. The ISIS neutron scattering facility at the Rutherford Appleton Laboratory near Oxford uses a high-energy beam of protons fired at a target in order to produce a shower of neutrons. The neutrons are used to probe deeply into matter to examine molecular structures.

Neutron scattering has led to improvements in everything from computer disks to shatterproof windscreens, from the design of new drugs to the development of powerful metal-hydride batteries.

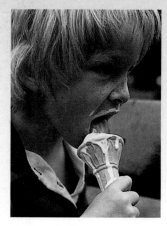

Neutron scattering has helped to make low-fat ice-cream with the right texture.

11.1 Alpha scattering

The use of high-energy particles to investigate the structure of matter is not new. Some of the earliest scattering experiments were carried out by Geiger and Marsden at Manchester University in 1909. They used naturally occurring high-energy particles, the alpha rays emitted by Radon-222. The target was a thin foil of gold and the detector was a scintillator, a material that emits a brief flash of light when it is hit by an alpha particle.

In 1909 the accepted model of the atom was J.J. Thomson's so-called 'plum-pudding' model. The atom was thought of as a cloud of positive charge of uniform density, with hundreds of electrons stuck in it, like the plums in a pudding. Geiger and Marsden knew that an alpha particle was relatively dense and positively charged. They were looking for small deflections as the alpha particle passed through the foil. It was the

Fig. 1 Geiger and Marsden's experimental set-up

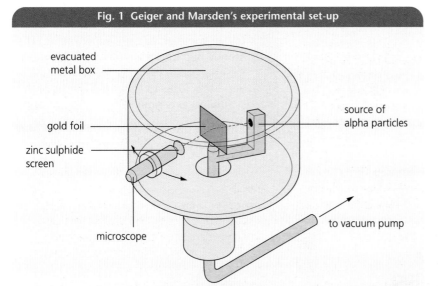

evacuated metal box

gold foil

zinc sulphide screen

microscope

source of alpha particles

to vacuum pump

Ernest Rutherford. Marsden remembered the day when Rutherford came into the lab. 'He said "See if you can get some effect of α-particles directly reflected from the metal surface." I do not think he expected any such result but it was one of those "hunches".... To my surprise I was able to observe this effect.'

Fig. 2 Alpha particle scattering

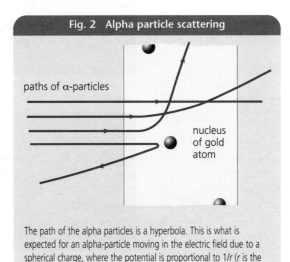

paths of α-particles

nucleus of gold atom

The path of the alpha particles is a hyperbola. This is what is expected for an alpha-particle moving in the electric field due to a spherical charge, where the potential is proportional to 1/r (r is the distance from the charge). (See Chapter 7.)

professor of physics, Ernest Rutherford, who made the crucial suggestion of looking for alpha particles scattered at large angles.

About 1 in every 8000 alpha particles was scattered at angles larger than 90°. This large-angle scattering could not be explained by the plum pudding model; there had to be a region of higher density and higher electric field strength within the atom. Rutherford used the results of the scattering experiment to predict the existence of the atomic nucleus.

Geiger and Marsden used alpha particles with an energy of 5 MeV. This kinetic energy is transferred to potential energy as the positively charged alpha particle does work against the electrostatic repulsion of the positively charged gold nucleus. An alpha particle, charge q, on a direct collision course with a gold nucleus, charge Q, will reach a distance, r, where all its kinetic energy has been transferred to potential energy. This is the distance of closest approach.

At the distance of closest approach:

$$E_k = E_p$$

For a spherical charge, Q,

$$E_p = qV \quad \text{where } V \text{ is the electric potential (Chapter 7)}$$

$$= \frac{Qq}{4\pi\varepsilon_0 r}$$

For a 5 MeV alpha particle approaching a gold nucleus of atomic number 79, this becomes

$$(5 \times 10^6 \times 1.6 \times 10^{-19}) \text{ joules} =$$

$$\frac{(79 \times 1.6 \times 10^{-19})\text{C} \times (2 \times 1.6 \times 10^{-19})\text{C}}{4\pi \times 8.85 \times 10^{-12} \text{ Fm}^{-1} \times r}$$

giving a value for r of 4.55×10^{-14} m. This gives an upper limit for the size of the gold nucleus. Modern measurements give a value of 6.5×10^{-15} m (or 6.5 fm, femtometres).

Rutherford went on to calculate the scattering **cross-section** for the nucleus. The cross-section for any nuclear reaction is the probability that the reaction will occur. Rutherford's cross-section equation is based on electrostatic scattering from a positive nucleus and it predicted how many alpha particles could be expected at each angle. The prediction was in good agreement with the experimental results and the concept of the nuclear atom was born.

In some ways Rutherford was lucky to get this agreement. The 5 MeV alpha particles were fast enough to be unaffected by any scattering off atomic electrons, yet not too fast so that relativistic effects need to be taken into account. If the alpha particles had moved much faster, or the target had a lower atomic number, the alpha particles might have penetrated the Coulomb barrier. The alpha particles would then have got close enough to the nucleus to be affected by the strong nuclear force and Rutherford's theory would not have agreed with the experimental observations.

1 Beta particles can be emitted with energies of several MeV, similar to that of the alpha particles used by Geiger and Marsden. Why was beta scattering less useful for examining the nucleus?

2 Geiger used aluminium, rather than gold foil, in some of his early experiments. The atomic number of aluminium is 13, much less than gold, which is 79. How would you expect this to affect the results of the scattering experiment?

3 Calculate the closest approach of a 4 MeV alpha particle to an aluminium nucleus.

11.2 Electron scattering

Higher energy particles are needed to find out about the nucleus in more detail. One way of getting a closer approximation for the size of the nucleus is to use high-energy electrons.

Electrons have a wave-like nature (see *AS Physics*, page 83). The wavelength, λ, can be calculated from the momentum, p, of the electron using De Broglie's relation:

$$\lambda = \frac{h}{p} \text{ where } h \text{ is Planck's constant.}$$

Electrons can be accelerated by allowing them to pass through a potential difference, V. This is exactly the process that happens in every cathode ray tube, or television.

As the electron is accelerated it gains energy, E:

$E = eV$,

where e is the charge on the electron $= 1.6 \times 10^{-19}$ C.

This energy will be equal to the final kinetic energy of the electron, $E_k = \frac{1}{2}mv^2$

$$eV = \frac{1}{2}mv^2$$

This gives

$$m^2v^2 = 2meV$$

so

$$p = mv = \sqrt{2meV}$$

The De Broglie wavelength is therefore

$$\lambda = \frac{h}{\sqrt{2meV}}$$

The larger the potential difference through which the electron is accelerated, the smaller its wavelength. For a potential difference of

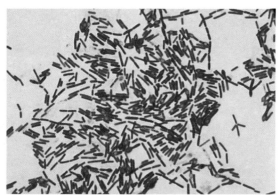

An optical microscope can show bacteria

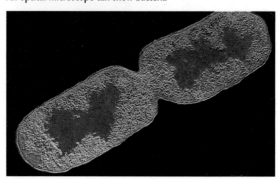

Magnification = 17 500. An ordinary transmission electron microscope can show the genetic material in this bacteria (in red), but ...

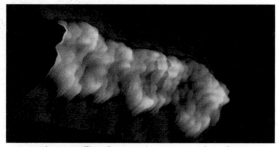

... a scanning tunnelling electron microscope can show the structure of that genetic material. Here you can clearly see the twisted double strands that form DNA. Magnification = 2 000 000.

only 100 V, the wavelength of the electron is 1.23×10^{-10} m. Compare this to the shortest wavelength of visible light, which is 400 nm or 4×10^{-7} m. The wavelength of the electron is more than 1000 times shorter.

Shorter wavelengths allow us to see more detail. We are limited in what we can see with light waves because of diffraction (see Chapter 3). Diffraction is more pronounced with longer wavelengths, so that if we can 'look' at objects with electrons we should be able to see much more detail. Transmission electron microscopes use this principle to allow us to look closer at matter.

In principle it should be possible to accelerate electrons to even greater speeds, and shorter wavelengths, and this could allow use to 'see' individual atoms. However, there are practical problems. The sample has to be sliced *very* thinly for the electrons to give a clear picture. It is also difficult to avoid imaging aberrations. The scanning tunnelling electron microscope uses a different principle and does allow individual atoms to be imaged.

By using much higher voltages still we can diffract an electron beam around the nucleus of an atom. By firing the electrons at a thin slice of material we can produce a pattern which is very similar to that produced by light passing through a diffraction grating (see Chapter 3).

Fig. 4 Electron diffraction pattern of oxygen nuclei

The diffraction of electrons provides a measurement of nuclear size. This diffraction pattern came from a beam with an energy of 125 GeV.

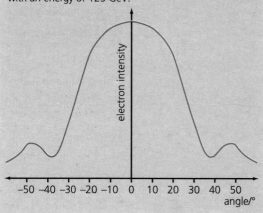

The angle at which the first minimum of a diffraction pattern appears is given by

$$\sin \theta = \frac{0.61\lambda}{D}$$

where D is the size of the obstacle. Electrons with an energy of 125 GeV have a De Broglie wavelength of 3.46×10^{-15} m, or 3.46 fm. In Fig. 4 the first diffraction minimum due to an oxygen nucleus is about 38°. This gives a value for the diameter of an oxygen nucleus of:

$$D = \frac{0.61 \times 3.46 \times 10^{-15} \text{ m}}{\sin 38°} = 3.4 \times 10^{-15} \text{ m}$$

Electron diffraction data gives us much more precise data for the radius of atomic nuclei. Diffraction experiments using different elements have shown that there is a link between the nucleon number, A, of a nucleus and its radius, R:

$$R = r_0 A^{\frac{1}{3}}$$

where r_0 is a constant representing the radius of a single nucleon.

Fig. 3 Electrons diffracting from a sample of material

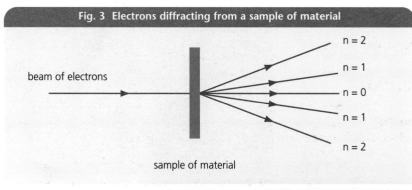

beam of electrons

n = 2
n = 1
n = 0
n = 1
n = 2

sample of material

Electrons with a wavelength of 2×10^{-11} m diffracting through graphite. The outer ring is due to rows of atoms 1.2×10^{-10} m apart.

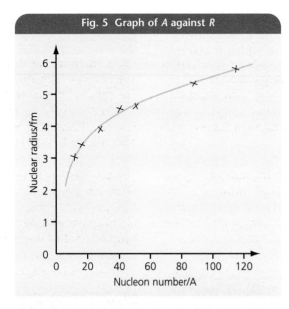

Fig. 5 Graph of A against R

Table 1 Nucleon numbers and nuclear radii for some elements

Nuclide	Nucleon number, A	Radius, R/fm
$^{12}_{6}$C	12	3.04
$^{16}_{8}$O	16	3.41
$^{28}_{14}$Si	28	3.92
$^{40}_{20}$Ca	40	4.54
$^{51}_{23}$V	51	4.63
$^{88}_{38}$Sr		
$^{115}_{49}$In		

1 fm = 10^{-15} m. Results from electron diffraction experiments.

4 Table 1 has values of nuclear radii for some isotopes. Complete the last two rows of the table.

5 The graph in Fig. 5 shows the relationship between R and A but to verify the equation

$$R = r_0 A^{\frac{1}{3}}$$

we would need a straight line graph. What graph would you plot to verify the law? Use data from Table 1 to plot the graph. What is signified by the gradient of your graph?

Very high energy electrons have also been used to probe deep inside the nucleus. Experiments at SLAC (the Stanford Linear Accelerator) in 1967 used 6 GeV electrons to investigate protons and neutrons. The pattern of scattering angles observed was characteristic of point-like particles within the proton and neutron. The scattering suggested that these point-like particles had fractional charge and spin of 1/2. These were exactly the properties that Gell-Mann had predicted for quarks (see *AS Physics*, Chapter 1).

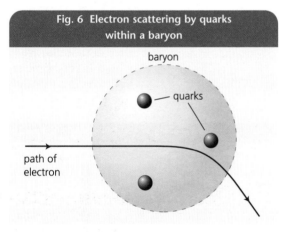

Fig. 6 Electron scattering by quarks within a baryon

KEY FACTS

■ High-energy electrons have a small De Broglie wavelength and can be used to measure nuclear diameters.

■ Nuclear radius depends on nucleon number,

$$R = r_0 A^{\frac{1}{3}}$$

11.3 X-ray scattering

It is possible to use electromagnetic radiation rather than particles to probe matter. However the wavelength has to be short so X-rays or gamma rays offer the only suitable tools with which to examine matter on an atomic scale.

X-rays interact with matter in a number of ways. X-rays photons can be *scattered* by atomic electrons or totally *absorbed.*

A *scattered* X-ray photon is deflected from its path by an atomic electron. If the electron is very tightly bound to the atom, or the photon has very little energy, the electron will remain in the atom and the X-ray photon will not lose any energy. This is known as *elastic* or *coherent* scattering.

Where the X-ray photon energy is great enough, it interacts with an atomic electron and knocks it out of its orbit, ionising the atom. In this case the X-ray photon does lose energy. The larger the scattering angle the more energy is lost. This is known as *Compton scattering*. The probability of Compton scattering taking place is proportional to the electron density in the material, which in turn depends on the atomic number of the material.

Fig. 7 Compton scattering

scattering angle
incident X-ray
ejected electron
target atom
nucleus
atomic electrons
scattered X-ray

When photon energy is greater than electron binding energy, the electron is ejected from the atom and the energy of the X-ray photon is reduced.

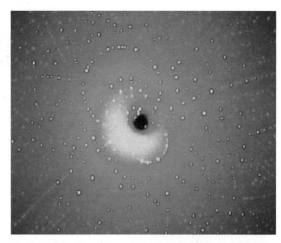

The X-ray diffraction pattern of lysozyme. The patterns are due to the elastic scattering of X-rays and can help determine the structure of crystals or biological molecules.

11.4 Neutron scattering

Neutrons are particularly useful for investigating matter since they are not charged. Neutrons do not interact with the electrons around an atom. The cross-section (probability) of neutron scattering is not strongly dependent on the atomic number, unlike electrons and X-rays. That means that it is easier to spot light atoms, like hydrogen, in the presence of heavier ones.

Neutrons interact with other nuclei quite weakly, so they can penetrate further into a material and because of this weak interaction, neutrons are non-destructive. Neutrons have wavelengths that are similar to typical atomic spacings, around 1 nm, which means that diffraction experiments can be performed. These can be used to study the form that molecules take.

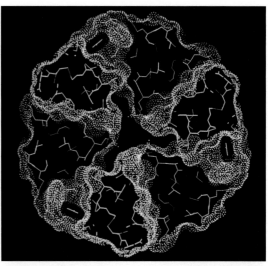

A model of an insulin molecule constructed from information from neutron scattering.

Although neutrons have no overall charge, they do have spin and this gives them a magnetic moment. In other words neutrons behave like tiny bar magnets. These are scattered by the magnetisation of materials on an atomic scale. This has led to neutron scattering being used to help to design new magnetic materials.

To look deep inside matter, physicists have to choose the right particle or radiation as a probe. It is also important to choose the right energy. Early experiments using naturally occurring projectiles like alpha particles were limited to energies of a few MeV. Electrons, protons and ions have all been used: since they are charged they have the advantage of being able to be accelerated to high energies by electric fields in linear accelerators or cyclotrons (see Chapter 7). A beam of charged particles can also be controlled by the use of magnetic fields. It is more difficult to produce a beam of high-energy neutrons. But the advantage of using uncharged projectiles means that neutrons can detect other properties of the target.

Perhaps the most difficult particles of all to use as a probe are neutrinos. These uncharged leptons are not affected by the electromagnetic force, or by the strong nuclear force. This makes them difficult to control, and difficult to detect. In June 2000, physicists at Fermilab announced that they had discovered one of the final missing pieces of the standard model, the Tau neutrino. They used a linear accelerator to direct a high-energy proton beam toward a block of tungsten. The collision produced many different particles, including neutrinos. Powerful magnets were used to remove all the charged particles from the beam. Then fifteen metres of shielding stopped all particles – except neutrinos. Amongst these were some of the very rare Tau neutrinos.

11.5 The future

As physicists have probed deeper and deeper into matter the energy of the bombarding particles has had to become greater and greater. Much of the early work was done with stationary targets, but greater energies

The SPEAR colliding electron-positron storage ring in 1974.

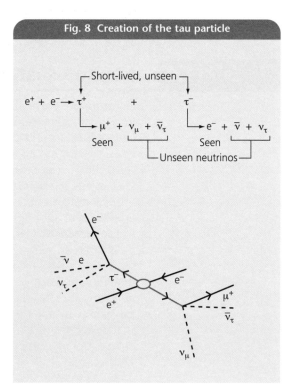

Fig. 8 Creation of the tau particle

can be created when the particles are accelerated towards each other.

Some of the outstanding discoveries of recent years have been achieved using colliders. In 1974 researchers at Stanford University accelerated electrons and positrons towards each other and discovered the fourth quark, which became known as the charmed quark. The tau particle, a heavier version of the electron, was discovered in similar experiments.

By 1994 researchers at Fermilab in the USA had discovered the sixth quark by colliding particles together at energies of around 2 TeV (Tera = 1×10^{12}). Although the 'top' quark seems to complete the standard model of particle physics, its discovery has simply raised more questions.

Why is the top quark so massive? Indeed why do all the quarks have different masses?

Are quarks really fundamental, or is there some deeper structure as yet unseen? Recent scattering experiments at Fermilab have discovered energetic scattering at wide angles. This is reminiscent of Rutherford scattering, which revealed that the atom has a nucleus. One possible interpretation of the results is that they due to collisions of even smaller objects within quarks - though this has not yet been observed by any other experiment.

Why are there three types of quarks and leptons of each charge?

Are all the fundamental forces really aspects of the same fundamental interaction?

These are some of the questions that the next generation of physicists will strive to answer. The tools for the job are already being

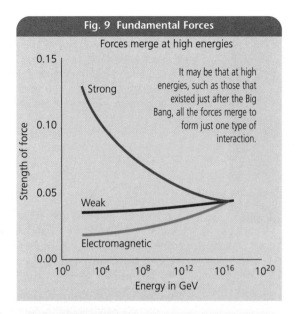

Fig. 9 Fundamental Forces
Forces merge at high energies

It may be that at high energies, such as those that existed just after the Big Bang, all the forces merge to form just one type of interaction.

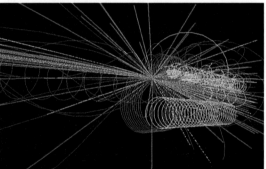

Artist's impression of the collision of two particles

constructed. By 2006 the LHC (Large Hadron Collider) at CERN in Geneva will begin operation. It will produce two proton beams colliding at 14 TeV. The results of these scattering experiments may help to answer some of the questions above.

1 When Rutherford was investigating the structure of the atom, α particles from a radioactive source travelled in a vacuum towards a thin gold foil. The diagram represents an α particle, of charge +2e, approaching a gold nucleus which has a charge of +79e.

Alpha particle

Gold nucleus charge = +79 e

Charge = +2e

a The α particle leaves the radioactive source at a speed of 1.7×10^7 m s^{-1} and approaches a gold nucleus along their line centres. Assume that the gold nucleus does not recoil.
Mass of α particle = 6.6×10^{-27} kg

(i) Describe the energy changes which the α particle experiences throughout its interaction with the gold nucleus.

(ii) Calculate the kinetic energy of the α particle as it approaches the gold nucleus when the distance between the centres of the particles is 3.5×10^{-13}. (6)

b Use the axes to sketch a graph to show how the kinetic energy of the α particle varies with the distance r between the centres of the two particles. (2)

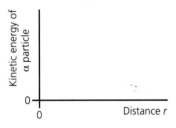

Kinetic energy of α particle

0

Distance r

0

AQA PH03 March 2000 Q6

2 a Two protons are separated by 1.2×10^{-14} m. Calculate:

(i) the electrostatic repulsive force between them,

(ii) the gravitational attractive force between them. (4)

b Show that the ratio of the gravitational force to the electrostatic force between two identical charged particles is independent of their separation. (2)

NEAB PH03 June 1998 Q 4

3 a (i) Define electric field strength, and state whether it is a scalar quantity or a vector quantity.

(ii) Complete the diagram below to show the electric field lines in the region around two equal positive point charges. Mark with a letter N the position of any point where the field strength is zero. (6)

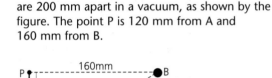

+

+

b Point charges A, of +2.0 nC, and B, of –3.0 nC, are 200 mm apart in a vacuum, as shown by the figure. The point P is 120 mm from A and 160 mm from B.

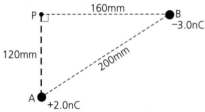

P ┌──────160mm──────● B

120mm

200mm

A ● +2.0nC

(i) Calculate the component of the electric field at P in the direction AP.

(ii) Calculate the component of the electric field at P in the direction PB.

(iii) Hence calculate the magnitude and direction of the resultant field at P. (6)

c (i) Explain why there is a point X on the line AB in part **b** at which the electric potential is zero.

(ii) Calculate the distance of the point X from A. (4)

AQA PH03 March 1999 Q4

4 a When α particles are projected at a thin metal foil in a vacuum enclosure they are scattered at various angles.

(i) In which direction will the maximum number of α particles coming from the foil be detected?

(ii) Describe the angular distribution of the scattered α particles around the foil.

(iii) What do the results suggest about the structure of the metal atoms? (XX)

b In this arrangement explain why
• the foil should be thin.
• the incident beam of α particles should be parallel and narrow. (2)

PH02 Q3 Feb 1996

5 In an experiment to investigate the structure of the atom, α particles were aimed at thin gold foil in a vacuum. A detector was used to determine the number of α particles deflected through different angles.

a State **two** observations about the α particles detected coming from the foil. (2)

b State **two** features of the structure of the atom which can be deduced from these observations. (2)

AQA PH02 June 1999 Q1

6 a Calculate the speed of electrons which have a de Broglie wavelength of 1.5×10^{-10} m. (2)

b Would you expect the electrons in part (a) to be diffracted by crystals in which the atom spacing is 0.10 nm? Explain your answer. (2)

AQA PH02 June 1999 Q7

Although these questions are largely based on the content of the specified chapter, they draw on content, ideas and skills from other parts of the AS and A2 specification.

You will need to make use of the data section (page *177*) in order to answer these questions.

Unless otherwise specified you should take the acceleration due to gravity, *g*, as 10 m s^{-2}.

1 A baby bouncer is designed to entertain babies before they can walk, by allowing them to bounce up and down. The baby is placed in a harness that is suspended by four rubber cords from a suitable doorway. The rubber cords are 1.2 m long and they each have a cross-sectional area of 1 cm^2. Rubber has a Young modulus of 20 MPa.

  a i) How much will the cords stretch when a baby of mass 10 kg is placed in the bouncer?

  ii) Assuming that the rubber cords obey Hooke's law, $F = kx$, over this extension, what is the spring constant, *k*, for one of the rubber cords?

  b The baby and harness are pulled down by another 10 cm and then released.

  i) What will the frequency of baby's oscillations be?

  ii) Calculate the baby's maximum speed.

  iii) Calculate the baby's maximum acceleration.

  c The baby's mischievous older brother pulls the baby bouncer back by a total of 30 cm from its equilibrium position. Explain what is likely to happen to the baby when it reaches the top of the first bounce.

2 **a** Waves are often classified as **transverse** or **longitudinal**. Explain the fundamental difference between these types of wave.

  b One of the differences between transverse and longitudinal waves is that light waves can be **polarised**.

  i) Explain what **polarised** means.

  ii) Describe how you could use polarisation to demonstrate that light is a transverse wave.

  c Reflected light is partially polarised. If light is reflected from a horizontal surface, the amount of polarisation depends on the angle of incidence. At one particular angle of incidence, known as the Brewster angle, the reflected ray is completely polarised.

At the Brewster angle the reflected and refracted rays are at 90° to each other. If the refractive index of glass is 1.5, find the Brewster angle for an air–glass interface.

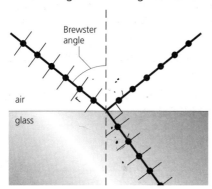

d Sugar solution is optically active. It can rotate the plane of polarisation of light. The amount of rotation depends on the concentration of the sugar solution. This effect is used to measure the concentration of sugar solution.

The rotation of the plane of polarisation is measured with a polarimeter.

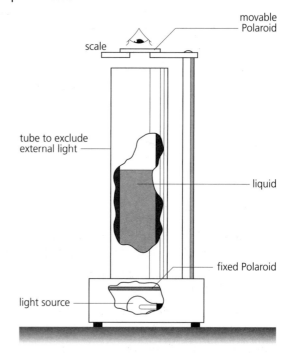

Initially, with no sugar solution in place, the lower Polaroid filter (the polariser) is placed at 90° to the second filter (the analyser). These polaroids are said to be crossed and there is no transmission of light through the polarimeter. The tube containing sugar solution is then placed between the two crossed polaroid filters. Light will be observed passing through the analyser. The analyser is then rotated through an angle, *q*, until no light is observed.

The angle *q* is given by; $q = a \, l \, c$

where *a* is the specific rotation of sugar solution (in degrees m^2 kg^{-1}), l = the length of the polarimeter tube (m) and *c* is the concentration of sugar solution (in kg of sugar per m^3 of water.)

An experiment is carried out using varying concentrations of sugar and the rotation of the plane of polarisation is measured in each case.

The following results were taken:

Concentration of sugar (kg m^{-3})	Angle of rotation (degrees)
50	19
80	31
110	44
140	55
170	65
200	74
230	89
260	100

i) Plot a suitable graph to verify that angle of rotation is proportional to concentration.

ii) If the length of the polarimeter tube was 20 cm, find a value for a, the specific rotation for sugar.

3 A diffraction grating is often used to examine the spectra of light from stars.

The diffraction grating equation is:

$nl = d \sin q$

a Explain the meaning of each of the terms in the equation.

b A diffraction grating with 500 lines per mm is used to create a spectrum of light from a star. The starlight contains particularly bright red and violet lines at wavelengths (λ) of 700 nm and 450 nm respectively.

i) What is the angular separation between these lines in the first order spectrum?

ii) Show that the red line from the second order spectrum overlaps with the third order violet line.

c The spectrum of light from the star has a number of dark lines superimposed on it. These are known as absorption lines. These absorption lines are characteristic of the elements in the cooler layer of gas which surrounds a star.

i) Explain how these dark lines arise.

ii) Explain how the lines give us information on both the chemical make-up and temperature of a star.

d The light from a telescope is often detected with a CCD (charge coupled device). CCDs depend on photons of light releasing charge in a semiconductor detector. Calculate the energy of photons of red ($\lambda = 700$ nm) and violet light ($\lambda = 450$ nm) from the star.

4 The flashgun in a disposable camera uses a capacitor to deliver a significant amount electrical energy in a short time. However, the capacitor can remain charged for some time and it can be dangerous to break into such a camera; there is certainly a risk of an electric shock.

a A disposable camera uses a 400 mF, 300 V capacitor to store charge.

i) How much charge will the capacitor hold when it is fully charged?

ii) How much energy will be stored by the capacitor?

b The typical duration for a flash is less than a microsecond. Estimate the power output of the flash.

c Safety instructions for dismantling the camera suggest that a 2 kW resistor is used to discharge the capacitor.

i) What is the time constant of this circuit?

ii) Sketch a graph showing how the potential difference across the capacitor changes with time.

iii) How long would it take for the potential difference across the capacitor to drop to less than 6 V?

iv) Why isn't it a good idea to use the blade of a screwdriver to discharge the capacitor?

5 Recently I bought a football training 'toy' for my young son, Jonathan. The toy is made from a plastic football fastened by a rubber cord to a belt that fastens around the child's waist. This stops the child from kicking the ball too far and saves the parent the trouble of going to fetch it. The ball has a mass of 0.25 kg and the 2 m long rubber cord has a spring constant of 25 N m^{-1}.

Jonathan can kick the football about 5 m into the air when it is not attached to the cord.

a How fast is the ball moving when it leaves his foot?

b Estimate the furthest distance that Jonathan can kick the ball horizontally when it is attached to the rubber cord.

c How far could Jonathan kick the ball vertically, when it is attached to the cord?

d Naturally enough Jonathan soon gets bored with this and starts to whirl the ball around his head in a horizontal circle.

i) What would you observe as Jonathan whirls the ball faster and faster? Explain what happens to the tension in the cord and to the length of the cord as the speed is increased.

ii) If Jonathan whirls the ball at a rate of 30 revolutions per minute, how much would the rubber cord stretch?

iii) What would be observed if Jonathan swung the ball in a vertical circle?

6 Use the following data in this question:

Gravitational constant = 6.7×10^{-11} N m² kg⁻²
Mass of Earth = 6.0×10^{24} kg
Radius of Earth = 6.4×10^6 m

A satellite of mass 1200 kg is to be placed in a circular orbit of radius 2.0×10^7 m around the Earth.

Calculate

   i) the speed of the satellite when in its orbit

   ii) the speed of the satellite when in its orbit

   iii) the change in gravitational potential of the satellite as it is placed into orbit from the surface of the Earth

   iv) the total energy which must be supplied to put the satellite into orbit (assuming the Earth's rotation provides negligible energy).

7 The diagram shows an electron gun that produces electrons with a kinetic energy of 6.0×10^{-16} J.

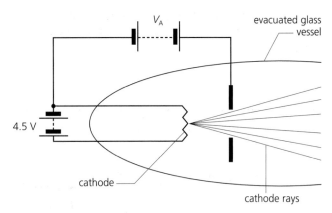

a i) Calculate the cathode–anode potential, V_A.

   ii) What part does the 4.5 V power supply play in producing electrons?

b After leaving an electron gun, a narrow beam of electrons of speed 3.6×10^7 m s⁻¹ enters a uniform electric field at right angles to the field. The electric field is due to two oppositely charged parallel plates of length 60 mm, separated by a distance of 25 mm, as shown in the diagram below. The potential difference between the plates is adjusted to 1250 V so that the beam just emerges from the field at P without touching the positive plate.

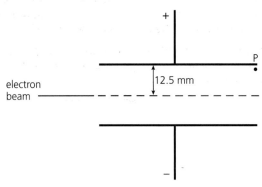

   i) Sketch the path of the beam in the field and beyond.

   ii) Calculate the time for which each electron is between the plates.

   iii) Use the data above to calculate the specific charge of the electron, e/m.

AQA (NEAB) PH09 June 2000 Q4

8 Portable televisions often have a loop antenna on top of the television. These are in the form of a single circular loop. The loop aerial works best when the magnetic flux density, **B**, of the magnetic component of the radio wave carrying the TV signal is normal to the plane of the loop.

Suppose that such a loop aerial has a radius of area $A = 0.01$ m². At a particular instant, the rate of change of the magnetic flux density is 0.16 T s⁻¹.

a What is the e.m.f. induced in the antenna? (Assume that **B** is uniform over the area of the coil).

b This e.m.f. results in a current flowing in the coil of 1 mA. If the coil is made from copper wire, find the diameter of the wire.

c The current leads to a magnetic field of 6×10^{-9} T. In which direction will this field act?

9 **a** A nuclear power station uses a moderator to slow down the neutrons emitted by fission. Why is it necessary to slow the neutrons down?

b Gas-cooled reactors use graphite (carbon-12) as the moderator. Pressurised water reactors use water as the moderator. Which of these is likely to be most effective at slowing down neutrons?

c Lead is used as shielding against the gamma radiation that is emitted from a nuclear reactor. The intensity of radiation, I, is related to the thickness of lead, x, by the equation: $I = I_0 e^{(-mx)}$ where I_0 is the intensity of radiation without shielding and m is the linear absorption coefficient for lead.

Measurements were taken of the intensity from a gamma source using varying thicknesses of lead.

   i) Explain what graph you would plot in order to find the linear absorption coefficient.

   ii) If the linear absorption coefficient for lead is 0.057 mm⁻¹, how many mm of lead would it take to reduce the intensity of gamma radiation to one half of its value without shielding?

10 Strontium-90 and plutonium-239 are radioisotopes that arise as waste products from nuclear fission.

Strontium-90 is a beta-emitter with a half-life of 27 years. Beta particles are emitted with an average energy of 0.54 MeV.

Plutonium-239 is an alpha emitter that has a half-life of 2.4×10^4 years. It emits alpha particles with an energy of 5.15 MeV.

a Write down an equation that represents the decay of strontium-90.

b Write down an equation that represents the decay of plutonium-239.

c Explain why the alpha particles emitted from plutonium-239 have a specific value for energy, whilst the beta particles vary in energy and only an average energy can be specified.

d Calculate the decay constant for strontium-90.

e Calculate the activity that you would expect from 100 g of strontium-90.

f What power is transferred by this amount of strontium-90?

g The specific heat capacity of strontium-90 is $308 \text{ J kg}^{-1} \text{ K}^{-1}$. Calculate the initial rate of temperature rise in a 100 g sample of strontium.

11 a i) The path of a charged particle through a cloud chamber appears as a thin line. What does this line consist of?

ii) How may the cloud chamber tracks of α particles be distinguished from those of β particles in the absence of a deflecting field?

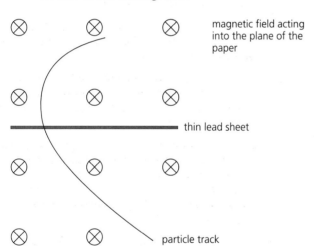

b The diagram shows the track of a charged particle which passes through a thin sheet of lead inside a cloud chamber. A uniform magnetic field acts into the plane of the paper.

i) Does the particle start from the top half or the lower half of the diagram? Explain your answer.

ii) Is the particle carrying a positive or negative charge? Explain your answer.

AQA (NEAB) PH06 June 2000 Q1

12 The radius of a nucleus, *R*, is related to its nucleon number, *A*, by

$R = r_0 A^{1/3}$, where r_0 is a constant.

The table lists the values of nuclear radius for various isotopes.

Element	$R/10^{-15}$ m	A
carbon	2.66	12
silicon	3.43	28
iron	4.35	56
tin	5.49	120
lead	6.66	208

a Use the data to plot a straight line graph and use it to estimate the value of r_0.

b Assuming that the mass of a nucleon is 1.67×10^{-27} kg, calculate the approximate density of nuclear matter, stating one assumption you have made.

AQA NEAB PH06 June 2000 Q5

13 Nuclear radii can be determined by observing the diffraction of high energy electrons, as shown in the diagram.

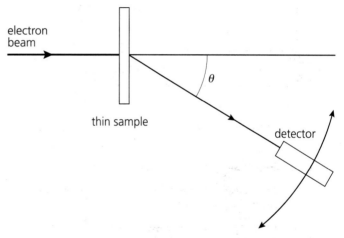

a Sketch a graph of the results expected from such an electron diffraction experiment (*y*-axis = intensity of diffracted electrons, *x*-axis = diffraction angle (*q*)).

b State why high energy electrons are used in determining nuclear size.

c Electron diffraction experiments have been performed on a range of different nuclei to give information about nuclear density and average separation of particles in the nucleus. Give the main conclusion in each case.

d Sketch the relationship between the radius of a nucleus and its nucleon number (*y*-axis = radius of nucleus, *x*-axis = nucleon number).

AQA (NEAB) PH06 June 1999 Q1

14 a In a synchrotron, charged particles are confined by magnets to a ring while being accelerated to high energies.

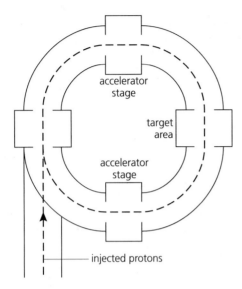

i) Sketch the diagram and on it indicate the direction of the magnetic field necessary to confine protons moving clockwise round the ring.

ii) Explain why it is necessary to increase the strength of the magnetic field as the energy of the particles increases.

iii) The particles radiate electromagnetic waves, known as synchrotron radiation, as they are moving round the ring. Why does this limit the energy of a charged particle in a synchrotron?

b A synchrotron is designed to accelerate antiprotons in stages through a total potential difference of 2.0 GV and make them collide with protons of equal energy moving in the opposite direction. In such a collision, a proton–antiproton pair is created, as represented by the equation

$$p + \bar{p} \rightarrow p + \bar{p} + p + \bar{p}.$$

i) Give the total kinetic energy, in GeV, before the collision.

ii) Calculate the total kinetic energy, in GeV, after the collision.

iii) This pair production is not possible if all the initial kinetic energy is carried by the antiproton only. Explain why.

AQA (NEAB) PH06 June 1998 Q3

Answers to text questions

Chapter 1

1

Gravitational potential energy	Elastic potential energy	Overall potential energy	Kinetic energy
max	min	max	0
		min	max
min	max	max	0

2 **a** Mark in a position at the minimum of the curve. According to classical physics an atom has no vibrational KE when the temperature is at 0 K.

b The atom would have enough energy to leave the potential 'well' and be able to move away from its neighbour (if all the atoms had this much energy, the solid would melt and then vaporise).

3 Potential energy stored = $\frac{1}{2}ke^2 = 0.5 \times 100$ N m^{-1} $\times (0.04)^2$
= 0.08 J.
If this is all transferred to KE, $E_k = \frac{1}{2}mv^2 = 0.08$ J,
$v = \sqrt{(2 \times 0.08/0.200)} = 0.89$ m s^{-1}.
So doubling the extension also doubles the maximum speed.

4 **a** g.p.e. stored = $mg\Delta h = 0.500$ kg $\times 9.8$ N kg^{-1} $\times 0.05$ m
= 0.25 J (to 2 s.f.).

b 0.25 J. This is also the total energy since there is no KE at the top of the oscillation.

c If all the g.p.e. is transferred to KE, $E_k = 0.25$ J $= \frac{1}{2}mv^2$.
So the maximum velocity will be $v = \sqrt{(2 \times 0.25/0.50)}$
= 1 m s^{-1}.

5 **a** $E = \frac{1}{2}kx^2$, so amplitude increases by a factor of $\sqrt{2}$.

b A thicker bar would be heavier and have a higher spring constant.
Both factors result in smaller oscillations for a given energy.

c A lower Young modulus gives lower k, so bigger oscillations.

6

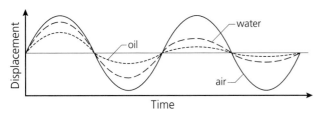

When the mass and spring are oscillating in a more viscous ('sticky') medium, there will be more resistance to the motion. There will be more energy transferred from the oscillations to the medium and the amplitude of the oscillations will die away more quickly. (There will be more damping.)

7 $f = 1/T$. $T = 12$ hours which is $12 \times 60 \times 60 = 43\,200$ seconds.
So $f = \frac{1}{43\,200} = 2.31 \times 10^{-5}$ Hz.

8 $\omega^2 = -a/x$. So the units of ω^2 are m s^{-2}/m = s^{-2}.
So ω has units of s^{-1}.
In fact ω has units of radians per second.

9

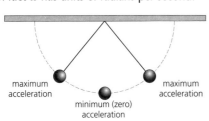

10 $a = -(2\pi f)^2 x = 4 \times \pi^2 \times (25\,000)^2 \times 6.25 \times 10^{-5} = 1.5 \times 10^6$ m s^{-2}.

11 When the frequency of rotation of the washing machine matches its natural frequency, there will be large-amplitude vibrations due to resonance. When the top surface of the washing machine has an acceleration due to its vibrations of more than 10 m s^{-2}, any object left on top will not be able to stay in contact with it. (The surface will accelerate down at a greater rate than gravity.) If the acceleration, a, is 10 m s^{-2}, then $x = a/\omega^2$
$= 10/(2 \times \pi \times 1000/60)^2 = 9.12 \times 10^{-4}$ m, i.e. an amplitude of just under 1 mm will be enough.

12 $x = 2 \times \cos(1.45 \times 10^{-4} \times 14\,400) = -1$ m. That is 1 m below the mean tide level.

13 **a** Frequency = 30/60 = 0.5 Hz.
So displacement, $x = 0.2 \times \cos(2 \times \pi \times 0.5 \times 0.5) = 0$ m

b Frequency = 30/60 = 0.5 Hz. So displacement,
$x = 0.2 \times \cos(2 \times \pi \times 0.5 \times 0.75) = -0.14$ m (0.14 m on the other side of the equilibrium position).

14 **a** $T = 2 \times \pi \sqrt{(1/1000)} = 0.20$ s (to 2 s.f.).

b $F = 1/T = 50$ Hz

Displacement (m)	Velocity (m s^{-1})	Kinetic energy (J)
0.020	0.00	0.00
0.015	4.16	8.64
0.010	5.44	14.80
0.005	6.08	18.51
0.000	6.28	19.74

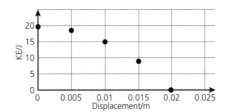

15 $T = 2\pi \sqrt{(l/g)}$. So $l = gT^2/4\pi^2 = 0.994$ m

16 **a** $T = 2\pi\sqrt{(l/g)} = 4.95$ s

b The pendulum does not oscillate because the bob is in free fall. There is no tension in the string, so the SHM formula is not valid.

17 The factors are:
mass because bigger masses accelerate more slowly
spring constant because stiffer springs give bigger forces, making the mass accelerate faster.

18 Although hanging vertically alters the overall length of the spring, it does not change the effects of mass and spring constant, so the period is unchanged.

19 Doubling k increases ω by $\sqrt{2}$, so:

a $f = \omega/2\pi$, so f increases by a factor of $\sqrt{2}$

b $E = \frac{1}{2}kx^2$, so for the same amplitude, energy doubles

c $v = \omega \sqrt{(A^2 - x^2)}$, so speed v increases by a factor of $\sqrt{2}$.

20 Frequency is proportional to $\sqrt{(k/m)}$, so you need to make the horn stiffer (higher k) or lighter (smaller m). You could use a smaller spherical tip, less-dense material, material with higher Young modulus or a shorter rod. A wider rod would be stiffer, but it would also be heavier: the net effect is not easy to predict.

21 The liquid will provide much more damping than air. Damping causes the frequency of maximum response to drop. If you tuned the horn in air, it would give a poor performance in the liquid.

Chapter 2

1 The table contains examples of mechanical waves, light is not a mechanical wave. Mechanical waves need a medium to sustain the vibrations, EM waves do not.

2 Compression waves on a spring, caused by a displacement of the spring.

3 The seagulls are 1.5 wavelengths apart. So $1.5\lambda = 150$ m. $\lambda = 100$ m.

4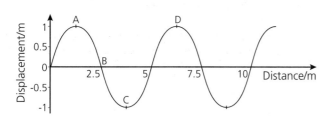

5 π radians = 180°. So $\pi/6$ radians = 30°. This is 30/360 = 1/12 of a wavelength, so the shortest distance is 3/12 = 0.25 m.

6 $T = 1/f = 1/256 = 3.91 \times 10^{-3}$ s.

7 $f = 1/T = 1/(60 \times 60) = 2.78 \times 10^{-4}$ Hz.

8 $\lambda = c/f = 330/256 = 1.29$ m.

9 $f = c/\lambda = 3 \times 10^8/1500 = 200\,000$ Hz or 200 kHz.

10 a The period = $0.015/6.5 = 2.3 \times 10^{-3} = 1/T$. $T = 433$ Hz

   b The gradient at any point gives the velocity.

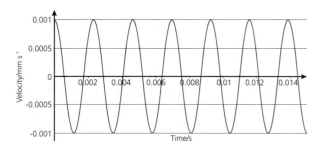

11 The P–S interval is about 10 minutes which is $10 \times 60 = 600$ s. $600 \times 3500 = 2.1 \times 10^6$ metres away or 2100 km.

12 The seismograph gives the distance, but not the direction to the epicentre.
   The epicentre could be anywhere at a given radius away. Three seismographs collected at three different locations are needed. The intersection of circles that are centred on the seismographs at A, B and C give an unambiguous reading.

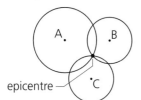

13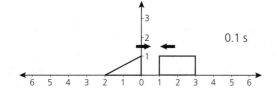

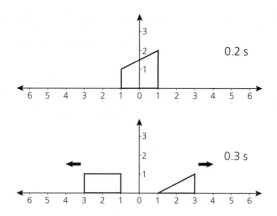

14 Fundamental is $\lambda/2$. So $\lambda = 60$ cm = 0.60 m. $f = c/\lambda = 330/0.60 = 550$ Hz.
   If the pipe is closed at one end, the fundamental is $\lambda/4$ so $\lambda = 120$ cm = 1.20 m.
   $f = c/\lambda = 330/1.20 = 275$ Hz.

15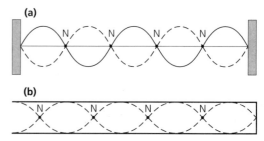

(a)

(b)

Chapter 3

1 The microphone would detect a series of quiet and loud points. A quiet point would occur when there was a difference of an odd number of ½ wavelengths between the distance travelled by the two sound waves. A loud point would occur when there was a difference of a whole number of wavelengths between the two waves. For example, in the middle of the speakers, each wave has travelled 5 m and there would be a loud point. At 4.75 m from one speaker, and 5.25 m from the other, the path difference is ½ wavelength and the microphone would detect a quiet point.

2 $\lambda = \omega s/D = 0.5 \times 3/5 = 1.5/5 = 0.3$ m.
   $f = c/\lambda = 330/0.3 = 1100$ Hz or 1.1 kHz.
   Since $s = \lambda D/\omega$, the three changes are:
   Increase the wavelength (lower frequency),
   Increase the distance between the observer and the loudspeakers,
   Or move the speakers closer together.

3 At longer wavelengths you need a longer path difference for constructive interference. That needs a bigger angle, so the fringe separation is bigger.

4 Fringes get further apart if you move the screen further from the slits or if you move the slits closer together.

5 The car passes through positions of cancellation and positions of strong signal. Using $c = f\lambda$ gives $\lambda = 100$ m. Using $s/\lambda = D/\omega$ gives $s = 100 \times 10\,000/1000 = 1000$, so the car passes through a maximum every 1 km.

6 Mobile phones also use radio waves. Reflections from walls will cause constructive and destructive interference, just as for the TV signal.

7 The reflector increases the signal strength by reflecting back a wave which constructively interferes. The reflecting sheet also stops the aerial picking up waves which have bounced off buildings behind the aerial. This prevents ghosting.

8 The aerial receives two radio waves, one direct from the transmitter and the other reflected from the aircraft. The two waves interfere. As the aircraft flies over, the path difference between the two radio waves changes, so that they are sometimes in phase and sometimes out of phase with each other. This leads to a fluctuating signal.

9 There are two reflected waves, one from the top of the oil film and one from the top surface of the water. These interfere. At some viewing angles the two waves will be in phase, but this will only happen exactly for a specific wavelength (i.e. when $2d = n\lambda$). So different wavelengths (colours) constructively interfere at different viewing angles and we see coloured patterns on the oil.

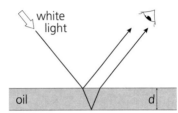

10 Low-frequency sounds have longer wavelengths, they can diffract more around the head and the shadowing effect is reduced.

11 The wavelength of radio waves used for TV is $c/f = 3 \times 10^8$ m s^{-1}/600 $\times 10^6$ = 0.5 m. The wavelength of medium-wave radio waves is $\lambda = 3 \times 10^8$ m s^{-1}/1000 $\times 10^3$ = 300 m. There is much more diffraction with the longer 'medium-wave' radio and so reception is possible in the 'shadow' of a hill.

12 Radio waves are much longer than light waves and so a radio telescope needs to have a much larger aperture to reduce diffraction problems and be able to 'see' more detail.

13 The wavelength of these microwaves is k = c/f = 3×10^8 m s^{-1}/10 $\times 10^9$ Hz = 0.03 m or 3 cm.

   a The gap is much larger than the wavelength so there would be little diffraction, and microwaves would be detected mainly in the region opposite the gap.

   b The gap is now a similar size to the wavelength, the microwaves would be significantly diffracted and would be detected well inside the region of geometric shadow.

14 Along the zero-order beam, path difference is zero, which is the same for all wavelengths – all colours interfere constructively.

15 The distance between each line is $d = 1/200\,000 = 5 \times 10^{-6}$ m. The maximum number of diffracted beams can be found by putting q = 90°, i.e. sin q = 1 into the equation: $n = d \sin q / \lambda$. This gives $n = 5 \times 10^{-6} \times 1/(600 \times 10^{-9}) = 8.33$. So there are 8 beams on each side of the central maximum, so $8 \times 2 = 16$, plus the zero-order, = 17 diffracted beams in total.

Chapter 4

1 Real capacitors gradually discharge as charges move across the imperfect insulating layer.

2 10 pF is the capacitance. The capacitor will store 10×10^{-9} C for each 1 V of potential difference applied across it. 0.1 V is the maximum potential difference that can be applied to this capacitor, before electrical breakdown occurs.

3 $Q = CV = 1 \times 10^{-6} \times 10 = 10$ mC.
   $Q = CV = 1 \times 10^{-6} \times 100 = 100$ mC.

The amount of charge stored is limited by the maximum potential difference that can be applied to the capacitor.

4 Because human skin has high resistance, a large p.d. is needed, otherwise no significant current would flow.

5 Using $E = \frac{1}{2}CV^2$, $V = \sqrt{(2E/C)} = 2683$ V.

6 $1/e^7 = 0.09\%$.

7 In one time constant the charge will drop to 0.368 of its original value. From the graph this happens after approximately 1 s, so Time constant = CR = 1s and $R = 1/1000 \times 10^6$ = 1000 Ω = 1 kΩ.

8 a $Q = CV = 1000 \times 10^{-9} \times 6 = 6 \times 10^{-6}$ C.

   b $T = CR = 1000 \times 10^{-9} \times 1 \times 10^6 = 1$ second.

   c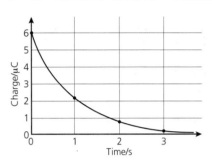

   d $Q = Q_0 e^{-t/CR} = 6 \times 10^{-6} \times e^{-1} = 2.21 \times 10^{-6}$ C.

   e $V = Q/C = (2.21 \times 10^{-6})/(1000 \times 10^{-9}) = 2.2$ V. So $I = V/R = 2.2/(1 \times 10^6) = 2.2 \times 10^{-6}$ A.

9 a Higher potential means that the initial charging rate will be higher (since $I = V/R$) and that the final charge stored will be greater (since $Q = CV$).

   b Higher resistance would mean a lower current, so that the capacitor would take longer to charge up.

   c Higher resistance means a lower current, so the capacitor would take longer to discharge.

10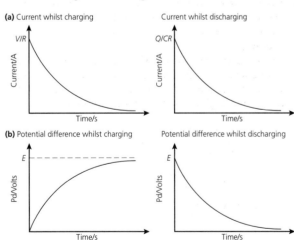

11 The sampling rate depends on the time constant, CR, of the circuit. $CR = 10 \times 10^{-6} \times 10 \times 10^3 = 0.1$ s. A sample rate of once per 1 ms would cover 10 time constants, which is satisfactory. (A sample rate of once per 100 ms would only sample once per time constant, not frequently enough. A sample rate of once per second is far too slow.)

12 High voltage is likely to cause insulation to break down, so separation, d, needs to be kept large. But capacitance is inversely proportional to d, so large d gives small capacitance.

13 Using $1/C = 1/C_1 + 1/C_2$ gives $C = 24$ mF.
The charge on each plate is $Q = CV = 0.024$ C.
Using $V = Q/C$, p.d.s are 400 V and 600 V for the 60 mF and 40 mF capacitors respectively.

14 A chain of three capacitors in series would have a working voltage of 3000 V, but only (50/3) mF capacitance. You would need to link six such chains in parallel.

Chapter 5

1 Earth completes one rotation each day, so $T = 24$ hours
$= 86\,400$ s.
$f = 1/T = 11.6 \times 10^{-6}$ Hz.

2 $f = 200/60 = 3.33$ Hz. $T = 1/3.33 = 0.3$ s.
$f = 500/60 = 8.33$ Hz. $T = 1/8.33 = 0.12$ s.

3 $\omega = 2\pi f$.
$f = 10$ rpm $= 10/60 = 1/6$ Hz.
$\omega = 2\pi \times 1/6 = 1.05$ rad s^{-1}.

4 $T = 1$ year $= 365 \times 24 \times 60 \times 60 = 31.5 \times 10^6$ s.
$\omega = 2\pi/T = 2\pi/(31.5 \times 10^6) = 200 \times 10^{-9}$ rad s^{-1}.

5 **a** $\omega = 2\pi/T = 2.09$ rad s^{-1}.
   b $v = r\omega = 5 \times 2.09 = 10.5$ m s^{-1}.

6 $v = r\omega$ and $\omega = 200 \times 10^{-9}$ from Q3. $v = 14.9 \times 10^{10} \times 200 \times 10^{-9}$
$= 29\,800$ m s^{-1}. Almost 30 km s^{-1}.

7 $a = v^2/r = 26^2/23 = 29.4$ m s^{-2} (about 3 g).

8 $a = r\omega^2 = 6 \times 10^6 \times (2\pi/(60 \times 60 \times 24))^2 = 0.03$ m s^{-2}.

9 $v = \sqrt{(a \times r)} = \sqrt{(3 \times 9.8 \times 3000)} = 297$ m s^{-1}. (300 m s^{-1} or 1080 km h^{-1}).

10 $r = v^2/a = 2572$ m.

11 **a** The gravitational attraction between the Moon and the Earth.
   b The contact force between the Y-fronts and the drum.
   c Friction and the contact force between the rails and the train's wheels.

12 $F = mv^2/r$. Estimate $m = 1000$ kg, $r = 20$ m, $v = 10$ m s^{-1}.
Gives $F = 5000$ N.

13 At the equator your weight is not quite balanced by the contact force. Weight – contact force = centripetal force. The contact force (shown on the scales) is a little less than your weight. There is no such effect at the pole so you appear to weigh more. (There is also an increase in gravity because the Earth is not perfectly spherical, the distance from the centre to the pole is less than from the centre to the equator.)

14 The hammer is moving at high speed in a circular path. It is only the tension in the thrower's muscles that keeps the hammer chain moving in a circle. When the thrower releases the hammer, it travels in a straight line, at a tangent to the circle from the point of the point of release, in accordance with Newton's first law.

15 The wet clothes attempt to move in a straight line, but are prevented from doing so by the inside surface of the drum of the spin-drier. This contact force provides the centripetal force that keeps the clothes moving in a circle. Drops of water can escape through the holes in the drum, and they obey Newton's first law and keep moving in a straight line.

16

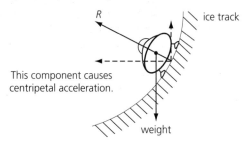

R
ice track
This component causes centripetal acceleration.
weight

The track is banked. The horizontal component of the contact force of the track acting on the bob-sleigh accelerates it round the bend.

17 $\tan \omega = v^2/gr$
or $v^2 = gr \tan \omega$
$v^2 = 9.8 \times 20 \times \tan 45° = 196$
$v = 14$ m s^{-1}.

18 At the top of the circle the balance would read zero. At the bottom of the circle the balance would read 2 kg. When the weight *just* doesn't fall on your head,
$v^2 = gr = 10 \times 1 = 10$
so at the bottom of the circle,
tension $= T_B = W + mv^2/r = 10 + 1 \times 10/1 = 20$ N.

19 $v = \sqrt{gr} = \sqrt{(10 \times 500)} = \sqrt{5000} = 71$ m s^{-1}.

20 $a = v^2/r = 100^2/500 = 20$ m s^{-2}.
   a $F = ma = 60 \times 20 = 1200$ N downwards.
   b $F = ma = 60 \times 20 = 1200$ N upwards.
The *resultant* force is constant around the circle.

Chapter 6

1 **a** $F_1 = -GmM_E/(R + h_1)^2$
where M_E = mass of the Earth and
R = radius of the Earth
h_1 = height of initial orbit
$F_2 = -GmM_E/(R + h_2)^2$
where h_2 = height of final orbit
$F_2/F_1 = (R + h_1)^2/(R + h_2)^2 = (7100)^2/(6900)^2 = 1.06$ times greater in the lower orbit.
   b Since F is providing the centripetal force, $a = 1.06$ times greater than before.
$v^2 = ra$ but r is 1.03 times less than before.
v^2 has increased by a factor of $1.06/1.03 = 1.03$
v will increase by a factor of 1.015.

2 $F = GM_PM_S/r^2 = M_Pv^2/r$ combining gives $v^2 = GM_S/r$
but time for one orbit $T = 2\pi r/v$, $v = 2\pi r/T$ which means
$4\pi^2r^2/T^2 = GM_S/r$
or $r^3 = (GM_S/4\pi^2)T^2$, $(GM_S/4\pi^2)$ is constant. Therefore $r^3 \propto T^2$.

3 Since $r^3 \propto T^2$, $T_{Pluto} = T_{Earth} \times (40)^{3/2} = 253$ Earth years.

4 The weight of a mass, m, on Earth = mg = GMm/R2. So ME = R2g/G. The radius of the Earth and free-fall acceleration were already known, so measuring G enabled ME to be calculated.

5 Work done in taking craft from surface of the Earth to infinity
$= GM_Em/R = 2.74 \times 10^{12}$ J.
Work done in taking craft from 185 km to infinity $= 2.67 \times 10^{12}$ J.
Difference = work done in lifting space craft into orbit $= 7 \times 10^{10}$ J.

6 Work done $= ((GmM_{Moon}/R) - GmM_{Moon})/(h + R) = 7.46 \times 10^8$ J
(where R is the radius of the Moon).

7 $v = \sqrt{(2GM_E/R)}$ which gives $R = 8.9 \times 10^{-3}$ m. If the Earth was crushed to this size, about 1 cm radius, it would be a black hole with a density
of 2×10^{30} kg m^{-3}.

8 **a** As the rocket accelerated upwards the scales would show an increased reading, since they are supporting the astronaut's weight and are causing an acceleration.
   b In orbit both astronaut and scales are falling towards the Earth at the same rate, so the reading is zero.

9 To simulate Earth gravity we need an acceleration of about 10 m s^{-2}.
$a = v^2/r$ gives $v = 100$ m s^{-1}.
Such a large space-station would only need to rotate once per minute. The astronauts would walk on the 'inside' of the outer circumference of the doughnut with their heads towards the centre.

10 • If the satellite is to stay above the same place then it must have the same axis of rotation as the Earth.
   • The centripetal force on the satellite is due to gravity, so the centre of its orbit must be the centre of the Earth.
   The only orbit which meets both conditions is an equatorial one.

11 $T = 2\pi r/v$ and $v = \sqrt{(GM_E/r)}$, $r = 7.1 \times 10^6$ m, and
   $v = 7.5 \times 10^3$ m s^{-1}
   Therefore $T = 5930$ s.

12 $R^2/r^2 = M_E/M_S = 3 \times 10^{-6}$. This gives $R = 1.7 \times 10^{-3}$ r. The neutral point is 0.998 of the way to the Sun or 1.493×10^{11} m from Earth.

13 $V = -GM_E/r$ so
   a −61 MJ kg^{-1}
   b −1.04 MJ kg^{-1}
   $\Delta V = -1.04 - (-63) = 60$ MJ kg^{-1}
   Potential is energy per unit mass, so 60 MJ kg^{-1} × m = $\frac{1}{2}mv^2$
   $v = 11.0 \times 10^3$ m s^{-1}.

14 a Potential energy gets less (i.e. more negative).
   b Kinetic energy increases.
   c The satellite speeds up.
   d The total energy gets less (i.e. more negative).
   The presence of the atmosphere means that more energy will be transferred to internal energy if the satellite and the surrounding atmosphere. This heating effect will reduce the kinetic energy and slow the satellite down.

Chapter 7

1 a 10 mT.
  b zero.

2 $F/\lambda = BI = 0.5/0.1 = 5$ N, assuming that the magnetic field is radial and therefore cuts the wires at right angles.

3 0.13 g corresponds to a force of approximately 0.0013 N.
  $B = F/I\lambda = 0.0013/1 \times 0.05 = 0.026$ T or 26 mT.

4 a flux is down into page
  b faster below lead plate.

5 Although the neon isotope has twice the charge and so twice the force acts upon it, it also has approximately twice the mass. The two isotopes will have paths of similar curvature and the results will overlap.

6 The radius is three times as large, and since $r = mv/Bq$, the mass must be three times as big.

7 a $r = mv/Bq < 0.375$ m
  b $n = 40\ 000$ m^{-1}, so using $B = m_0 nI$ gives $I = 4.0$ A.

8 Ignoring movement of the nucleus, the proton can reach a point where $V = 10$ MV. Using $V = Q/(4\pi e_0 r)$ gives $r = 1.2 \times 10^{-15}$ m.

9 Using $V = Q/(4\pi e_0 r)$ and $E = Q/(4\pi e_0 r^2)$ gives $E = V/r$
  a $E \approx 200\ 000$ V m^{-1}
  b Same answer, although there would be more charge on the sphere.

10 a $V = W/q = W/e = 13.8$ V
   b Using $V = Q/(4\pi e_0 r)$ gives $r = 1.04 \times 10^{-10}$ m, so diameter of atom $\approx 2 \times 10^{-10}$ m
   c Using $E = Q/(4\pi e_0 r^2)$ gives $E = 1.33 \times 10^{11}$ V m^{-1}

11 a Kinetic energy.
   b Potential energy (electrostatic).
   c Around 2.5×10^{-13}, 250 fm.

12 a 8 keV, 1.3×10^{-15} J
   b $\frac{1}{2}mv^2 = 1000 \times 1.3 \times 10^{-15}$

$$v^2 = \frac{2.6 \times 10^{-12}}{1.673 \times 10^{-27}}$$
$$v = 1.2 \times 10^6 \text{ m s}^{-1}$$

c $$r = \frac{mv}{BQ} = \frac{1.673 \times 10^{-27} \times 1.2 \times 10^6}{0.8 \times 1.602 \times 10^{-19}}$$
$$= 0.016 \text{ m, 16 mm}$$

d $$t = \frac{x}{v} = \frac{\pi \times 0.016}{1.2 \times 10^6}$$
$$= 4.2 \times 10^{-8} \text{ s, 42 } \mu s$$

e $$f = \frac{1}{T} = \frac{1}{2 \times 4.2 \times 10^{-8}}$$
$$= 1.2 \times 10^7 \text{Hz, 12 MHz}$$

13
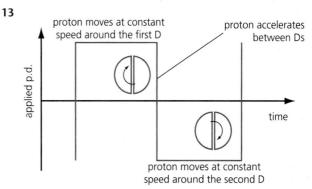

14 A large radius can achieve higher speeds for a given magnetic field strength. Can compensate for relativistic effects (mass change of high speed protons) by varying the magnetic field. Magnetic field does not have to cover the whole area of the circle. Acceleration can continue for longer, so higher speeds possible.

15 The particles need to be kept on a path of fixed radius. From r = mv/BQ, as v increases, B must increase to compensate. At very high speeds, approaching the speed of light, the mass of the particles starts to increase noticeably. Again, B must be increased to keep r constant.

Chapter 8

1 The blade is a conductor cutting through flux, so an e.m.f. is induced. The blade cuts through an area of 452 m^2 every 6 seconds in a flux density of 20 μT. The flux cut is therefore 452 m^2 × 20 × 10^{-6} T
  = 0.00904 Wb.
  Using $E = \Delta F/\Delta t$, the e.m.f. is 0.00904 Wb / 6 s = 0.0015 V.

2 Total flux through the disc = BA = 0.1 × π × 0.3^2 = 0.028 Wb
  Emf = rate of change of flux, so 3 × 10^{-3} = 0.028/t, t = 0.106 s.
  The disc rotates once every 0.106 s or at 565 rpm.

3 The emf will be greater at higher velocities but it won't be possible to measure it. Any voltmeter will involve putting a conductor across the wings, which itself will be inside the magnetic field and will itself have the same emf induced across it. The two emfs will balance and no current will flow.

4 Factors are speed of rotation, area of coil, number of turns and flux density.
  3000 rpm gives ω = (3000 × 2π rad)/60 seconds = 314 rad s^{-1}
  Using $E = NAB\omega$, E = 5000 × (0.50 m × 0.10 m) × 0.015 T × 314
  = 1180 V.

5   a   At 200 kV, current is $I = P/V = 10^9$ W/200 000 V = 5000 A, so power loss in cables is $P = I^2R = (5000)^2 \times 10 = 250$ MW, a 25% loss.

    b   At 400 kV this drops to 6.25%.

Chapter 9

1   $^{235}_{92}U + ^1_0n \rightarrow ^{236}_{92}U \rightarrow ^{133}_{54}Xe + ^{100}_{38}Sr + 3\,^1_0n$
    There are a number of possible answers, just make sure that the mass numbers on the right-hand side of the equation add up to 236 and that the atomic numbers add up to 92.

2   mass of 94 protons = $94 \times 1.0073 = 94.686$ u.
    mass of 145 neutrons = $145 \times 1.0087 = 146.262$ u.
    total mass of constituents = 240.947 u.
    nuclear mass = 239.052, so mass defect = 1.896 u.

3   From question 2, the mass defect of Pu-239 = 1.896 u.
    Convert this to kg:
    mass defect = $1.896 \times 1.660 \times 10^{-27} = 3.147 \times 10^{-27}$ kg
    binding energy = $3.147 \times 10^{-27} \times (3 \times 10^8)^2$
    $= 2.833 \times 10^{-10}$ J or 1.769×10^9 eV.

4   Originally the total mass was:
    239.052 u (Pu-239) + 1.009 (neutron) = 240.061 u
    After the fission the mass is:
    (Br) + 149.920 (Nd) + 3×1.009 (neutrons)
    + 0.000548 (beta particle) = 239.870 u
    The mass defect is 0.191 u. This is an energy release of 178 MeV per fission.

5   Mass change = $E/c^2 = (400 \times 10^3)/(3 \times 10^8)^2$
    $= 4.44 \times 10^{-12}$ kg (not quite detectable with kitchen scales!).

6   The products of a carbon fission would have less binding energy per nucleon than the original carbon nucleus, so a carbon fission would need more energy to cause it than it could release.

7   1/20 s = 50 ms. This means $3^{50} = 7.2 \times 10^{23}$ fissions. Each fission releases 200 MeV, so $7.2 \times 10^{23} \times 200 \times 10^6 \times 1.6 \times 10^{-19} = 2.3 \times 10^{13}$ J.

8   a   To prevent the critical mass being reached.

    b   Water could act as a moderator, slow down escaping neutrons and increase the chances of further fission reactions occurring.

9   As time goes on there is a build up of fission products; these absorb neutrons and slow down the chain reaction.

10 a   Thermal neutrons have a kinetic energy comparable to that of particles their size in a hot gas.

    b   Uranium-235 absorbs thermal neutrons more easily than it absorbs fast neutrons.

11 The coolant in a PWR is water and this can become radioactive when exposed to a neutron flux. For that reason it is important that the primary cooling system is entirely contained. In a gas-cooled reactor, the primary cooling system can lead outside the shielding because the coolant nuclei (carbon and oxygen) do not absorb neutrons so much.

12 Advantages: water acts as a moderator, so an extra moderator is not needed, which leads to a much more compact design. Water has a high specific heat capacity.
    Disadvantages: the water can become radioactive. Water can liberate oxygen and hydrogen – both chemically reactive gases.

13 a   The hydrogen will absorb neutrons to become deuterium.

    b   The absorption of neutrons by oxygen is a thousand times less frequent than that of hydrogen and it would take three neutrons (a billion times less frequent) to produce an unstable isotope of oxygen.

    c   H-3 (tritium) emits β.

14 a
    momentum: $mv_1 = mv_2 + 12mv_3$
    kinetic energy: $\frac{1}{2}mv_1^2 = \frac{1}{2}mv_2^2 + \frac{1}{2}12mv_3^2$
    $10^{10} = v_2^2 + 12v_3^2$
    so, $10^{10} = v_2^2 + 12((10^5 - v_2)/12)^2$
    $10^{10} = v_2^2 + 12((10^{10} + v_2^2 - 2 \times 10^5 v_2)/144)$
    $12 \times 10^{10} = 12v_2^2 + 10^{10} + v_2^2 - 2 \times 10^5 v_2$
    $0 = 13v_2^2 - 2 \times 10^5 v_2 - 11 \times 10^{10}$
    $0 = (13v_2 + (11 \times 10^5))(v_2 - 10^5)$
    $v_2 = -11/13 \times 10^5 = 0.85 \times 10^5$ m s^{-1} backwards.

    b   Concentrating on the 'mean' neutron:
    $\frac{1}{2}m\bar{c}^2 = \frac{3}{2}kT$
    $\bar{c}^2 = 3kT/m$
    $c = 1.98 \times 10^7$ m s^{-1}.

15 a   The coolant should not absorb neutrons at all for safety considerations. The moderator should preferably not absorb neutrons, but should interact with them significantly to absorb their energy. Control rods should strongly absorb neutrons.

    b   Boron or cadmium.

16 a   900 MW is 9×10^8 J per second. This corresponds to a mass loss of:
    $E = mc^2 = 9 \times 10^8$
    $m = (9 \times 10^8)/c^2 = 1.00 \times 10^{-8}$ kg, or 10 mg
    10 mg per second.

    b   Energy inefficiency.

17 a   Using $A = A_0 \exp(-\lambda t)$ (see Chapter 10)
    If $A/A_0 = 0.01$, then:
    $\exp(-\lambda t) = 0.01$, $-\lambda t = \ln 0.01 = -4.605$, so $t = 4.605/\lambda$
    Now, $\lambda = \ln 2/\text{half-life} = 0.693/24\,000 = 2.89 \times 10^{-5}$ year^{-1}.
    So $t = 4.605/(2.89 \times 10^{-5}) = 159 \times 10^3$ years.

    b   This is an underestimate of the time taken to decay because Pu-239 will decay into a radioisotope which is also radioactive. In fact there will be a decay series of radioactive products.

18 The rods are physically hot, due to the energy released by their own radioactivity. The water helps to dissipate this heat. The water provides a radiation barrier, to absorb emitted gamma rays, etc.

19 a   Alpha and gamma.

    b   The products of fission present in used fuel produce beta radiation. Neutrons will have transformed some nuclei to produce new radionuclides.

20 a $^{16}_8O + 3\,^1_0n \rightarrow ^{19}_8O$.

    b $^{19}_8O \rightarrow ^{19}_9F + ^{0}_{-1}e^- + \bar{v}$.

    c   Fluorine is enormously different from oxygen in its chemical behaviour. Oxygen atoms 'disappearing' from molecules in the concrete would cause the break down of the molecules and weaken the structure of the concrete.

21 $^7_3Li + ^1_0n \rightarrow ^3_1H$ (tritium) $+ ^4_2He$ or $^7_3Li + ^1_0n \rightarrow ^3_1H + ^4_2He + ^1_0n$.

Chapter 10

1   53 protons, 53 electrons and $131 - 53 = 78$ neutrons

2   Hydrogen ^1_1H: deuterium ^2_1H: tritium ^3_1H

3   Alpha particles are relatively massive (8000 × more massive than the beta particle) and so they are not easily deflected. The

electric and magnetic fields used by early experimenters were simply not strong enough.

4   $5 \times 10^6/10 = 500\ 000$ ion pairs.

5   Alpha particles have a short range in air, only a few cm, even those reaching the body would be stopped by the outer layers of skin. So alpha emitters outside the body present little risk. However, if an alpha source is ingested all of its energy is deposited in living tissues, the lining of the lungs for example, which makes it very hazardous.

6   $^{241}_{95}\text{Am} \rightarrow \,^{237}_{93}\text{Np} + \,^{4}_{2}\text{He}$

7   $^{14}_{6}\text{C} \rightarrow \,^{14}_{7}\text{N} + \,^{0}_{-1}\text{e}$ (An anti–neutrino is also emitted)

8   The short, thick tracks on the left are due to alpha particles which are short range and densely ionising. The meandering tracks on the right are due to beta particles which are less densely ionising and more easily deflected from their path (because of their lower mass)

9   The beta has the greater range in air. An alpha particle has many more collisions causing ionisation per cm than a beta particle. It deposits much more of its energy in a short distance and so comes to a stop long before the beta particle.

10 $1\ \text{MeV} = 1 \times 10^6 \times 1.6 \times 10^{-19}\ \text{J} = 1.6 \times 10^{-13}\ \text{J}$.
    $f = E/h = (1.6 \times 10^{-13})/(6.63 \times 10^{-34}) = 2.41 \times 10^{20}\ \text{Hz}$

11 Using $E = hf$ for each possible transition:
    0.90 MeV → 0 MeV, 2.2×10^{20} Hz.
    0.90 MeV → 0.28 MeV, 1.5×10^{20} Hz.
    0.90 MeV → 0.66 MeV, 5.8×10^{19} Hz.
    0.66 MeV → 0 MeV, 1.6×10^{20} Hz.
    0.66 MeV → 0.28 MeV, 9.2×10^{19} Hz.
    0.28 MeV → 0 MeV, 6.8×10^{19} Hz.

12 Alpha and beta particles are absorbed and scattered much more than gamma rays. An inverse–square law would apply to point sources of alpha and beta radiation in a vacuum, where there would be no absorption or scattering.

13 To keep as large a distance as possible between the gamma source and the experimenter. To avoid any contamination, i.e. to make sure that no cobalt is transferred to the experimenter.

14 The average background count is 12.6 per minute. (This has to subtracted from all the other values)
    a   A graph of x (y–axis) Vs $(1/\sqrt{c})$ should be a straight line. Any intercept on the y-axis will be due to a difference between the measured distance and the true distance to from the source to the active region of the GM tube. This difference is referred to as 'd' in the text.
    $y = 0.3407x - 0.0078$
    b $d = 0.008$ m , or 8 mm.

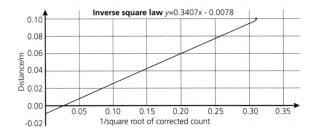

c   The readings at larger distances are lower and therefore subject to higher statistical errors.
d   More samples could be taken at small distances.
The readings at higher distances could be taken over much longer time periods. In practice GM tubes are not very efficient at counting gamma rays and are less reliable at high count rates

(due to the 'dead–time' between registering a count and becoming sensitive to the next gamma ray). A scintillator would be a better detector to use.

15 Alpha particles are densely ionising and much more likely to cause lots of damage to a cell in a short time, making cell repair more difficult.

16 Strontium tends to get concentrated on the bone surfaces, irradiating the bone marrow where new blood cells are being formed. These rapidly dividing cells are radiosensitive and large amounts of damage will be caused, possibly leading to leukaemia.

17 5×10^{-10} g is $(5 \times 10^{-10})/99 = 5.05 \times 10^{-12}$ of a mole.
    This is $5.05 \times 10^{-12} \times 6.022 \times 10^{23} = 3.04 \times 10^{12}$ nuclei
    Activity $= \lambda N = 3.2 \times 10^{-5} \times 3.04 \times 10^{12} = 9.73 \times 10^7$ (97 MBq)

18 a   48 000 yrs is two half–lives, so activity will have dropped to one quarter, = 5 MBq.
    b $\lambda = \ln 2/T_{1/2} = 2.89 \times 10^{-5}$ yr^{-1}
    c $A = 20 \times 10^6 \times \text{e}^{-(2.89 \times 10^{-5} \times 100\ 000)} = 1.11 \times 10^6$ Bq or 1.11 MBq.

19 Low count rates and lack of reliable calibration data make accurate work difficult for such old samples.

20 $A = -\lambda N$ so we need $N = A/\lambda = 100/(3.833 \times 10^{-12}) = 2.60 \times 10^{13}$ atoms of C-14. This will need approximately 2.1×10^{25} atoms of carbon.
    This is $(2.1 \times 10^{25})/(6.02 \times 10^{23}) = 34.7$ moles. Which would have a mass of $34.7 \times 12 = 416$ g.

21 Valuable artefacts, like the Turin shroud, cannot have large samples taken from them to check the date. Accelerator mass spectrometry limits the damage that is done by dating.

22 Mass difference between helium–5 and the combined mass of the products is $5.0123 - (4.002604 + 1.008\ 665) = 0.00103$. This extra mass is converted to energy and the reaction is possible.

23 $^{5}_{3}\text{Li} \rightarrow \,^{1}_{1}\text{p} + \,^{4}_{2}\text{He}$

Chapter 11

1   Beta particles are much lighter than alpha particles. They are scattered much more by the atomic electrons than the alpha particles were. Much higher energy electrons are needed to 'see' the nucleus.

2   The lower atomic number means less charge in the nucleus, which means that alpha particles would need to be closer to the nucleus before appreciable scattering took place. There would be less large angle scattering.

3   $E_p = qV = Qq/4\pi e_0 r$, so $r = Qq/4\pi e_0\, E_p$
    $= (2 \times 1.6 \times 10^{-19} \times 13 \times 1.6 \times 10^{-19})/(4\pi \times 8.85 \times 10^{-12} \times 4 \times 10^6 \times 1.6 \times 10^{-19})$
    $= 9.35 \times 10^{-15}$ m, or 9.35 fm.

4   From the data for $^{51}_{23}\text{V}$, $r_0 = 4.63/3.708 = 1.25$ fm.
    Sr has nucleon number 68 and radius $1.25 \times (68)^{1/3} = 5.10$ fm
    In has nucleon number 115 and radius $1.25 \times (115)^{1/3} = 6.07$ fm

5   Plotting R Vs $A^{1/3}$ should give a straight line with gradient r_0.
    The graph gives a value of 1.3 fm for r_0 (the gradient)

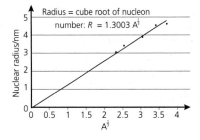

Glossary

Absolute zero   The lowest possible temperature: all molecular motion stops at absolute zero.

Absorption spectrum   A material selectively absorbs radiation emitted by a source, and an oberver of source and material detects this as an absorption spectrum, e.g. absorption of a star's light by clouds of interstellar gas. This can produce a series of dark lines or bands that are characteristic of the absorbing material.

Acceleration, a   The rate of change of velocity (measured in m s^{-2}).

Activity   The number of decays (or emissions) per second in a radioactive source (measured in becquerel's, Bq).

Alpha particle   Strongly ionising, short range radiation emitted by some radioisotopes. An alpha particle is two neutrons and two protons tightly bound together.

Ammeter   An instrument of low resistance connected in series with a component to measure the current.

Angular frequency, f   The number of rotations per second (measured in hertz, Hz). Sometimes given as revolutions per minute, r.p.m., though this is not SI

Angular velocity, ω   The speed of rotation, measured by the angle turned through per second (measured in rad s^{-1}).

Anode   Positive electrode or positive terminal.

Antinode   The point on a standing wave where a quantity reaches a maximum. Usually refers to maximum displacement.

Antiparticles   A particle identical in mass to another more common particle, but different in other properties, e.g.. charge, baryon number and strangeness. A bar over the particle letter, e.g. p, indicates that it is an antiparticle.

Aperture   The opening to a camera or telescope which admits light.

Atomic mass unit, u   A small unit of mass used in nuclear physics. 1 u is defined as one-twelfth of the mass of a carbon-12 atom (1 u = 1.66043 × 10^{-27} kg).

Atomic number   The number of protons in the nucleus of an atom is its atomic number. The atomic number is also the number of electrons in the neutral (i.e. not ionised) atom.

Avogadro constant   The number of particles in a mole of anything: N_A = 6.023 × 10^{23} particles per mole.

Back e.m.f. on break   A high e.m.f. of opposing polarity to the original p.d., caused by the rapid collapse of a magnetic field when a circuit is broken.

Background radiation   The average level of radiation in the environment. It arises from both natural sources, such as radioactive rocks, and artificial sources, such as X-rays used in medicine.

Beta particle   A high speed electron emitted from the nucleus of some radioisotopes.

Binding energy   For an atomic nucleus this is the energy needed to pull it apart, i.e. to separate the individual neutrons and protons.

Black body   A perfect absorber of (heat) radiation. Black bodies are also the best possible emitters. A black body absorbs all of the radiation that falls upon it and reflects none. The temperature of a black body determines the amount of radiation that it emits at each wavelength.

Black hole   An astronomical body that is so dense that its gravitational field is strong enough to prevent even light escaping from it.

Boltzmann constant, k   The gas constant for a single ideal gas molecule ($k = R/N_A$ = 1.381 × 10^{-23} J K^{-1}).

Boundary layer   A layer of slow-moving fluid next to a surface. It may have significant thermal resistance.

Capacitance, C   The charge stored per volt. For parallel plates, the positive charge stored on one plate is used in the calculation.

Capacitor   A device which stores electrical charge (and so electrical energy).

Cathode   Negative electrode or negative terminal.

Centre of gravity   The point at which the weight of a body acts.

Centre of mass   For some applications, an object can be treated as if all its mass is concentrated at one point. This point is called the centre of mass. If the resultant force acting on a body passes through the centre of mass then the body will accelerate in a straight line. If the resultant force does not pass through the centre of mass the body will also spin.

Centripetal   Towards the centre.

Charge   A fundamental property of matter; charged objects experience electrostatic forces; charge may be positive, zero or negative.

Chromatic dispersion   The splitting of waves into different wavelengths during refraction e.g. the coloured spectrum produced by a prism.

Cloud chamber   A device which gives a tiny cloud trail along the track of a charged particle.

Coherent   Describes waves which are of the same frequency, polarisation and amplitude and in a constant phase relationship.

Component   A vector may be replaced by several (usually two) different vectors known as components. Components are usually at right angles to each other, typically horizontally and vertically, and together have exactly the same effect as the original vector.

Compression (wave)   A point in a longitudinal wave where the density and pressure is at a maxiumum.

Conduction (heat)   The transfer of heat through a material without any bulk movement of the material.

Constructive interference   Interference which results in an increased amplitude.

Convection   The transfer of heat caused by the movement of a hot fluid (liquid or gas) into cooler regions (see also natural convection and forced convection).

Conventional current   Consists of positive charge flow. Flows from positive supply terminal, around circuit, to negative.

Critical damping   An amount of damping which is just sufficient to prevent oscillation.

Current, I   The rate of flow of charge in a circuit (measured in amperes, A).

Cyclotron   The cyclotron is a small flat cylindrical can, split into halves called Ds. Charged particles such as protons are accelerated by potential difference between the Ds and made to travel in near-circular motion by a magnetic field. The increasing speed of the charged particles causes them to spiral outwards. The potential difference alternates so that the particles always experience accelerating force when moving between the Ds.

Daughter nucleus Fission produces a small number of free neutrons and two nuclei which are slightly less than half of the size of the initial or parent nucleus. These are the daughter nuclei.

de Broglie relationship Particles, such as electrons, can display wave wave behaviour. Their wavelength, λ, a wave property, depends on their momentum, p, a particle property, as described by de Broglie's relationship:

$$\lambda = \frac{h}{p} \text{ or } p = \frac{h}{\lambda}$$

Damping Any mechanism which absorbs energy of oscillations, causing a reduction of amplitude.

Decay chain Many nuclides decay into nuclides which are also radioactive. There may be a series or chain of decays before a stable nuclide results.

Decay constant, λ The probability that a radioactive nucleus will decay in a given time period.

Dead time The time immediately after an ionising event when a G—M tube cannot detect further ionisations.

Destructive interference Interference leading to decreased wave amplitude, and ultimately to complete cancellation.

Dielectric An insulator which raises the capacitance of a capacitor.

Diffraction The spreading out of the edges of waves to occupy areas which would otherwise be in 'shadow'.

Diffraction grating A grating of many narrow slits, each causing diffraction. These diffracted waves then interfere.

Displacement, s The distance travelled in a certain direction from a given point. It is a vector quantity (measured in metres, m).

Doppler effect The change in frequency of waves emitted by an object as it moves towards or away from an observer.

Doppler shift The shift in frequency due to the movement of a transmitter and/or detector.

Dynamo A device which transfers kinetic energy to electrical energy.

E.m.f. Abbreviation for electromotive force.

Efficiency The ratio of useful energy output to total energy input, or power output to power input.

Elastic A material that stretches under a load and then returns to its original dimensions when the load is removed is said to be elastic.

Elastic collision If the total kinetic energy before and after a collision is the same, the collision is said to be elastic i.e. kinetic energy is conserved in an elastic collision.

Elastic limit When an object is subjected to a force which is just large enough to cause permanent deformation, it is said to have reached its elastic limit.

Electric field A region of space in which charged objects experience a force.

Electric field strength, E At any point in an electric field, this is the force per unit charge on a tiny test charge placed at that point.

Electrical potential, V The work done per unit charge in bringing a tiny test charge from infinity to a point in an electric field.

Electromagnetic induction The generation of e.m.f. in a conductor when it cuts flux or is in a changing magnetic field.

Electromagnetic waves Waves which propagate by swapping energy between electric and magnetic fields: includes radio waves, microwaves, infrared radiation, visible light, ultraviolet radiation, X-rays and gamma rays.

Electromotive force The energy per coulomb produced by a source of electricity; also the p.d. across a source when no current flows.

Electron Charged particle of charge $\approx 1.6 \times 10^{-19}$ C and mass $\approx 9 \times 10^{-31}$ kg. The main charge carrier in metals.

Electronvolt (eV) A unit of energy used in atomic and nuclear physics. It is the energy gained by an electron when it is accelerated through a potential difference of 1 volt (1 eV = 1.6×10^{-19} J).

Emission spectrum The range of wavelengths emitted by a luminous source is known as its emission spectrum. It may be a line, band or continuous spectrum.

Energy Energy is the stored ability to do work.

Energy level Electrons in an atom can only have specific energy values. These are known as the atom's energy levels.

Equilibrium position The usual resting place of a system.

Excitation When an electron absorbs energy and moves to a higher atomic energy level, the atom is said to be in an excited state.

Exponential decay The name given to a mathematical relationship which has a constant reduction period, such as radioactive decay or the discharge of a capacitor.

Feynman diagrams A representation of the exchange of particles in an interaction.

Fission The splitting of a large atomic nucleus, usually uranium or plutonium, into two smaller nuclei. The process releases a few free neutrons and a large amount of energy.

Fixed points Measurements made at standard temperatures which are used to calibrate thermometers.

Fundamental The fundamental frequency is the lowest natural frequency of oscillation of a system.

Fundamental particles Constituents of all matter. These include quarks (make up protons, neutrons, etc.), leptons (these include electrons and neutrinos) and bosons.

Fusion The joining together of two light nuclei, typically isotopes of hydrogen, to form a heavier nucleus, such as helium. Energy is released in this process.

Gamma radiation, gamma ray Penetrating, short wavelength ionising radiation emitted by some radioisotopes.

Geostationary Describes an orbit that keeps a satellite over exactly the same point on the Earth.

Gravitational field The region around a mass where another mass would experience a gravitational attraction.

Gravitational field strength, g The force exerted on a unit mass by a gravitational field (measured in N kg^{-1}). On Earth, g is approximately equal to 10 N kg^{-1}.

Gravitational potential energy The energy due to the position of a mass, m, in a gravitational field. In a uniform field, such as that close to the surface of the Earth, the change in potential energy due to an increase in height, Δh, is $\Delta E_p = mg\Delta h$, where g is the gravitational field strength.

Gravitational potential, V The potential energy of a unit mass in a gravitational field. It is the work done in moving a unit mass from infinity to that point (measured in J kg^{-1}).

Ground state An atom is said to be in its ground state when its electrons all occupy the lowest possible allowed energy levels.

Half-life, $t_{1/2}$ The time taken for the number of radioactive nuclei in a source to drop to half its original value.

Heat Energy transferred from one place to another because the places are at different temperatures.

Induced e.m.f. The e.m.f. induced in a conductor as a result of cutting or changing magnetic flux.

Inelastic collision In an inelastic collision, the total kinetic energy of the system decreases, i.e. kinetic energy is transferred as other forms of energy. Momentum *is* conserved in inelastic collisions.

Inertia A body's resistance to acceleration.

Instantaneous Values measured over an infinitesimally short period of time, Δt. For example, the instantaneous speed of an object can be calculated from the distance travelled in a very small time interval, Δt.

Intensity The power through a given area (measured in W m^{-2}).

Interference The addition of waves which leads to changes in amplitude.

Internal energy The sum of all kinetic and potential energies of the component parts of a system. In ideal gases, equal to total kinetic energy.

Inverse square law The intensity of gamma radiation from a point gamma source is inversely proportional to the square of the distance from the source. If you double the distance between yourself and the source, you will receive one quarter of the radiation dose. This relationship is known as an inverse square law. It is important in other areas of physics, e.g. the strength of the gravitational field due to a spherical mass or the strength of an electric field due to a point change.

Ion An atom which has gained or lost one or more electrons.

Ionisation The removal of electron(s) from an atom, or the addition of electron(s) to an atom.

Ionisation chamber A device relying on charged particles ionising air. The ionisation current is proportional to the number of particles.

Ionising radiation Radiation capable of ejecting electrons from any atoms with which it collides; emanates from the nuclei of radioactive atoms.

Isotope Atoms of an element can exist in different forms. These forms, called isotopes, have the same number of protons and electrons but different numbers of neutrons.

Isotropic The same in all directions.

Kinetic energy The energy stored in a moving mass ($E_K = \frac{1}{2}mv^2$).

Laser A device which produces intense light by stimulated emission from excited molecules (**l**ight **a**mplification by **s**timulated **e**mission of **r**adiation).

Latent heat The heat which you need to supply to a material to change its phase: e.g. heat is needed to convert water into steam.

Linear accelerator (linac for short) An accelerator consisting of a line of tubes positioned end to end. Charged particles are accelerated by the alternating potential difference applied to the tubes.

Longitudinal Describes a wave where oscillations are in the direction of wave travel.

Magnetic flux density, *B* The strength of a magnetic field, measured by the force on a current-carrying wire or moving charge (SI unit is the tesla, T).

Mass defect, mass difference The difference between the mass of a nucleus and the total mass of the nucleons which make up that nucleus.

Moderator The material, often graphite or water, used in a nuclear reactor to slow down neutrons.

Mole The amount of material containing the same number of particles as 12 g of the isotope carbon-12.

Momentum The linear momentum of a body = mass × velocity. It is a vector quantity, measured in kg m s^{-1}.

Natural frequency For a vibrating system this is the frequency at which the system oscillates when disturbed.

Neutron A particle of zero charge found in the nucleus of almost all atoms. A free neutron is unstable and decays to a proton and an electron with a half-life of 11 minutes.

Neutron star The very dense remnant left after the supernova of a star.

Newton The S.I. unit of force. 1 newton is the force that will accelerate a mass of 1 kg at 1 m s^{-2}.

Node (waves) The point on a standing wave where a quantity is zero. Usually refers to zero displacement.

Nucleon A particle that exists in the nucleus of an atom, i.e. neutrons and protons.

Ohm's law The current through a conductor is proportional to the p.d., if temperature and other physical conditions stay constant.

Pair production In a pair production event a photon's energy is manifested as the masses of an electron and a positron.

Parent nucleus An unstable nucleus that decays to produce a daughter nucleus.

Path difference The difference in the distances travelled by two waves, usually expressed in terms of the wavelength.

P.d. Abbreviation for potential difference (q.v.).

Period Time taken to complete one cycle of oscillation, one complete cycle of vibration, one complete wave or one complete rotation in circular motion.

Permeability In magnetism, this is a term related to the ease with which a magnetic field can go through (permeate) a material.

Permittivity A material with high permittivity will permit large charges to build up with a small electric field strength.

Phase A measurement of the relative timing of two oscillations of the same frequency.

Photoelectric effect The emission of electrons from a metal surface caused by light of sufficiently high frequency.

Photon A quantum of electromagnetic radiation. It carries an amount of energy, E, that depends upon the frequency of the radiation. $E = hf$, where h is Planck's constant.

Plane wave the shape of a wavefront arriving from a distant source.

Plastic A material which does not return to its original dimensions when a deforming force is removed is said to be plastic.

Point source of waves A source which produces circular wavefronts as though coming from a single point in space.

Polarised A transverse wave is polarised when the vibration of the wave is confined to one direction.

Positron A particle of same mass as electron and equal but opposite charge; antielectron.

Potential difference The energy transferred per coulomb when charge moves through a circuit (measured in J C^{-1} or V).

Potential energy The stored ability to do work. A body may have potential energy due to its position in a field, e.g. a mass raised above the surface of the Earth has **gravitational** potential energy due to its position in the Earth's gravitational field. **Elastic** potential energy is due to work done in changing the shape of an object, e.g. a stretched rubber band has elastic potential energy.

Power, *P* The rate at which work is done. It can also be thought of as the rate at which energy is transferred (measured in watts, W).

Pressure, P The normal force per unit area; pressure = force/area (measured in pascals, Pa; 1 Pa = 1 N m^{-2}; also in bars, atmospheres, mmHg).

Progressive wave A wave which transfers energy from one place to another.

Propagation The process by which a wave spreads itself through space.

Proton A positively charged particle found in the nucleus of all atoms. Thought to be stable.

Quantum (plural : quanta) This can refer to the smallest quantity of some property (such as energy) or to a discrete particle that carries that quantity.

Quantum theory This theory states that some physical quantities, like the energy of an electron in an atom, can only have certain discrete values. For example, charge is quantised in units of the charge of an electron; it is not possible to have a charge equivalent to 1.5 electrons.

Radian (rad) One radian is the angle subtended at the centre of a circle by an arc whose length is equal to the radius (2π radians = 360°).

Radioisotope A form of a nucleus which is radioactive.

Radiosensitive cells that are particularly vulnerable to ionising radiation.

Rarefaction A point in a longitudinal wave where the density and pressure of the medium are at a minimum.

Refraction The change of direction of waves which results from a change of speed.

Refractive index Light slows down in more dense media. The absolute refractive index of a material is the speed of light in a vacuum divided by the speed in the material.

Relative permittivity The factor by which a dielectric raises the capacitance of a parallel plate capacitor.

Relativistic speed A velocity near to the speed of light.

Resistance, R A measure of a component's tendency to oppose electrical current; ratio of p.d. to current ($R = V/I$).

Resolving Distinguishing between separate parts of an image by an optical instrument.

Resonance This occurs when a system accepts energy from a driving source at its natural frequency – the amplitude increases greatly.

Resultant A single vector which is the result of combining several vectors.

Root mean square, r.m.s. The square root of the average of the squares of the values; a useful average if quantities can be both positive and negative: e.g. r.m.s. of (+3, –4, +6, –5, 0) is 4.14, but arithmetic mean is 0.

SI Stands for Système Internationale and refers to the system of units based on the kilogram, metre and second. SI units are used by nearly all scientists.

Scalar A physical quantity which has magnitude but no direction. Mass, speed, temperature and potential difference are examples of scalar quantities.

Secondary wavelet Every point on a wavefront is a disturbance of the medium, and so acts as a tiny point source of waves called secondary wavelets.

Simple harmonic motion Oscillation where acceleration is always towards the equilibrium position and is proportional to the displacement.

Special relativity Einstein's theory of mechanics, published in 1905. The theory gives results which are identical to Newton's laws except when relative velocities approach the speed of light.

Spontaneous A spontaneous event is one that occurs without an external cause e.g. radioactive decay is a spontaneous event.

Standing wave A state of oscillation of a system which can be regarded as resembling a wave standing still.

Stationary wave Alternative term for standing wave.

Stress The force per unit cross sectional area (measured in Pa).

Strong nuclear force One of the fundamental forces. The strong nuclear force acts between nucleons over a very short range and holds the nuclei of atoms together.

Superconduction At low temperatures, some materials lose all electrical resistance: they become perfect conductors.

Superposition The process of adding waves together, often used to produce an interference pattern.

Synchrotron An accelerator in which particles gain energy as they travel in a circular or near circular path of constant radius.

Tesla (T) Unit of magnetic flux density.

Thermionic emission The emission of electrons from a heated cathode.

Threshold frequency The minimum frequency of light which can cause photoelectric emission.

Transformer A device which uses electromagnetic induction to change the voltage or current of an a.c. supply.

Transverse Describes a wave where vibrations are at right angles to direction of wave travel.

Ultrasonics The study and use of waves which travel as sound waves, by compression and rarefaction, at inaudible frequencies above 20 kHz.

Unresolved When two images overlap to such an extent that they cannot be distinguished.

Vector A physical quantity which has a direction as well as a magnitude. Force, velocity and electric field strength are examples of vector quantities.

Velocity selector A device using electric and magnetic fields at 90°. Only particles of a particular velocity go straight through.

Velocity, v The rate of change of displacement measured in m s^{-1}.

Voltage An alternative term for potential difference.

Voltmeter An instrument of very high resistance connected in parallel with a component to measure the potential difference.

Wave–particle duality The term used to describe the fact that light can behave as a wave or a particle. Subatomic particles, such as electrons, also show wave and particle properties.

Wavelength, λ The distance travelled by a wave in one period of oscillation; the length in space of one cycle.

Weber (Wb) The unit of magnetic flux, Wb = tesla × m^2.

Weight, W Force on a mass, m, due to a gravitational field, measured in newtons, N ($W = mg$).

Work Work, W, is done by a force, F, when it moves its point of application in the direction of the force. If there is an angle θ between the direction of the force and the displacement, s, then $W = Fs \cos \theta$. Work is a scalar quantity (measured in joules, J).

Work function The energy needed to remove an electron from a material in thermionic or photoelectric emission processes.

X-rays Very penetrating, ionising radiation from the short wavelength (high frequency) end of the electromagnetic spectrum. An X-ray is produced by rapid deceleration of a charged particle or by a high-energy electron transition in an atom.

Fundamental constants

Quantity	Symbol	Value	Units
speed of light in vacuo	c	3.00×10^8	m s^{-1}
charge of electron	e	1.60×10^{-19}	C
the Planck constant	h	6.63×10^{-34}	J s
the Avogadro constant	N_A	6.02×10^{23}	mol^{-1}
molar gas constant	R	8.31	J K^{-1} mol^{-1}
the Boltzmann constant	k	1.38×10^{-23}	J K^{-1}
the Stefan constant	σ	5.67×10^{-8}	W m^{-2} K^{-4}
the Wien constant	α	2.90×10^{-3}	m K
electron rest mass	m_e	9.11×10^{-31}	kg
electron charge/mass ratio	e/m_e	1.76×10^{11}	C kg^{-1}
proton rest mass	m_p	1.67×10^{-27}	kg
proton charge/mass ratio	e/m_p	9.58×10^7	C kg^{-1}
neutron rest mass	m_n	1.67×10^{-27}	kg
gravitational field strength	g	9.81	N kg^{-1}
acceleration due to gravity	g	9.81	m s^{-2}

Mathematical constants and equations

$e = 2.72$ $\pi = 3.14$ 1 radian = 57.3°

circumference of circle = $2\pi r$

area of circle = πr^2

area of cylinder = $2\pi rh$

volume of cylinder = $\pi r^2 h$

area of sphere = $4\pi r^2$

volume of sphere = $\frac{4}{3}\pi r^3$

arc = $r\theta$

$\sin^2 \theta + \cos^2 \theta = 1$

For small angles, $\sin \theta \approx \tan \theta \approx \theta$

$y = mx + c$ – equation of a straight line

Properties of solids

At 293 K

Substance	Density	Electrical resistivity	Yield strength	Young modulus	Melting point	Specific latent heat of fusion	Specific heat capacity
	kg m^{-3}	Ω m $\times 10^{-8}$	Pa $\times 10^{6}$	Pa $\times 10^{9}$	K	J kg^{-1} $\times 10^{4}$	J kg^{-1} K^{-1}
alumina, ceramic	3800	–	–	245	2300	–	800
aluminium	2710	2.65	50	71	932	38	913
brass	8500	8.0	450	100	1300	–	370
brick, building	2300	–	–	–	–	–	–
carbon, graphite	2300	–	–	1200	–	–	710
carbon, diamond	3300	–	–	207	3800	–	525
concrete	2400	–	–	14	–	–	3350
constantan	8880	47	–	170	1360	–	420
copper	8930	1.7	75	117	1356	21	385
epoxy resin	1120	–	–	4.5	–	–	1400
gold	19300	2.4	–	71	1340	7	132
iron	7870	10	165	206	1810	27	440
lead	11340	21	12	18	600	2.6	126
marble	2600	–	–	–	–	–	880
perspex	1190	–	–	3.0	350	–	1500
phosphor bronze	8900	7	420	120	–	–	–
platinum	21450	11	–	150	2042	11	136
polystyrene	1050	–	–	3.1	510	–	1300
quartz fibre	2660	–	–	73	2020	–	788
rubber	910	–	–	0.02	300	–	1600
silver	10500	1.6	180	70	1230	10	235
stainless steel	7930	96	230	200	1800	–	510
steel, piano wire	7800	–	–	210	1700	–	–
titanium carbide	4500	–	–	345	–	–	–
zinc	7140	5.9	–	110	693	10	385

Properties of liquids

At 293 K

Substance	Density	Melting point	Boiling point	Specific latent heat of vaporisation	Specific heat capacity	Refractive index
	kg m^{-3}	K	K	J kg^{-1} × 10^4	J kg^{-1} K^{-1}	
benzene	879	279	353	40.0	1700	1.50
ethanol	789	156	352	85.0	2500	1.36
ethoxyethane (ether)	714	157	308	35.0	2300	1.35
mercury	13600	234	630	29.0	140	1.73
methanol	791	179	337	112	2500	1.33
propan-1,2,3-triol	1260	293	563	83.0	2400	1.47
propanone (acetone)	780	178	330	52.0	2210	1.36
water, pure	998	273	373	226	4190	1.33

Properties of gases

At S.T.P.

Substance	Density	Specific heat capacity, C_p	Ratio of specific heat capacities
	kg m^{-3}	J kg^{-1} K^{-1}	
air	1.29	993	1.40
ammonia	0.771	2190	1.31
carbon dioxide	1.98	834	1.30
chlorine	3.21	478	1.36
helium	0.179	5240	1.66
hydrogen	0.090	14300	1.41
methane	0.717	2200	1.31
nitrogen	1.25	1040	1.40
water vapour	0.800	2020 (at 373 K)	–

Electric insulators

At 293 K

Solid	Resistivity Ω m	Liquid	Resistivity Ω m
acrylic (typical)	10^{19}		
bakelite	10^9	ethanol	10^3
barium titanate	–	silicone oil	–
glass	10^{11}	transformer oil	10^{11}
mica	10^{14}	water	10^3
neoprene	10^{10}		
paper, waxed	10^{14}		
paraffin wax	10^{15}		
perspex	–		
polyethane	10^{15}		
polystyrene	10^{14}		
polyvinyl chloride	10^{12}		
porcelain	10^{12}		
rubber	10^{13}		
sulphur	10^{15}		
teflon	10^{13}		

Table of isotopes

1u = 1 atomic mass unit = 1.661×10^{-27} kg
1u is equivalent to 931.3 MeV

Name	Symbol	Proton number Z	Nucleon number A	Atomic mass u
electron	$e^{\pm}$	± 1	–	0.00055
proton	p	1	1	1.00728
neutron	n	0	1	1.00867
hydrogen	^{1}H	1	1	1.00783
	^{2}H	1	2	2.01410
	^{3}H	1	3	3.01605
helium	^{3}He	2	3	3.01603
	^{4}He	2	4	4.00260
	^{5}He	2	5	5.01230
	^{6}He	2	6	6.01890

Fundamental particles

Class	Name	Symbol	Rest energy / MeV
leptons	photon	γ	0
	neutrino	ν_e	0
		ν_μ	0
	electron	$e^{\pm}$	0.511004
	muon	$\mu^{\pm}$	105.659
mesons	pion	$\pi^{\pm}$	139.576
		π^0	134.972
	kaon	$K^{\pm}$	493.821
		K^0	497.762
baryons	proton	$p^{\pm}$	938.257
	neutron	n	939.551

Properties of quarks

Type	Charge	Baryon number	Strangeness
u	$+\frac{2}{3}$	$+\frac{1}{3}$	0
d	$-\frac{1}{3}$	$+\frac{1}{3}$	0
s	$-\frac{1}{3}$	$+\frac{1}{3}$	-1

Useful equations

Statics

$F = \mu R$

Dynamics

$v = u + at$

$s = \left(\dfrac{u+v}{2}\right)t$

$s = ut + \dfrac{at^2}{2}$

$v^2 = u^2 + 2as$

$p = mv$

$F = \dfrac{\Delta(mv)}{\Delta t}$

$P = Fv$

$\text{efficiency} = \dfrac{\text{power output}}{\text{power input}}$

Refraction

$_1n_2 = \dfrac{\sin\theta_1}{\sin\theta_2} = \dfrac{c_1}{c_2} = \dfrac{n_2}{n_1}$

$\sin\theta_c = \dfrac{1}{n}$

Electricity

$\in = \dfrac{E}{Q}$

$\in = I(R + r)$

$R_{\text{series}} = R_1 + R_2 + R_3 + \ldots$

$\dfrac{1}{R_{\text{parallel}}} = \dfrac{1}{R_1} + \dfrac{1}{R_2} + \dfrac{1}{R_3} + \ldots$

$P = I^2R$

$\rho = \dfrac{RA}{l}$

Alternating current

$I_{\text{r.m.s.}} = \dfrac{I_o}{\sqrt{2}}$

$V_{\text{r.m.s.}} = \dfrac{V_o}{\sqrt{2}}$

Solids

$\text{Young modulus} = \dfrac{F/A}{e/L}$

Thermal properties

$$c = \frac{\Delta Q}{m \Delta T}$$

$$l = \frac{\Delta Q}{m}$$

$$pV = \frac{1}{3} N m \overline{c^2}$$

$$\frac{1}{2} m \overline{c^2} = \frac{3}{2} kT = \frac{3RT}{2N_A}$$

Nuclear physics

$$E = mc^2$$

Photoelectric effect

$$E = hf$$

$$hf = \phi + E_k$$

$$hf = E_1 - E_2$$

Wave–particle duality

$$\lambda = \frac{h}{p}$$

$$\lambda = \frac{h}{\sqrt{2meV}}$$

Gravitation and electrostatics

$$F = \frac{-Gm_1m_2}{r^2}$$

$$g = \frac{F}{m}$$

$$g = -\frac{GM}{r^2}$$

$$g = -\frac{\Delta V}{\Delta x}$$

$$V = -\frac{GM}{r} \quad \text{(radial field)}$$

$$F = \frac{1}{4\pi\varepsilon_0} \frac{Q_1 Q_2}{r^2}$$

$$E = \frac{F}{Q}$$

$$E = \frac{V}{d} \quad \text{(uniform field)}$$

$$E = \frac{1}{4\pi\varepsilon_0} \frac{Q}{r^2} \quad \text{(radial field)}$$

$$V = \frac{1}{4\pi\varepsilon_0} \frac{Q}{r} \quad \text{(radial field)}$$

Electromagnetism

$$\Phi = BA$$

$$F = \frac{B}{l}$$

$$\Phi = BQV$$

$$\varepsilon = \frac{N\Delta\Phi}{\Delta t}$$

Simple harmonic

$$a = -\omega^2 x$$

$$v = \pm\omega\sqrt{x_0^2 - x^2}$$

$$T_{\text{pendulum}} = 2\pi\sqrt{\frac{l}{g}}$$

$$T_{\text{spring}} = 2\pi\sqrt{\frac{m}{k}}$$

$$a = -\omega^2 x = -(2\pi f)^2 x = -4\pi^2 f^2 x$$

$$x = A\cos(2\pi ft)$$

$$v = \pm 2\pi f\sqrt{(A^2 - x^2)}$$

$$v = \pm 2\pi f\sqrt{(A^2 - x^2)}$$

Period of an oscillating spring

$$T = 2\pi\sqrt{\left(\frac{m}{k}\right)}$$

Period of an oscillating pendulum

$$T = 2\pi\sqrt{\left(\frac{l}{g}\right)}$$

Radioactivity

$$I = k\frac{I_0}{x^2}$$

$$\frac{\Delta N}{\Delta t} = -\lambda N$$

$$N = N_0 e^{-\lambda t}$$

$$T_{1/2} = \frac{\ln 2}{\lambda}$$

$$E = mc^2$$

Circular motion

$$\omega = \frac{v}{r}$$

$$\omega = \frac{2\pi}{T}$$

$$a = \frac{v^2}{r} = r\omega^2$$

$$F = \frac{mv^2}{r} = mr\omega^2$$

Capacitors

$$Q = CV$$

Energy stored $= E = \frac{1}{2}CV^2 = \frac{1}{2}QV$

Time constant $= CR$

$$Q = Q_0 e^{-t/RC}$$

Waves

$$c = f\lambda$$

$$\lambda = \frac{ws}{D}$$

$$d\sin\theta = n\lambda$$